MASTERING PUBLIC SPEAKING

MASTERING PUBLIC SPEAKING

TENTH EDITION

George L. Grice
Radford University, Professor Emeritus

Daniel H. Mansson
Penn State Hazleton

John F. Skinner
San Antonio College

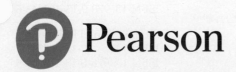

Director, Portfolio Management: Karon Bowers
Content Producer: Barbara Cappuccio
Content Developer: Karen Moore
Portfolio Manager Assistant: Dea Barbieri
Product Marketer: Christopher Brown
Field Marketer: Kelly Ross
Content Producer Manager: Melissa Feimer
Content Development Manager: Sharon Geary
Managing Editor: Maggie Barbieri
Content Developer, Learning Tools: Amy Wetzel
Art/Designer: Kathryn Foot
Digital Studio Course Producer: Amanda Smith
Full-Service Project Manager: SPi Global
Compositor: SPi Global
Printer/Binder: LSC Communications, Inc.
Cover Printer: LSC Communications, Inc.
Cover Design: Lumina Datamatics, Inc.
Cover Credit: Matvienko Vladimir/Shutterstock

Library of Congress Cataloging-in-Publication Data
Names: Grice, George L. author. | Mansson, Daniel H. author. | Skinner, John F. author.
Title: Mastering public speaking / George L. Grice, Radford University;
    Daniel H. Mansson Penn State Hazleton; John F. Skinner, San Antonio College.
Description: Tenth edition. | Boston : Pearson, 2017. | Includes
    bibliographical references and indexes.
Identifiers: LCCN 2017037904 | ISBN 9780134623115 (student edition) | ISBN 0134623118
Subjects: LCSH: Public speaking.
Classification: LCC PN4129.15 .G75 2017 | DDC 808.5/1—dc23 LC record available at https://lccn.loc.gov/2017037904

1   17

Instructor's Review Copy:
ISBN-10:   0-13-462344-4
ISBN-13: 978-0-13-462344-3

Access Code Card:
ISBN 10:   0-13-462341-X
ISBN 13: 978-0-13-462341-2

à la carte Edition:
ISBN-10:   0-13-462343-6
ISBN-13: 978-0-13-462343-6

Student Rental Edition:
ISBN 10:   0-13-462311-8
ISBN 13: 978-0-13-462311-5

To Wrenn, Evelyn, Carol, and Leanne

To Ulla, Henric, and Vivian;
and the memory of
my father and role model, Hans-Uno Månsson;
my grandfather, Åke Svensson; and
my host-father, Ernest Domoney

and

To the memory of John F. Skinner,
author, teacher, colleague, and friend

Brief Contents

Contents

8 Organizing the Body of Your Speech 100

9 Supporting Your Speech 115

10 Introducing and Concluding Your Speech 131

11 Outlining Your Speech 146

In 1993, George Grice and John Skinner authored the first edition of *Mastering Public Speaking* to show students both the *hows* and the *whys* of public speaking. This was the first major public speaking textbook to devote an entire chapter to speaker and listener ethics and another chapter to managing speaker nervousness. It also introduced students to the 4 S's, a practical mnemonic device for organizing each major idea in a speech.

The text's instructional approach mirrored a view of the public speaking instructor as a "guide on the side" rather than a "sage on the stage." A primary goal was to empower students to take responsibility for their own learning by challenging them to make the decisions required of public speakers.

In 2013, Daniel Mansson joined the revision of the ninth edition of *Mastering Public Speaking* and he remains an author for the tenth edition. Although Daniel has added new research and new speaking strategies to the text, we adhere to our original goals by incorporating into our text many credible examples, both actual and hypothetical, which help inspire and encourage students to achieve the full potential of public speech.

To support our goals, we also wanted to help instructors shape the public speaking classroom into a community of caring, careful thinkers. We sought to improve the quality of feedback in the classroom by analyzing the elements of sound critiques and providing a helpful model for discussing speeches.

We live in a changed world in the early 21st century. Technology has altered our expectations of what a public speech can accomplish and how it can be delivered; new research tools have sent us scrambling to ensure that we know as much about these emerging technologies as do most of our students. However, in our view, the fundamentals of public speaking remain the same, regardless of the changes that surround us. Sensitive audience analysis, adequate research, clear organization, and dynamic delivery remain the key ingredients for effective speeches. Therefore, our basic instructional approach in this text remains constant: We seek to engage students in the principles, practice, and ethics of public speaking—both as speakers and as listeners.

What's New in the Tenth Edition

Revel ™

Revel is an interactive learning environment that deeply engages students and prepares them for class. Media and assessment integrated directly within the authors' narrative lets students read, explore interactive content, and practice in one continuous learning path. Thanks to the dynamic reading experience in Revel, students come to class prepared to discuss, apply, and learn from instructors and from each other.

Learn more about Revel

www.pearson.com/revel

Rather than simply offering opportunities to read about and study public speaking, Revel facilitates deep, engaging interactions with the concepts that matter most. For example, when learning about public speaking anxiety, students are prompted to complete the PRPSA to assess their current level of anxiety. (They may take the assessment at a later point to see if their level of anxiety has changed.) By providing opportunities to read about and practice communication in tandem, Revel engages students directly and immediately, which leads to a better understanding of course material. A wealth of student and instructor resources and interactive materials can be found within Revel; we are excited to have retained the interactivity our users have come to rely on and to offer many new opportunities for engagement. Highlights include:

- **Short Speech Excerpts**
  Abundant in-text speech excerpts, many new to this edition, let students listen to audio clips while they read, bringing examples to life in a way that a printed text cannot. Many of these excerpts are from student speeches, while other new samples are from famous speeches, like FDR's fireside chats.

- **Videos and Video Quizzes**
  Video examples of sample speeches and expert advice throughout the narrative boost mastery, and many videos are bundled with correlating self-checks, enabling students to test their knowledge. Students will also benefit from new video galleries which are collections of video clips that illuminate aspects or samples of a topic, such as "successful central ideas" or "effective inclusive language." In addition, we provide video clips of influential speeches (like Barack Obama's Tucson memorial speech) and video content on real world speaking situations (like the ethical questions surrounding Melania Trump's 2016 RNC speech).

Video Self-Check: Human Trafficking

3 questions

▶ 00:04 / 01:20   info 🔊 ———●— CC ⚙ ⤢

1. Nikita's statement, "Human trafficking is this generation's newest form of slavery" serves as her:

   ○ Central idea.

   ○ Specific purpose.

   ○ Closure statement.

   ○ Final key idea.

Next

- **Interactive Figures**

  Interactive figures help students understand hard-to-grasp concepts through interactive visualizations. Examples in the tenth edition include Figure 4.1: The Process of Listening, Figure 5.2: Maslow's Hierarchy of Needs, Figure 10.1: The Outward Method of Speech Development, and Figure 16.1: The Continuum of Persuasion.

Figure 10.1   The Outward Method of Speech Development

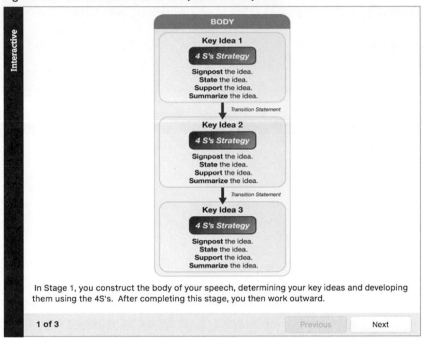

In Stage 1, you construct the body of your speech, determining your key ideas and developing them using the 4S's. After completing this stage, you then work outward.

1 of 3

- **Author Audio: Final Words of Encouragement**

  Each chapter now ends with an audio feature starring author Daniel Mansson, who shares personal and professional anecdotes—including his experiences of taking the introductory speech course as an ESL student—to help students learn and grow on their journey to improve their speaking skills.

Chapter 10 Final Words of Encouragement

Author Daniel Mansson, Penn State Hazleton

- **Assessment Opportunities**

  Revel offers students many unique opportunities to assess their content knowledge and understanding. In addition to the aforementioned video quizzes, students can complete no-stakes assessment in the form of "Key Points" quizzes, in which they drag and drop a term or concept to the correct definition or example in an interactive table. Finally, instructors and students alike benefit from formal end-of-module and end-of-chapter assessments (revised to match the content of our new edition) to ensure that students comprehend the chapter's learning objectives.

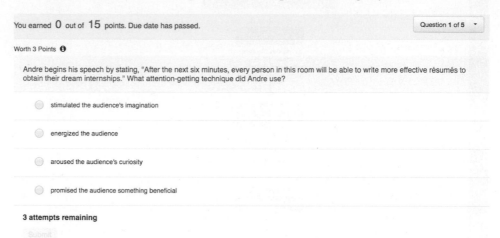

You earned **0** out of **15** points. Due date has passed.   Question 1 of 5 ▾

Worth 3 Points ⓘ

Andre begins his speech by stating, "After the next six minutes, every person in this room will be able to write more effective résumés to obtain their dream internships." What attention-getting technique did Andre use?

○ stimulated the audience's imagination

○ energized the audience

○ aroused the audience's curiosity

○ promised the audience something beneficial

3 attempts remaining

Submit

- **Integrated Writing Opportunities**

  To help students connect chapter content with personal meaning, each chapter offers two varieties of writing prompts: the Journal prompt, which elicits free-form topic-specific responses addressing topics at the module level, and the Shared Writing prompt, which encourages students to share and respond to each other's brief responses to high-interest topics in the chapter.

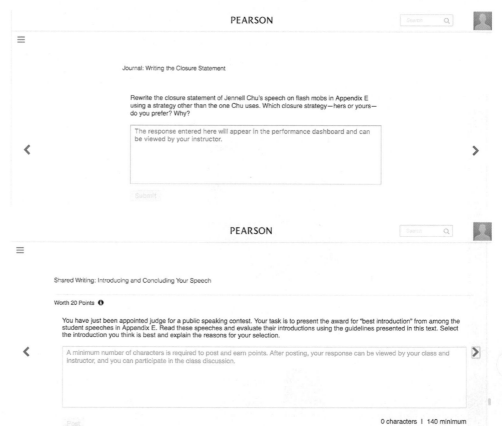

PEARSON

≡

Journal: Writing the Closure Statement

Rewrite the closure statement of Jennell Chu's speech on flash mobs in Appendix E using a strategy other than the one Chu uses. Which closure strategy—hers or yours—do you prefer? Why?

The response entered here will appear in the performance dashboard and can be viewed by your instructor.

Submit

PEARSON

≡

Shared Writing: Introducing and Concluding Your Speech

Worth 20 Points ⓘ

You have just been appointed judge for a public speaking contest. Your task is to present the award for "best introduction" from among the student speeches in Appendix E. Read these speeches and evaluate their introductions using the guidelines presented in this text. Select the introduction you think is best and explain the reasons for your selection.

A minimum number of characters is required to post and earn points. After posting, your response can be viewed by your class and instructor, and you can participate in the class discussion.

Post   0 characters | 140 minimum

For more information about all the tools and resources in Revel and access to your own Revel account for *Mastering Public Speaking,* Tenth Edition, go to www.pearson.com/revel.

As you read this new edition of *Mastering Public Speaking*, you will notice several structural changes. Drawing from suggestions of talented reviewers, colleagues, and students, as well as our own experience, we have retitled two chapters (Chapters 16 and 17), shifting some of the content between the two. We added a new appendix on question-answer periods, modified the internal structure of several chapters, and replaced three of our six full speech samples in Appendix E (Sample Speeches). We also revised and updated many of our features, including Ethical Decisions, Theory into Practice, and Speaking with Confidence. In addition, we have replaced and updated many student and professional examples, using actual classroom and contest speakers for many of these.

Specific changes to each chapter include:

- Chapter 1, "An Introduction to Public Speaking," builds on a solid overview of public speaking to help students understand—and embrace—the reasons *why* they should value the skills they will gain from this course. In particular, we offer an updated overview of the academic, personal/social, professional, and public benefits of public speaking. In Revel, we support this goal with a photo gallery highlighting the work of some of our nation's most influential speakers.

- Chapter 2, "The Ethics of Public Speaking," highlights ethical speech dilemmas from recent events and considers the quandary of ethical "grey zones." The chapter also offers an expanded discussion of the types of plagiarism so students can recognize and prevent this ethical failure. In Revel, students will consider the ethical dilemma of Melania Trump's 2016 RNC speech.

- Chapter 3, "Speaking with Confidence," continues to focus on how to *manage*, rather than *control*, speaker nervousness. We offer a streamlined set of public speaking skills as well as physical and psychological strategies to address anxiety, including new content on burning off energy and taking care of the body before a speech. In Revel, students take the Personal Report of Public Speaking Anxiety (PRPSA) to assess their current level of anxiety.

- Chapter 4, "Listening," offers a stronger focus on the benefits of good listening skills (including a new Table 4.1 that overviews the academic, personal/relational, professional, and social/legal benefits of listening). It also offers new content on the dangers of ethnocentric listening in a multicultural world. Students will also benefit from hearing from human communication expert Melissa Beall in Revel.

- Chapter 5, "Analyzing Your Audience," offers a streamlined organization that allows students to learn better from shorter, more focused modules on audience demographics (now including sexual orientation), psychographics, and needs. In addition, the chapter offers a new section to help students obtain relevant information about their audience. Revel also offers significant support for students learning about Maslow's hierarchy of needs, including an interactive figure and table, as well as a new video.

- Chapter 6, "Selecting Your Speech Topic," is reorganized to help students walk through this important process in the most natural and logical way possible, beginning with generating ideas and ending with the creation of the central idea of the speech. Students may also interact with a mind map in Revel.

- Chapter 7, "Researching Your Speech Topic," contains reorganized and specific modules on primary and secondary research, including Internet research, library research, and qualitative and quantitative research via interviews, questionnaires, and focus groups. Throughout this chapter and other parts of the book, we emphasize the importance of critically evaluating the material students come across. New annotated sample notes and references in Revel provide students with a helpful example to get started with their own research journey.

- Chapter 8, "Organizing Your Speech," is full of new examples and samples (many from our own teaching experience) to help students walk through the process of organizing their ideas in an appropriate and coherent fashion. We also now highlight moving from specific purpose, to central idea, to key ideas in our examples. An interactive visual of this process offers additional support in Revel.

- Chapter 9, "Supporting Your Speech," continues to provide students with a comprehensive overview of the many types of supporting material, now clarified by a new video gallery in Revel. Updated examples support student learning throughout.

- Chapter 10, "Introducing and Concluding Your Speech," now highlights eight (instead of seven) attention getting strategies and four (instead of three) essential functions of a conclusion, in addition to the five functions of the introduction of a speech. Students will see new video samples of effective introductions and conclusions throughout Revel. Additionally, we've divided our content on the Outward Method of Speech Development into a separate module, allowing students to better focus on this process that will support the creation of their speeches.

- Chapter 11, "Outlining Your Speech," now offers a speech sample that is consistent across the working, formal, and speaking outlines so that students can observe the evolution of a single speech through the outlining process. In Revel, audio annotations assist students' analysis of the outlines they read. A new student interview in "Speaking with Confidence" underscores the value of the outlining process.

- Chapter 12, "Wording Your Speech," provides a refocused module on wording the speech carefully to share intended meaning, complete with contemporary examples and images of incorrect word choice. The new "Speaking with Confidence" feature highlights one student's experience with word choice when speaking on a particularly controversial topic. In Revel, students practice their word choice by viewing a powerful photograph and journaling with vivid language.

- Chapter 13, "Delivering Your Speech," has a new module on "Delivering Speeches Online," helping students address specific delivery challenges in a mediated context, such as using technology, engaging an audience virtually, and dealing with limited feedback and a lack of personalization. Revel offers additional support with a new, instructive video on mediated presentations.

- Chapter 14, "Using Presentational Aids," now considers speaker credibility in relation to presentational aids in addition to covering Prezi presentations. We also provide tips for using presentational aids (like pictures and handouts) in online speaking situations. Students will find this chapter's Revel video gallery on aid types particularly useful.

- Chapter 15, "Speaking to Inform," continues to place an emphasis on guidelines that are more focused and specific to informative speaking, supported by a new "Speaking with Confidence" feature that highlights a student who struggles to inform rather than persuade. In Revel, this chapter kicks off with a segment of a cooking demonstration with celebrity chef Cat Cora, reminding students that informative presentations are all around us.

- Chapter 16, "Speaking to Persuade," has a new title and a new organization that offers students a more readable and focused overview of persuasive speaking. Separate and heavily revised modules on Aristotle's modes of persuasion and establishing common ground help students better reach their audience. The final module on organizing the persuasive speech now offers content on Monroe's Motivated Sequence (previously in Chapter 17) as well as the comparative advantage and refutation patterns. Student speech videos and instructive video overviews support this heavily revised content in Revel.

- Chapter 17, "Developing Persuasive Arguments," has been renamed to better represent the content of the chapter. It continues to offer a solid overview of logic and argument to help students incorporate these essentials into their persuasive speeches. (They may test their knowledge of argument types with a video self-check in Revel.) The chapter also offers a new "Ethical Decisions" box on contradictory evidence as well as a look at a current student's experience with argument and evidence in the new "Speaking with Confidence" interview.

- Chapter 18, "Speaking on Special Occasions," now features a section on commencement speeches as well as new annotated sample speeches for the Speech of Presentation and the Acceptance Speech. Additionally, we added a "Speaking with Confidence" box to highlight one student's experience with these speech types. Revel provides substantial video support, with special occasion speeches by familiar faces including Catherine Middleton, John Elway, and Matthew McConaughey.

- New Appendix D on "Question–Answer Periods" helps students prepare for these unique audience interactions.

- Appendix E, "Sample Speeches," offers three new student speeches, including a eulogy sample. Several of the speeches in the appendix contain full video in Revel, further enhancing student learning.

Special Features

There are many special features that are an integral part of the learning materials in this book. We've included these to help students understand and learn public speaking concepts. We have retained the following popular instructional features:

- **Learning Objectives** appear at the beginning of each chapter and are additionally highlighted in their related sections and the chapter summary to help reinforce students' reading and learning.

- **Theory into Practice** boxes, several of which have been newly revised and edited, reinforce the text's instructional approach and help students understand and apply communication concepts and strategies to enhance their public speaking competence. In Revel, many include interactive opportunities that allow students to focus on one aspect at a time, listen to audio excerpts, or walk through an example that illustrates the concept.

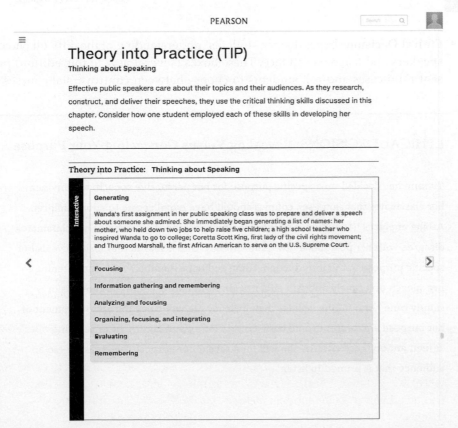

- **Key Points** boxes appear throughout the book to reinforce instruction and aid student review. They summarize important material and offer helpful guidelines throughout the public speaking process. As noted, Revel takes them one step further as no-stakes interactive quizzes that students can use to review and interpret concepts.

Key Points: **Functions of a Speech Conclusion**

> Review the following functions of a speech conclusion. When you're ready, click "Check Your Understanding" below.
>
> | Function | Example |
> | --- | --- |
> | **Restate the topic or purpose.** | Today, I've shared with you a few of the many benefits of making your own household cleaners. |
> | **Restate the key ideas.** | We've discussed the money that you can save by making your own cleaners, in addition to the health and environmental benefits that come when you use natural products—like vinegar—over chemical cleaners. |
> | **Activate audience response.** | With all of these benefits in mind, take a small step into the world of natural cleaners. Try replacing just one of your products—say, your all purpose cleaner—with a homemade recipe using ingredients you can pronunce! |
> | **Provide closure.** | As the great naturalist John Muir once said about time in nature, "Wash your spirit clean." Now you can do the same for your home, using inexpensive products safe for your wallet, your body, and the Earth. |
>
> Check Your Understanding

Interactive

- **Ethical Decisions** boxes deepen students' understanding of the difficult choices speakers and listeners can face. These boxes (several new to this edition) present mini cases and ask students to choose between controversial courses of

---

ETHICAL DECISIONS: Revealing Versus Concealing Your Purpose

Yvonne has decided on a specific purpose for her persuasive speech: to convince her classmates that same-sex couples should have equal access to adopt children. As she analyzes her audience's attitudes, she concludes that some of her classmates disagree with her position, a few quite strongly. She is fearful that if she reveals her specific purpose in the introduction, some audience members will stop listening to her speech objectively and will either begin formulating counterarguments or simply tune her out. She decides that, instead, she will delay the announcement of her purpose and present some basic criteria for a good family. After securing agreement on these criteria, she will then reveal her purpose for speaking—to an audience that is primed to listen.

action. Thought-provoking questions follow each scenario, providing spring-boards for engaging in classroom debates and, in Revel, writing online Journal entries.

- **Speaking with Confidence** boxes (several new to this edition) feature the stories of real students from public speaking classes throughout the country who explain how this text helped them build their confidence in public speaking. Additionally, Revel offers audio versions of this feature.

Speaking With Confidence

◀ Listen to the Audio

If you fail to attain your audience's attention in the introduction, you won't have it in the rest of your speech. My introduction's success in my speech on Virtual Cyber Charter Schools was important not only for the rest of my speech but also because it would become the audience's first impression of me. I asked the audience members to close their eyes and picture a classroom, not one of rows of desks, but one with a computer and headset that existed in virtual space. By starting off with this place I knew well and wanted to share, I felt confident in my ability to deliver an effective introduction.

- **Sample Speeches** appear in selected chapters and in Appendix E as models for students to learn from or critique. In Revel, some of the speeches include audio and/or video components.

Instructor and Student Resources

Key instructor resources include an Instructor's Manual (ISBN 0-13-462377-0), TestBank (ISBN 0-13-462346-0), and PowerPoint Presentation Package (ISBN 0-13-462373-8). These supplements are available on the catalog page for this text on Pearson.com/us (instructor login required). MyTest online test-generating software (ISBN: 0-13-462345-2) is available at www.pearsonmytest.com (instructor login required). For a complete list of the instructor and student resources available with the text, please visit the Pearson Communication catalog, at www.pearson.com/communication.

Pearson MediaShare

Pearson's comprehensive media upload tool allows students to post videos, images, audio, or documents for instructor and peer viewing, time-stamped commenting, and assessment. MediaShare is an easy, mobile way for students and professors to interact and engage with speeches, presentation aids, and other files. MediaShare gives professors the tools to provide contextual feedback to demonstrate how students can improve their skills.

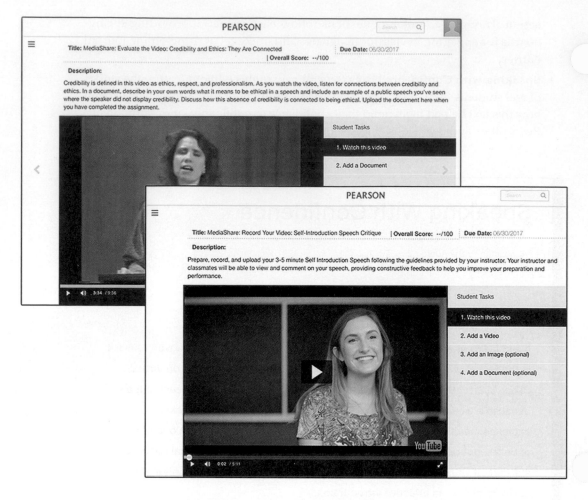

The best of MediaShare functionality, including student video submissions with grading and video quizzes, is now available to use and assign *within Revel*, making Revel an even more complete solution for Communication courses. By placing these key components of MediaShare within Revel, students have one all-inclusive space to practice and have their performance assessed while actively learning through interactive course content. Revel with MediaShare is an unparalleled immersive learning experience for the Communication curriculum.

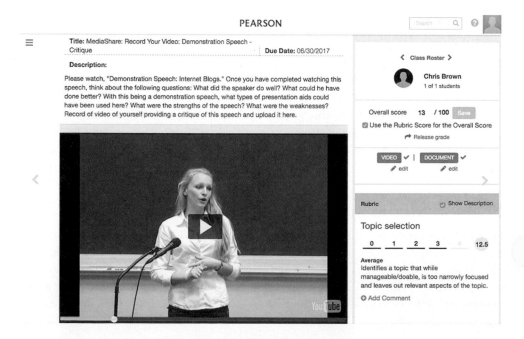

- Use MediaShare to assign or view speeches, video-based assignments, role plays, and more in a variety of formats including video, Word, PowerPoint, and Excel.

- Assess students using customizable, Pearson-provided rubrics or create your own around classroom goals, learning outcomes, or department initiatives.

- Set up assignments for students with options for full-class viewing and commenting or private comments between you and the student.

- Record video directly from a tablet, phone, or other webcam.

- Embed video from YouTube via assignments to incorporate current events into the classroom experience.

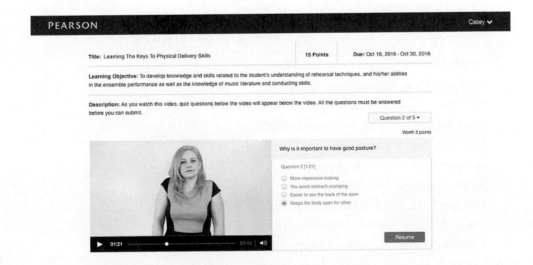

- Set up quiz questions on video assignments to ensure students master concepts and interact and engage with the media.

- Import grades into most learning management systems.

- Ensure a secure learning environment for instructors and students through robust privacy settings.

Acknowledgments

We are, first and foremost, grateful to the many university, college, and community college educators whose encouragement and support contributed to the success of previous editions of this textbook. The tenth edition of *Mastering Public Speaking* is the product of more than just the authors. Although we have tried to speak with one voice for the sake of our readers, the truth is that many voices resonate throughout this text: the voices of our teachers, our colleagues, our editors, and our students. Wherever possible, we have tried to acknowledge their contributions. For all their influence on this text, we are thankful.

On the copyright page of this textbook is a list of Pearson professionals who have done the heavy lifting and guided this edition to completion. We thank the entire editorial, production, and marketing staffs for their time, talent, and contributions to this tenth edition.

We are indebted to two problem solvers extraordinaire: our editor, Karon Bowers, and Karen Moore, content developer. Thank you for your faith in this project, wise counsel, and responsiveness to our input, questions, and requests. We also continue to acknowledge Carol Alper, our development editor for six of our ten editions, and a wonderful part of the co-authors' lives. We hope you are enjoying your well-deserved retirement.

This is the second edition written or revised without our friend and co-author John F. Skinner. Yet, as we reviewed previous editions, we experienced, once again, his insights, scholarship, wit, respect for language, and the conversational tone he established with readers. John, you will forever be a part of *Mastering Public Speaking* and a part of our lives.

Mastering Public Speaking has been shaped and refined by the close readings and thoughtful suggestions of a number of reviewers. We would like to thank the following reviewers for their comments on this edition:

Susan Cunningham, *San Antonio College*

John Hosty, *Kankakee Community College*

Shellie Michael, *Volunteer State Community College*

Daryle Nagano, *Los Angeles Harbor College*

Lauri Zumwalt, *Kankakee Community College*

We would also like to acknowledge reviewers of previous editions:

Linda Anthon, *Valencia Community College*

Suzanne Atkin, *Portland State University*

Barbara L. Baker, *Central Missouri State University*

Lana Becker, *Ivy Tech Community College*

Elizabeth Bell, *University of South Florida*

Jim Benjamin, *University of Toledo*

Kathy Berggren, *Cornell University*

Tim Borchers, *Moorhead State University*

Sue E. Brilhart, *Southwest Missouri State University*

Gwendolyn Brown, *Professor Emerita, Radford University*

Carl R. Burgchardt, *Colorado State University*

Barbara Ruth Burke, *University of Minnesota, Morris*

Sharon Cline, *University of North Dakota*

Dolly Conner, *Radford University*

Pamela Cooper, *Northwestern University*

Michael Cronin, *Professor Emeritus, Radford University*

Sherry Dewald, *Red Rock Community College*

Thomas E. Diamond, *Montana State University*

Terrence Doyle, *Northern Virginia Community College*

Rebecca J. Franko, *California State Polytechnic University, Pomona*

Sandy French, *Radford University*

John Fritch, *Southwest Missouri State University*

Kristin Froemling, *Radford University*

Robert W. Glenn, *University of Tennessee*

Deborah Anne Gross, *Gwynedd Mercy College*

Trudy L. Hanson, *West Texas A&M University*

Dayle C. Hardy-Short, *Northern Arizona University*

Deborah Hatton, *Sam Houston State University*

Kimberly Batty Herbert, *Clovis Community College*

Susan Kilgard, *Ann Arundel Community College*

Leslie A. Klipper, *Miramar College*

Mary Kaye Krum, *formerly of Florence-Darlington Technical College*

Linda Kurz, *University of Missouri, Kansas City*

Nancy Legge, *Idaho State University*

Bruce Loebs, *Idaho State University*

Stacey M. Macchi, *Western Illinois University*

Chris McCollough, *Columbus State University*

Sean McDevitt, *Lakeland College*

Patricia Palm McGillen, *Mankato State University*

David C. McLaughlin, *Montana State University*

David B. McLennan, *Peace College*

Dante E. Morelli, *Suffolk County Community College*

David Mrizek, *San Antonio College*

Eileen Oswald, *Valencia Community College*

Jolinda Ramsey, *San Antonio College*

Jeff Rhoads, *Estrella Mountain Community College*

Rosemarie Rossetti, *Ohio State University*

Jim Roux, *Horry-Georgetown Technical College*

Edward H. Sewell, *Virginia Polytechnic Institute and State University*

Suzanne Skinner, *San Antonio College*

Deborah Stieneker, *Arapahoe Community College*

Frances Swinny, *Professor Emerita, Trinity University*

Jason J. Teven, *California State University, Fullerton*

Cory Tomasson, *Illinois Valley Community College*

Beth M. Waggenspack, *Virginia Polytechnic Institute and State University*

Kimberly Warren-Cox, *Jackson State Community College*

Sue Weber, *University of Pennsylvania*

Doris Werkman, *Portland State University*

Karin Wilking, *San Antonio College*

Dianna R. Wynn, *Midland College*

We also appreciate the many talented individuals who prepared the array of supplemental materials listed in the "Instructor and Student Resources" section in this preface. Their contributions to the effective teaching and learning of public speaking are immeasurable.

Finally, we are indebted to all our public speaking students who have crafted their messages, walked to the front of their classrooms, and informed, persuaded, entertained, and challenged us. Without their ideas and experiences, writing and revising this book would have been impossible, just as without tomorrow's students it would be unnecessary.

An Invitation

I welcome your feedback about the tenth edition of *Mastering Public Speaking*. Please contact me by email at the following address:

dhm14@psu.edu

I look forward to hearing from you.

Daniel H. Mansson Ph.D.

AN INTRODUCTION TO PUBLIC SPEAKING

REWRITING THE BOOK
THE LIBRARY OF BIRMINGHAM

→ **LEARNING OBJECTIVES**

After studying this chapter, you should be able to

1.1 Identify the four benefits of studying public speaking.

1.2 Define communication, including its five basic levels.

1.3 Explain the model of communication in terms of the seven elements.

1.4 Use the eight critical thinking skills in developing and evaluating speeches.

The word began as the spoken word. Long before anyone devised a way to record messages in writing, people told stories and taught lessons. Societies flourished and fell; battles were waged and won all on the basis of the spoken word. Ancient storytellers preserved their cultures' traditions and history by translating them orally to eager audiences. Crowds might wander away from unprepared, unskilled speakers, but the most competent, skilled storytellers received widespread attention and praise.

After the development of script and print, people continued to associate marks on the page with the human voice. Even today, linked as we are by Twitter, texts, and Facebook updates, a speaker standing at the front of a hushed room makes a special claim on our attention and our imagination. As you develop and deliver speeches in this class—and in future years as you deliver reports, sell products, present and accept awards, or campaign for candidates—you continue an ancient oral tradition.

In this chapter, we introduce you to the exciting world of public speaking. We hope you learn why public speaking matters (and why you should study it) in addition to gaining a better understanding of the communication process. Finally, we explain the model of communication and introduce you to critical thinking skills that will help you develop and evaluate speeches.

Why Study Public Speaking?

1.1 Identify the four benefits of studying public speaking.

Today's college students are expected to complete a wide variety of general education courses. For many students, it may be difficult to understand how these courses are related to their intended future careers or personal goals and needs. One of our former students, Jenaveve, who majored in electrical engineering, asked us how this public speaking course would be beneficial to her future employment. We asked Jenaveve if she wanted to become a lead project engineer. "Of course," she said. We then asked her if safety and procedural accuracy are important to electrical engineers. Again, Jenaveve answered affirmatively. We continued to talk about how important it is for a lead project engineer to inform her team members about both safety and operational procedures. At the end of our conversation, Jenaveve understood that electrical engineers are also expected to be competent speakers.

There are many benefits to studying public speaking regardless of one's academic major. In fact, Aristotle argued this very point more than 2,000 years ago. This claim has been supported in several recent research studies focusing on the benefits and impacts of studying public speaking.[1] These studies indicate that students who study public speaking enjoy academic, personal/social, professional, and public benefits. Our observations and feedback we've received from students and instructors also support the importance of developing and using the skills, principles, and arts that are the subject of this textbook.

Academic Benefits

Do your instructors require you to participate in class? Are you expected to deliver group or individual presentations? Do you ever discuss your academic progress with your instructors? The answer to each of these three questions is most likely "yes." Thus, studying, practicing, and evaluating public speaking often leads to *academic benefits,* such as improved skills in the following areas:

- Classroom communication skills
- Critical thinking skills
- Group work skills
- Organization skills
- Research skills
- Writing skills

These are also *transferable* skills that can help you throughout your academic studies and in your chosen career.

Personal/Social Benefits

Think about your best friends or the instructors you most like and respect. Are they good conversationalists? Is it easy to understand them when they explain something to you? Are they outgoing and assertive? In general, we are attracted to outgoing and assertive people who are good communicators. In fact, research suggests that studying public speaking also may lead to personal and social benefits, such as enhanced

- Awareness and appreciation of other cultures
- Relationships with friends, family members, and romantic partners
- Self-awareness
- Self-esteem
- Understanding of social and environmental responsibilities

Mastering public speaking requires practice, but your efforts will reward you with increased knowledge, relational skills, and confidence.

Journal: Personal/ Social Benefits

How do you think you will benefit personally or socially from studying public speaking? Why are these benefits important to you?

Professional Benefits

Whether you are currently working in your desired field or looking to enter into a particular industry after graduation, you're likely concerned about the current job market as well as prospects for promotion or professional development once you are established with an organization. How do employers make decisions about whom to hire or promote, particularly if several candidates have equally impressive resumes or experiences? In many cases, they make their final decisions based on how well they connect with the candidates and how well the candidates present themselves. Not only will your initial job search involve an interview, it may also include a "job talk" in which you introduce yourself and your skills to the employer. So, it is no surprise then that several studies suggest that studying public speaking may benefit you professionally, including improved

- Ability to obtain employment
- Career advancement (i.e., upward mobility in your workplace)
- Collaboration skills with coworkers
- Conflict resolutions at work
- Salary negotiation skills

Public Benefits

Take a moment to think about some people who have benefited our society, whether a celebrity advocating for refugees or a fellow student advocating for stricter recycling policies on campus. What do these people have in common? They are most likely good communicators who use their skills to inform others about valuable issues and persuade them to take action. Therefore, public speaking can help you play a role in creating and sustaining a society of informed, active citizens. A democratic society is shaped in part by the public eloquence of its leaders and public figures. But a democratic society is also shaped by the quiet eloquence of everyday citizens:

- The police officer who informs residents of a crime-plagued area how to set up a Neighborhood Watch program.
- The social worker who addresses the city council and secures funding for a safe house for abused and runaway children.
- The neighbor who leads the PTA and advocates for the creation of an afterschool science enrichment program.

Actress Emma Watson, a United Nations Women Goodwill Ambassador, uses her public platform as an actor to advocate for gender equality and education for girls and women.

Key Points: Benefits of Studying Public Speaking

1. Academic benefits
2. Personal/social benefits
3. Professional benefits
4. Public benefits

In each of these instances, the speaker used the power of the spoken word to address a need and solicit an appropriate audience response. Active civic participation requires citizens to "speak out" about injustices and inequities. And though we increasingly use social media to alert and quickly mobilize groups of people, activism will always involve one or more individuals stirring groups of people through public speech.

While we recognize effective speaking when we meet someone who always says just the right thing or who says things in funny and colorful ways, few of us have been trained to speak well. That's a shame in light of the academic, personal/social, professional, and public benefits public speaking can offer. To appreciate the power of communication, you must understand just what it is. That requires a look at some definitions of communication and at some of its essential components.

Definitions of Communication

1.2 Define communication, including its five basic levels.

The word *communicate* comes from the Latin verb *communicare*, which means "to share." Simply stated, when you communicate, you share, or make common, your knowledge and ideas with someone else.

Some scholars view communication primarily as a *process*. For example, Thomas Scheidel provides a process perspective when he defines communication as "the transmission and reception of symbolic cues."[2] Other scholars see communication as an outcome or a *product* and define it simply as "shared meaning." We believe both perspectives are valid: Communication is both a *process* and a *product*. **Communication**, then, is the sharing of meaning by sending and receiving symbolic cues.

Figure 1.1 represents Charles Ogden and I. A. Richards's triangle of meaning,[3] an illustration of the three elements necessary for communication: interpreter, symbol, and referent.

The word *interpreter* refers to both the sender and the receiver of a message. The **interpreter** is simply the person who is communicating, with words or other symbols.

communication

The process of sharing meaning by sending and receiving symbolic cues.

interpreter

Any person using symbols to send or receive messages.

Figure 1.1   The Triangle of Meaning

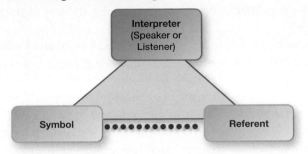

The second element of this model, the **symbol**, is anything to which people attach or assign a meaning. Symbols can be pictures, drawings, words, or objects. For example, your school most likely has a school logo of some sort. When you wear these logos, such as the West Virginia University Mountaineer or the University of North Carolina-Wilmington Seahawk, you communicate that you are affiliated with that particular school. Even colors can function as symbols; political pundits reduce us to living in blue or red states. Police officers' uniforms and squad cars are symbols of their authority. Facial expressions, posture, and gestures also convey messages of speakers and listeners. The most familiar symbols, however, are words. Many words refer to particular objects, places, and people: *chair*; *Stockholm, Sweden*; and *Chiwetel Ejiofor*, for example. Other words refer to concepts, such as *freedom of expression*, *existentialism*, and *fair play*.

The third and final element of the triangle of meaning is the **referent**, the object or idea for which the symbol stands. Both the sender and the receiver of a message have a referent for the symbols used. This referent depends on each individual's knowledge and experience. People cannot exchange referents in the way they can exchange objects. For example, someone can hand you a paper clip, and that paper clip is the same in your hand as it is in your friend's hand. Your friends, however, cannot transfer their ideas or information to you. All they can do is to code their ideas into symbols and hope that the ideas you decode will be similar to the ones they intended. In short, as senders, we select a symbol based on our referent. That symbol, in turn, triggers the receiver's referent.

Countless jokes and situation comedy plots revolve around interpreters who attach different referents to the same symbol. However, miscommunication can sometimes be serious and divisive. Consider the experience of Muslim American Zayed M. Yasin, the Harvard student whose graduation speech was one of three the selection committee chose in the spring of 2002. A furor began when the campus newspaper, the *Harvard Crimson*, published the titles of the three student commencement speeches. Yasin's speech, to be delivered less than 9 months after September 11, 2001, was titled "Of Faith and Citizenship: My American Jihad." His aim, he said, was to rescue the word *jihad* from extremists who had co-opted it to justify terrorism. He defined the term as a spiritual quest, "the determination to do right and justice even against your personal interests."[4] Some of the definitions of the Arabic word *jihad* are "striving," "effort," and "struggle," but many of those who protested the selection of Yasin's speech equated the term *jihad* with a "holy war." After the protests began on his campus,

symbol
Anything to which people attach meaning.

referent
The object or idea each interpreter attaches to a symbol.

What does this gesture symbolize for many people in the United States?

Yasin met with members of the selection committee, retitled his speech "Of Faith and Citizenship" for the printed program, and delivered the text of the speech without changing a word.[5]

As this example demonstrates, communication is clearest when all its interpreters attach similar referents to the message being communicated. You can, no doubt, think of experiences you have had when people misinterpreted what you said because they attached different referents to your words. The most important thing to remember about the triangle of meaning and the process of communication is this: *Words and other symbols have no inherent meaning. People create meaning; words do not*. A word takes on the meaning that each interpreter attaches to it. We will revisit this idea in Chapter 12, Learning Objective 12.1, when we discuss connotative and denotative language.

What does the triangle of meaning have to do with public speaking? As you will discover throughout this book, this model applies to public speaking just as it does to all other forms of communication. If speakers and listeners always used specific symbols, interpreted them objectively, and attached similar referents to them, then few communication problems would arise from the content of the message. As a result, your work in a public speaking class could be limited to improving your organization and polishing your style of delivery. Yet many of our communication problems can be traced directly to difficulties in the relationships between interpreters, the symbols they use, and the referents behind those symbols.

As a public speaker, you must try to ensure that the message your audience hears matches as closely as possible the message you intended. You do that by paying particular attention to your content, organization, and delivery, all major subjects of this book. To understand the complexity of public speaking, you need to realize how it relates to other levels of communication. See Table 1.1 for a discussion of these levels.

You will develop public speaking skills more quickly and easily if you understand and use the connections between public communication and the four other levels of communication. You communicate intrapersonally when you brainstorm areas of expertise on which you can speak. You may use interpersonal and group communication

> **Journal: Communication Breakdown**
>
> Think of an embarrassing experience that resulted from a breakdown in communication because you and someone else did not share similar referents. What referent(s) caused the confusion? Can you think of another example of miscommunication based on individuals having different referents for the same message?

TABLE 1.1 Levels of Communication

Communication can occur on five levels. Each level is distinguished by the number of people involved, the formality of the situation, how the messages are sent, and the opportunities for feedback. Public speaking, the subject of this book, incorporates elements of all these levels. A brief look at each will help you better understand public speaking.

Intrapersonal communication *is cognition or thought—in other words, communication with yourself*. Much intrapersonal communication is geared toward a specific, conscious purpose: evaluating how you are doing in a particular situation, solving a problem, relieving stress, or planning for the near or distant future. You use intrapersonal communication when you give yourself a silent pep talk before you speak or, as you walk to the front of the room, you tell yourself to turn to the audience, pause, look at your listeners, and speak clearly.

Interpersonal communication, *sometimes called dyadic communication, occurs when you communicate with one other person*. Face-to-face or phone conversations between friends, colleagues, or acquaintances are common forms of interpersonal communication. You use interpersonal communication skills when you meet with your instructor to discuss your speech or when you interview an expert to gather information on your topic.

Group communication *generally takes place when three or more people interact and influence one another to pursue a common goal*. The important thing to remember is that the people involved have a sense of group identity. They believe and accept that they belong together for some reason, whether they face a common problem, share similar interests, or simply work in the same division of a company. You may practice your speech in front of friends and then follow that with a group discussion of the strengths and areas for improvement of your speech.

Public communication *occurs when one person speaks face to face with an audience*. Compared with the levels just discussed, public communication is a more one-directional flow of information. Whether the audience is 20 or 20,000, public communication always involves one person communicating to an audience that is physically present (or virtually present, in the case of an online speech).

Mass communication *occurs when a person or group communicates to an audience through some form of print or electronic medium*. The audience may be so large or so diffused that it cannot be gathered in one place; thus, some type of medium—newspaper, magazine, radio, television, or computer, among others—must be placed between the speaker or writer and the intended audience. One important characteristic of mass communication is that audience feedback is delayed. If an article inspires or angers you, you may post a response. You have taken the opportunity to send feedback, but it is delayed.

to determine topics that interest your classmates. As you research and develop your speech, you will use mass communication to access information published electronically or in print. And as you deliver your public speeches, you will give yourself intrapersonal feedback about the job you are doing and the positive responses we hope you'll be receiving.

Once you understand the definition of communication (as well as its five levels), you are ready to develop a more detailed understanding of the seven elements of communication discussed in the next section.

Elements of Communication

1.3 Explain the model of communication in terms of the seven elements.

Now let's look at the elements of communication to see how they apply, specifically, to the complex activity of public speaking. Remember, the better you understand how communication works in general, the better you will be able to make it work for you in specific speaking situations. Just as important, knowing these elements will let us see where some common communication problems arise.

Today, the most widely accepted model of communication has seven components, as illustrated in Figure 1.2, the communication elements model of public speaking. Although we can identify the individual elements of the communication process, we cannot assess them in isolation. Contemporary scholars emphasize the transactional, interactive nature of communication. Each element simultaneously influences, and is influenced by, the other elements.

A sender (the speaker) encodes a message and sends it through a channel to a receiver (listener), who decodes the message. The receiver then provides feedback and sends it through a channel to the original sender. Therefore, we serve as both senders and receivers when we communicate with others. These interactions take place in an environment with different levels of internal and external noise.

Figure 1.2   The Communication Elements Model of Public Speaking

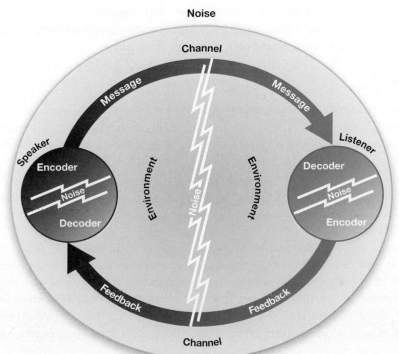

Speaker

speaker
The sender, source, or encoder of the message.

encoding
The process of selecting symbols to carry a message.

Human communication starts with a person, the **speaker**. As you will learn in the following sections and in Chapter 13, Learning Objective 13.4, we not only communicate verbally, but also nonverbally (through gestures, eye contact, and so on). Therefore, the speaker could also be called the *sender*, the *source*, or the *encoder*. **Encoding** is the process of putting ideas into symbols. We encode so much and so well that we are aware of the process only when we find ourselves "at a loss for words" while either speaking or writing.

Message

message
Ideas communicated verbally and nonverbally.

Linked to the speaker is the **message**, the ideas actually communicated. Speech communication scholar Karlyn Kohrs Campbell captures the connection between messages and people when she writes:

> Ideas do not walk by themselves; they must be carried—expressed and voiced— by someone. As a result, we do not encounter ideas neutrally, objectively, or apart from a context; we meet them as someone's ideas.[6]

The ideas of the message originate with the speaker, who determines the form that the message will initially take. However, others who may participate in the communication process further shape that message.

Listener

listener
The receiver or decoder of the message.

decoding
The process of attaching meaning to symbols received.

The message is sent to a **listener**—the decoder or receiver. This element is also known as a *decoder* or *receiver* because not all messages are verbal. This person shapes the message by **decoding** it—that is, attaching meaning to the words, gestures, and voice inflections received. Is every listener's decoded message identical to the one the speaker encoded? Remember our earlier discussion of the triangle of meaning; communication involves more than a single message. The truth is, there are as many messages as there are communicators involved. As long as these messages are similar, communication is usually effective.

The message does not stop as it is received. Instead, it is transformed—added to or diminished—as it is joined by other messages that originate with each listener. It is a mistake to assume that a person in the communication process is either a sender or a receiver of messages. We perform both roles simultaneously.

Feedback

feedback
Verbal and nonverbal responses between communicators about the clarity or acceptability of messages.

The interactions between listeners and senders provide the fourth element in our model of communication—**feedback**. Feedback includes all messages, verbal and nonverbal, sent by listeners to speakers. If you tell a joke, your listeners will tell you through laughter and visual feedback whether they understood the joke and how they evaluated it. If you are paying attention, you will know who liked it, who disliked it, who didn't understand it, and who was offended by it. Note that "if you are paying attention" is the particularly important phrase. In order to be effective, feedback must be received and interpreted correctly.

Feedback from your audience can be deliberate and conscious (as when members raise their hand or nod their heads) or it can be unintentional and unconscious (as when their facial expressions appear bored or tired). As a speaker, you should be aware and responsive to both types. Also know that feedback can be either immediate or delayed. Immediate feedback is provided when the listener (receiver) replies instantly after having received the message. Delayed feedback occurs when there is a substantial period of time between the message and the feedback, such as in email conversations.

Channel

The fifth element of our model is the **channel**, or medium—the means through which a message is sent. Each speaker sending a message and each listener providing feedback uses a channel. In public speaking, the medium is vibrations in the air between speaker and listener, set in motion by the speaker's voice. Vocal elements such as rate, volume, and pitch also carry part of the message. Visual elements—another channel for the message—include eye contact, facial expression, gestures, movement, and presentational aids. As a public speaker, you must learn to use and control all these channels. Students who take their public speaking class online will likely record their speeches and share them online for their instructor and fellow students. Therefore, the Internet becomes the channel through which they send their messages to the receivers, which would result in delayed feedback. In other situations, such as in mass communication, the channel may be your television, radio, or the Internet.

channel
The means through which a message is sent.

Environment

The sixth element of the communication model is the **environment**. Three factors shape an environment: (1) the occasion during which the communication occurs, (2) the larger social context in which the communication takes place, and (3) the physical setting where the communication occurs.

The *occasion* refers to the reasons why people have assembled. Circumstances may be serious or festive, planned or spontaneous. Occasions for communication may be as relaxed and informal as a party with friends, as rule-bound as a college debate, or as formal and traditional as a commencement address.

The larger *social context* involves a variety of people and opinions that can vary by culture and affect the appropriateness of the messages that you communicate. For instance, if the members of your audience are from a collectivist (group-oriented) culture (such as Latin America or Asia), they may be persuaded by cooperation more than by competition, which may play better in an individualistic culture such as the United States. However, although cultural tendencies do exist, a speaker would be advised to avoid stereotyping the audience; there will always be individual differences in any collected audience.

The *physical setting* for your classroom speeches is probably apparent to you. You know the size of the room and the number of people in the audience. You know whether the seating arrangement is fixed or flexible. You know whether the room has a lectern or wifi. You know, or may soon discover, potential problems with the setting: The table at the front of the room is wobbly, the air seems stuffy, and one of the fluorescent lights flickers. Each of these distracting elements is a form of noise—the final element for which any accurate model of communication must account.

environment
The occasion, social context, and physical setting for communication.

Noise

Noise is anything that distracts from effective communication. The reality is that some form of noise is always present when we are communicating with others. Three forms of noise exist, distinguished by their sources. First is **physical noise**—anything you can hear or feel in the immediate environment that interferes with communication. This could be the sounds of traffic, the loud *whoosh* of an air conditioner or a heater, the voices of people talking and laughing as they pass by a classroom. However, some physical noise may not involve a sound at all. If your classroom is so cold that you

noise
Anything that distracts from effective communication.

physical noise
Distractions originating in the physical environment.

Effective public speakers adapt their speaking styles to the physical settings and the occasions for their speeches.

physiological noise

Distractions originating in the bodies of communicators.

psychological noise

Distractions originating in the thoughts of communicators.

Journal: Noise

What is one example of noise present around you right now? Is it physical, physiological, or psychological? How could you minimize any effects of this noise that might distract you from your reading?

Key Points: Elements of Communication

1. Speaker
2. Message
3. Listener
4. Feedback
5. Channel
6. Environment
7. Noise

shiver or so hot that you fan yourself, then its temperature is a form of physical noise. If the room's lighting is poor, then that form of noise will certainly affect the communication occurring there.

A second type of noise is **physiological noise**; a bad cold that affects your hearing and speech, a headache, and an empty growling stomach are examples. Each of these bodily conditions can shift your focus from communicating with others to thinking about how uncomfortable you feel, and creates a form of intrapersonal communication.

The third and final type of noise is **psychological noise**. This term refers to mental rather than bodily distractions. Anxiety, worry, daydreaming, anticipation, and even joy over some recent event can distract you from the message at hand.

Each form of noise—physical, physiological, and psychological—can occur independently or in concert. For example, a speaker may be distracted by a sore throat as well as the sounds of a sniffling classmate. An audience member might have trouble listening because he's daydreaming about summer and because construction on campus makes it difficult to hear the speaker. Nonetheless, some form of noise is always present, so as a speaker you must try to minimize its effects in public communication. For example, by varying your rate, volume, and pitch, or through lively physical delivery, you can combat some noise and rivet the audience's attention to your message.

As you can see, public speaking is more complicated than just saying the right words or having cool presentation slides. Communication is dynamic and transactional. Speaker, message, listener, feedback, channel, environment, and noise all interact to influence one another. Unlike that paper clip—the same in every hand that holds it—the message that emerges in communication will never be identical to what any one speaker intended.

Part of mastering public speaking begins with basic skills: organizing a presentation with an identifiable introduction, body, and conclusion; providing previews, summaries, and transitions; deciding whether the oral message needs the support of presentational aids; and using appropriate grammar, pronunciation, and articulation.[7] However, to design, develop, and deliver a speech that is appropriate to you, your audience, and the communication context requires some higher-order thinking. Public speaking involves choices and, to choose appropriately, you must sharpen your critical thinking skills.

The Public Speaker as Critical Thinker

1.4 Use the eight critical thinking skills in developing and evaluating speeches.

We began this chapter by discussing benefits you gain from studying and practicing public speaking. One of those benefits is that public speaking uses and develops your critical thinking skills. **Critical thinking** is "reasonable reflective thinking that is focused on deciding what to believe or do."[8] If you have ever questioned the answers you were offered, looked for patterns you thought no one else had noticed, or followed a hunch to solve a problem in your own way, you have already begun to cultivate your critical thinking ability.[9] You probably also recognize its importance to your personal and professional life. The authors of a national assessment of educational progress underscored the importance of developing critical thinking skills as follows:

> In a world overloaded with information, both a business and a personal advantage will go to those individuals who can sort the wheat from the chaff, the important from the trivial. . . . Quality of life is directly tied to our ability to think clearly amid the noise of modern life, to sift through all that competes for our attention until we find what we value, what will make our lives worth living.[10]

Drawing from the works of Stuart Rankin and Carolyn Hughes, Robert Marzano and his colleagues have identified eight categories of critical thinking skills (See Table 1.2). As a public speaker, you will exercise all of these skills, sometimes in a different order or in combination, as you develop and deliver your speeches.

Most professional endeavors—whether exploring a therapeutic target in a lab environment or designing a lesson plan on the Revolutionary War for a fifth-grade class—require the critical thinking skills you will develop to be a competent speaker.

critical thinking

The logical, reflective examination of information and ideas to determine what to believe or do.

TABLE 1.2   Eight Categories of Critical Thinking Skills

This Skill . . .	Enables the Public Speaker to . . .
Focusing	Define problems, set goals, and select pieces of information.
Information gathering	Formulate questions and collect data.
Remembering	Store information in long-term memory and retrieve it.
Organizing	Arrange information so that it can be understood and presented more effectively.
Analyzing	Clarify existing information by examining parts and relationships.
Generating	Use prior knowledge to infer and elaborate new information and ideas.
Integrating	Combine, summarize, and restructure information.
Evaluating	Establish criteria and assess the quality of ideas.

SOURCE: Adapted from Robert J. Marzano, Ronald S. Brandt, Carolyn Sue Hughes, Beau Fly Jones, Barbara Z. Presseisen, Stuart C. Rankin, and Charles Suhor, *Dimensions of Thinking: A Framework for Curriculum and Instruction*, Alexandria, VA: Association for Supervision and Curriculum Development (1988), 66, 70–112. Reprinted by permission. The Association for Supervision and Curriculum Development is a worldwide community of educators advocating sound policies and sharing best practices to achieve the success of each learner. To learn more, visit ASCD at www.ascd.org.

Journal: Critical Thinking

Consider a challenging personal situation you recently encountered, whether debating a political topic with a friend or attempting to get your finances in order. In what ways did you think critically to address the issue? Did you employ any of the eight categories of critical thinking skills discussed in this section? If so, how?

To see how one student used these eight critical thinking skills to develop, deliver, and evaluate her speech, read "Theory into Practice: Thinking about Speaking."

Theory into Practice (TIP)

THINKING ABOUT SPEAKING

Effective public speakers care about their topics and their audiences. As they research, construct, and deliver their speeches, they use the critical thinking skills discussed in this chapter. Consider how one student employed each of these skills in developing her speech.

- **Generating** Wanda's first assignment in her public speaking class was to prepare and deliver a speech about someone she admired. She immediately began generating a list of names: her mother, who held down two jobs to help raise five children; a high school teacher who inspired Wanda to go to college; Coretta Scott King, first lady of the civil rights movement; and Thurgood Marshall, the first African American to serve on the U.S. Supreme Court.

- **Focusing** Wanda recalled how Marshall's commitment to justice for all was one of the reasons she aspires to attend law school. So she decided to focus her speech on Marshall.

- **Information gathering and remembering** She devised a research plan and began to gather her supporting materials. Remembering the moving tributes following Marshall's death, Wanda located some of these articles and also found several books about him.

- **Analyzing and focusing** She analyzed her audience, the occasion, and the information she had collected and began to focus her speech further. Wanda decided that a biography of Marshall's life was far too encompassing for a 3- to 5-minute speech. She also chose not to discuss his more controversial decisions on abortion and capital punishment.

- **Organizing, focusing, and integrating** Wanda organized her key ideas and integrated her supporting materials around two central images: closed doors and open doors. First, she would describe some of the doors closed to African Americans during much of Marshall's life: equal education, housing, public transportation, and voting. She would recount that Marshall, the great-grandson of a slave, was denied admission to the University of Maryland Law School. Second, she would tell how Marshall fought to open these doors by expanding access to housing, public transportation, and voting. And she would, of course, note that it was Marshall who successfully argued the case of *Brown v. Board of Education of Topeka* (1954), which declared racial segregation in public schools unconstitutional. She would conclude her story by observing that it was Marshall who litigated the admission of the first African American to graduate from the University of Maryland Law School.

- **Evaluating** Wanda evaluated each of these examples as she prepared her speech to ensure that her ideas were well supported.

- **Remembering** As she constructed her speaking notes, Wanda used only a brief, key word outline to help her remember her ideas.

› SUMMARY

An Introduction to Public Speaking

Why Study Public Speaking?

1.1 Identify the four benefits of studying public speaking.

Public speaking teaches skills that can benefit you academically, personally/socially, professionally, and publicly.

Definitions of Communication

1.2 Define communication, including its five basic levels.

- Communication is the process of sharing meaning by sending and receiving symbolic cues.
- Communication involves individuals (interpreters) attaching referents (meanings) to a variety of symbols (words, gestures, and voice qualities).
- The five levels of communication are intrapersonal, interpersonal, group, public, and mass communication.

Elements of Communication

1.3 Explain the model of communication in terms of the seven elements.

Communication involves seven key elements: speaker, message, listener, feedback, channel, environment, and noise.

The Public Speaker as Critical Thinker

1.4 Use the eight critical thinking skills in developing and evaluating speeches.

Developing and delivering a public speech exercises eight critical thinking skills: focusing, information gathering, remembering, organizing, analyzing, generating, integrating, and evaluating.

THE ETHICS OF PUBLIC SPEAKING

→ LEARNING OBJECTIVES

After studying this chapter, you should be able to

2.1 Define ethics.

2.2 Describe how ethical principles should guide your actions as a speaker and a listener.

2.3 Apply the six common ethical speaking guidelines.

2.4 Apply the four common ethical listening guidelines.

2.5 Apply the principles of civility to your behavior in the classroom.

2.6 Conduct secondary research in accordance with antiplagiarism and fair use principles.

O n July 18, 2016, Melania Trump delivered her first speech to the nation during the Republican National Convention in Cleveland, Ohio. Shortly thereafter, journalist Jarrett Hill noted that several statements in Mrs. Trump's speech were the same, or very similar to, Michelle Obama's speech during the 2008 Democratic National Convention. During the weeks and months that followed, Mrs. Trump's speech was widely discussed on news outlets and social media platforms with many arguing that parts of the speech were plagiarized from Mrs. Obama's speech.[1]

Similarly, on September 8, 2016, Nigerian President Muhammadu Buhari delivered a speech to the Nigerian people in which parts were lifted verbatim from President Obama's 2008 victory speech. President Buhari was so disappointed and embarrassed that he fired his speech writer and apologized for the unfortunate incident.[2]

When we think about public speaking ethics, we are likely drawn to thoughts of plagiarism—the unattributed use of another's ideas, words, or patterns of organization. Plagiarism is a serious offense with serious consequences, whether a failing grade, university expulsion, or—as in the case of President Buhari—international embarrassment. Certainly, ethical speakers must avoid plagiarism at all costs, yet doing so is only part of speaking ethically. Ethical speakers show their audience that they are believable, dependable, competent, trustworthy, and caring. (This is known as developing *credibility* with the audience, a topic you will learn more about in Chapter 16, Learning Objective 16.4.) They also understand and respect their audiences, which they demonstrate by honoring an unwritten contract with their listeners. The terms of this contract require that audience members try to learn, listen without prejudging the speaker or his/her ideas, and, ultimately, evaluate the message and offer feedback. Speakers assume responsibility for being well prepared, communicating ideas clearly in order to benefit the audience, and remaining open to feedback for improvement. In this chapter, we focus on these mutual responsibilities as we examine ethical speaking, ethical listening, and plagiarism.

Definition of Ethics

2.1 Define ethics.

It is virtually impossible to read a newspaper or listen to a newscast today without encountering the topic of ethics. We hear of politicians selling out to special-interest groups, stockbrokers engaging in insider trading, accountants "cooking the books," and contractors taking shortcuts in construction projects. We read stories of people who agonized over the decision to allow—and in some cases help—a terminally ill loved one to die.

When we talk about **ethics**, we refer to the standards we use to determine right from wrong, or good from bad, in thought and behavior. Our sense of ethics guides the choices we make in all aspects of our professional and private lives. You should not be surprised that your academic studies include a discussion of ethics. You are, after all, educating yourself to function in a world where you will make ethical decisions daily. We will now examine why it is important for you to ensure that you communicate ethically.

Principles of Ethics

2.2 Describe how ethical principles should guide your actions as a speaker and a listener.

In discussing communication ethics, Donald Smith noted that communication is an ethically neutral instrument: "Speaking skill per se is neither good nor bad. The skill can be used by good persons or bad persons. It can be put to the service of good purposes [or]

Journal: What is Ethics?

Before reading this section, jot down one or two sentences describing your own definitions of ethics or ethical behavior. Does your understanding match the definition in this section? How would you add to or change the text's definition?

ethics
Standards used to determine right from wrong, good from bad, in both thought and action.

Speakers and listeners alike have ethical responsibilities. If "sexual relations" refers to intercourse, then former president Bill Clinton did not lie by saying, "I did not have sexual relations with that woman [Monica Lewinsky]." However, most audience members would probably assume Mr. Clinton's statement meant that his relationship with Miss Lewinsky was not sexual in nature, which was clearly untrue. Who owns the responsibility to ensure the speaker's message is perceived as intended? In this situation, Mr. Clinton withheld some important facts, but he did not lie.

bad purposes. . . ."[3] In this course, you will learn fundamental communication skills that will empower you as both a speaker and a listener. How you exercise these skills will involve ethical choices and responsibilities.

Two principles frame our discussion of ethics.

- First, *both the speakers who encode and send messages as well as the listeners who receive and decode the messages* have ethical responsibilities. Assume, for example, that a classmate lets you know that he plans to argue in a persuasive speech that "hate speech"—such as protests at military funerals—should be constitutionally protected and is good for the country. Another classmate objects to that position and spreads false claims about what the speaker intends to argue. Students who knew the facts of this case might agree that both students acted unethically. As this example demonstrates, all parties involved in the communication process share ethical obligations.

- Second, *ethical speakers who encode and send messages as well as the listeners who receive and decode messages possess attitudes and standards that pervade their character and guide their actions before, during, and after their speaking and listening.* Ethical speakers and listeners do more than just abstain from unethical behaviors. Ethics is as much a frame of mind as it is a pattern of behavior. Ethics is a working philosophy you apply to your daily life and bring to all speaking situations.

Consider the actions of the speaker in the following incident:

> Lisa presented a persuasive speech on the need for recycling paper, plastic, and aluminum products. To illustrate the many types of recyclables and how overpackaged many grocery products are, she used as an effective visual aid: a paper grocery bag filled with empty cans, paper products, and a variety of plastic bottles and containers. After listening to her well-researched, well-delivered speech, with its impassioned final appeal for us to help save the planet by recycling, the class watched in amazement as she put the empty containers back in the bag, walked to the corner of the room, and dropped the bag in the trash can! After a few seconds, someone finally asked, "You mean you're not going to take these home to recycle them?" "Nah," said Lisa. "I'm tired of lugging them around. I've done my job."

You may or may not believe that people have an ethical responsibility to recycle. But regardless of your views on that issue, you likely question the ethics of someone who insists, in effect, "Do as I say, not as I do." Lisa's actions made the entire class question her sincerity. Ethical standards cannot be turned on and off at an individual's convenience. Lisa certainly could have benefited from ethical speaking guidelines we present in the next section.

Ethical Speaking

2.3 Apply the six common ethical speaking guidelines.

Maintaining strong ethical attitudes and standards requires sound decision making at every step in the speech-making process. In this section, we present six guidelines to help you with these decisions.

Speak to Benefit Your Listeners

First, *ethical public speakers communicate in order to benefit their listeners as well as themselves.* Speakers and listeners participate in a transactional relationship; both should benefit from their participation. Listeners give speakers their time; in return, speakers should provide information that is interesting or useful.

Journal: Principles of Ethics

Consider the following scenario. A friend of yours—who is also a public speaking classmate—sells a legal and inexpensive supplement that claims to enable both men and women to enhance their workout performances. Your friend delivers an excellent speech in which he informs the audience about the supplement and how it works. However, he does not disclose that he sells the supplement and receives a commission for each person he convinces to make a purchase. When the class is over, you see several classmates asking your friend for more information on where to purchase the supplement. What do you do? Do you stay quiet or do you tell your classmates that your friend profits from the sales? Would you be more, less, or equally conflicted about this ethical quandary if your friend's speech were persuasive rather than informative?

Informative speakers have an obligation to benefit their audience. As in the following example, however, speakers sometimes lose sight of that responsibility.

> Assigned to give an informative speech demonstrating a process or procedure, plant lover Evelyn decided to show how to plant a seed in a pot. Her instructor was worried that this subject was something everyone already knew. Evelyn was, after all, speaking to college students who presumably could read the planting instructions on the back of a seed packet. The instructor did not want to discourage Evelyn but wanted the class to benefit from her speech.
>
> Without saying, "You cannot speak on this topic," the instructor shared her concerns with Evelyn. She found out that Evelyn had several other plant-related topics in mind. Evelyn agreed that a more unusual topic would be more interesting to the class and more challenging for her to deliver. On the day she was assigned to speak, Evelyn presented an interesting speech demonstrating how to propagate tropical plants by "air layering" them. Evelyn got a chance to demonstrate her green thumb, and her classmates learned something most had never heard of before.

You may often speak for personal benefit, and this is not necessarily unethical. You may, for instance, urge a group to support your candidacy or to buy your product. It is appropriate to pursue personal goals but not at the expense of your listeners. As one popular book on business ethics states, "There is no right way to do a wrong thing."[4] Speakers whose objective is to persuade should do so openly and with the goal of benefiting both the audience and themselves. A public speaker may try to inform, convince, persuade, direct, or even anger an audience. Ethical speakers, however, do not deceive their listeners. They are up front about their intentions, and those intentions include benefiting the audience.

Speak Up about Topics You Consider Important

Second, ethical public speakers make careful decisions about whether or not to speak. If an issue is trivial, silence is sometimes the best option. There are times, though, when speakers have an ethical obligation to convey information or when they feel strongly about an issue or an injustice. *Ethical communicators speak up about topics they consider important.* Our nation's history has been shaped by the voices of Thomas Jefferson, Frederick Douglass, Susan B. Anthony, Martin Luther King Jr., Cesar Chavez, and other advocates. You may never have the sweeping historical impact of these famous speakers, but you do have an opportunity to better the communities of which you are a part. You have a chance to share information your classmates can use to help them get more from their college experience or function better in their careers and personal lives. You can educate others about problems you believe need to be confronted. This class provides a training ground to hone your skills as speaker and listener. Use these skills as you move from involvement in class and campus issues to improvement of your community.

Choose Topics That Promote Positive Ethical Values

Third, *ethical speakers choose topics that promote positive ethical values.* Unless you are assigned one, selecting a topic is the first ethical choice you will likely make. You give your topic credibility simply by selecting it; and, as an ethical speaker, your choice should reflect what you think is important to your listeners.

In the course we teach, many student speeches have expanded our knowledge or moved us to act on significant issues. But consider this list of speech topics that some students have proposed:

- How to download copyright protected music and movies for free
- How to avoid paying taxes
- How students can get free snacks from a campus snack machine
- How to receive credit for the same paper in two different classes

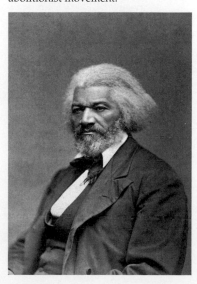

The formerly enslaved American orator Frederick Douglass used his voice to call attention to the abolitionist movement.

Even though they were all informative rather than persuasive speeches, each of these how-to topics implies that its action is acceptable. We suggest that all these speakers disrespected their listeners, failed to consider the values they were promoting, and presented unethical speeches.

Use Truthful Supporting Materials and Valid Reasoning

Fourth, *ethical speakers use truthful supporting materials and valid reasoning*. Listeners have a right to know both the speakers' ideas and the material supporting their claims. Ethical speakers are well informed and should test the truthfulness and validity of their ideas. They should not knowingly use false information or faulty reasoning.

One student gave a persuasive speech to urge his classmates to contact their state representatives to vote for a particular education bill. To help his audience with this task, he distributed a list of legislators with their phone numbers and addresses. After the speaker finished his speech, the instructor informed the speaker that the bill he supported had been passed by the legislature and signed by the governor the previous week. The premise that the bill had not yet been passed was false. Not getting caught in a factual or logical error does not free the speaker of the ethical responsibility to present complete, factual information. If you speak on a current topic, use the most recent information you can find and try to be as well informed as possible.

Consider the Consequences of Your Words and Actions

Fifth, *ethical speakers concern themselves with the consequences of their speaking*. Mary Cunningham observed, "Words are sacred things. They are also like hand grenades: Handled casually, they tend to go off."[5] Ethical speakers respect the power of language and the process of communication.

It is difficult to track, let alone to predict, the impact of any one message. Individuals may form opinions and behave differently because of what you say or fail to say. Incorrect information and misinterpretations may have unintended and potentially harmful consequences. If you provide an audience with inaccurate information, you

Speakers must remember that their words and messages have consequences—sometimes life or death consequences.

may contaminate the quality of their subsequent decisions. If you persuade someone to act in a particular way, you are partly responsible for the impact of the person's new action.

A colleague's student recently delivered an informative speech about rock-climbing safety. In her speech, she demonstrated how to tie the "figure 8 knot" that is used to connect the rope to the climber's harness. Although the speaker had her listeners' best intentions in mind, an experienced rock climber in the class pointed out that she offered several problematic directions as well as misleading information. The oversight was certainly not intentional, but you can imagine the potentially devastating consequences of the listeners going rock climbing and not using the correct, safe "figure 8 knot." Our colleague therefore respectfully asked the speaker to clarify the "figure 8 knot" at the end of the class period to ensure all listeners knew how to tie the knot correctly.

Strive to Improve Your Public Speaking

Finally, *ethical speakers strive to improve their public speaking*. Speakers who use the guidelines we have presented accept their obligation to communicate responsibly. Their ideas have value, are logically supported, and do not deceive their listeners. We would argue, however, that this is not enough.

Ethical speakers are concerned not only with *what* they say but also with *how* they say it. As a result, they work actively to become more effective communicators. This course provides you with an opportunity to begin mastering public speaking. You will learn how to select, support, evaluate, organize, and deliver your ideas. Your professional and public life beyond the classroom will extend your opportunities to speak publicly. Speakers have "the opportunity to learn to speak well, and to be eloquent [advocates of] truth and justice." If they fail to develop these abilities, they have not fulfilled their "ethical obligation in a free society."[6]

> **Key Points: Guidelines for Ethical Speaking**
>
> 1. Speak to benefit your listeners.
> 2. Speak up about topics you consider important.
> 3. Choose topics that promote positive ethical values.
> 4. Use truthful supporting materials and valid reasoning.
> 5. Consider the consequences of your words and actions.
> 6. Strive to improve your public speaking.

Ethical Listening

2.4 Apply the four common ethical listening guidelines.

The guidelines for ethical speaking we've just discussed probably make perfect sense to you. If some seem intimidating, if you feel that the future of free expression in a democratic society rests squarely on your shoulders, remember that no individual bears such a responsibility alone. Your listeners are obligated to adhere to four basic principles, and you share these ethical responsibilities as you listen to others' speeches.

ETHICAL DECISIONS

GRAY ZONES

Many ethical decisions are not clear cut or black and white, but rather fall into a "gray zone," making a clear course of action challenging to determine. Ethical gray zone issues involve "situations that might be unethical, undesirable or uncomfortable but are probably not severe enough to prompt legal action or reporting."[7] These gray zone situations often require people to make a decision about whether or not they can live with certain outcomes or certain knowledge, such as knowing that they have lied to spare a friend's feelings.

So, how do we deal with such gray zone issues? Let's assume that one of your closest friends is in your public speaking class. She has a great deal of public speaking anxiety and also tends to evaluate herself very harshly. To be honest, her first speech did not go particularly well. She spoke so softly that it was difficult to hear her and she rarely made eye contact. You also found her body movements stiff and awkward. After class she seemed relieved and said, "I think I did OK. What did you think of my speech?"

What would you do in this gray zone situation, knowing that your friend needs to improve but is very sensitive to criticism?

Seek Exposure to Well-Informed Speakers

First, *ethical listeners seek out speakers who expand their knowledge and understanding, introduce them to new ideas, and challenge their beliefs.* These listeners reject the philosophy, "My mind's made up, so don't confuse me with the facts." A controversial speaker visiting your campus can expand your knowledge or intensify your feelings about a subject, whether you agree or disagree with the speaker's viewpoint. Even in situations in which you are a captive audience, such as this class, ethical listening should be the standard.

Avoid Prejudging Speakers or Their Ideas

Second, *ethical listeners listen openly without prejudging speakers or their ideas.* This may be difficult. Listening without bias may require that we temporarily suspend impressions we have formed based on the speaker's past actions or our current views of the speaker's topic or position. But the rewards of doing so can be great, as in this example:

> Mai's first speech in class completely confused her classmates. She seemed nervous and unsure of herself and what she was going to say. The point of her speech eluded everyone. Class discussion after the speech focused primarily on Mai's delivery and some of the distracting mannerisms she exhibited and needed to control. When she went to the front of the room to begin her next speech weeks later, no one was really expecting to be impressed, but they were.
>
> Mai's second speech dealt with the problem of homelessness. Her opening sentence told the class that three years before, she had been living on the street. She had their attention from that point on. In addition to citing recent newspaper and magazine articles, Mai had conducted a great deal of research. She had interviewed the directors of local shelters and a number of the homeless people who took refuge there, and she quoted these individuals. Her speech was well organized and well delivered. It was both educational and inspiring.
>
> When discussing the speech later, classmates kept referring to her first speech and noting the remarkable improvements Mai had made. One person was blunt, but apparently summed up the feelings of a number of listeners that day: "Mai, I wasn't expecting much from you because your first speech was so unclear to me, but today you had a topic that you obviously care about, and you made us understand and care about it, too. I can't get over the difference between those two speeches!"

Speakers often present views that may be controversial. Whether or not we as the listeners agree with them, we should withhold judgment until after listening to what they say.

When listening to your classmates, assume that you may learn something important from each speaker and therefore listen intently. Information and ideas are best shared in an atmosphere of civility and mutual respect.

Evaluate the Speaker's Logic and Credibility

Listening eagerly and openly does not imply a permanent suspension of judgment. The third standard is that *ethical listeners evaluate the messages presented to them.* A listener who accepts a premise without evaluating its foundation is like someone who buys a used car without looking under the hood. The warning "Let the buyer beware" is good advice not only for consumers of products but also for consumers of messages.

As a listener, you should critically evaluate a speaker's ideas. Is each idea logically constructed? Is each idea supported with evidence that is relevant, sufficient, and authoritative? In Chapter 9, Learning Objective 9.3, and Chapter 17, Learning Objective 17.2, you will learn specific strategies to help you answer these questions as you listen to evaluate a speaker's evidence and logic.

Beware of the Consequences of Not Listening Carefully

Fourth, *ethical listeners concern themselves with the consequences of their listening.* As the following example illustrates, listeners who assimilate only part of a speaker's message because they fail to listen actively to the entire message are responsible for the distorted message that results.

> Eduardo, a fellow student in Elia's public speaking class, gave an informative speech about the ocular disease macular degeneration, the leading cause of vision loss in the United States. He was inspired to research and present this topic because of his grandmother's experience with the disease. Elia's great-aunt was recently diagnosed with the same condition, so her mind immediately started racing with the information she heard her family discuss—such as an implantable telescope that could improve the remaining sight for those suffering with severe cases. At the end of class, Elia rushed up to Eduardo to share her sympathies and to ask if his grandmother was aware of some of the newer treatment options, like the implantable device. Eduardo stared at her blankly and asked, "Did you hear the end of my speech? My grandmother wasn't a candidate for that treatment, nor will she benefit from any of the new research because she passed away two years ago."

Elia may have been embarrassed and have offended Eduardo with her lack of close listening, but neither party suffered long-term consequences. In other cases, however, the outcome of not listening is more serious. When you fail to listen to someone's directions and are late for an interview, you miss an employment opportunity. When you fail to follow a doctor's or pharmacist's instructions, you put your health at risk. In both of these examples, the listener, not the speaker, bears responsibility for the breakdown in communication.

At other times, the listener and the speaker may share responsibility for unethical behavior. For example, audience members who become victims of scams because they did not listen critically share responsibility for their victimization with the speaker. Voters who tolerate exaggerated, vague, and inconsistent campaign statements from those who ask to represent them are similarly complicit in ethically lax political campaigns and partially responsible for the results of those campaigns.

In the past, views of communication ethics implied a dotted line across the front of a classroom, with ethics being solely the speaker's responsibility. In contrast, we view ethics as a shared responsibility of the speaker and each listener. An absence of ethical motives among speakers and listeners devalues the currency of communication.

Key Points: Guidelines for Ethical Listening

1. Seek exposure to well-informed speakers.
2. Avoid prejudging speakers or their ideas.
3. Evaluate the logic and credibility of the speaker's ideas.
4. Beware of the consequences of not listening carefully.

Journal: Careful Listening

Share a personal example of a time when a lack of critical listening caused confusion or negative consequences, either because you did not listen carefully to someone or because someone did not listen carefully to you. Who was ethically responsible for the missed message—the speaker, the listener, or both? Explain your answer.

Civility in the Classroom

2.5 Apply the principles of civility to your behavior in the classroom.

As Keith gave his first graded speech in his public speaking class, he thought, "This is going well." Then from the audience came a buzzing sound. He stumbled over a few words as he noticed his classmate Eden reaching into her bag to retrieve her phone. When the entire class saw Eden begin to respond to a text message, the instructor asked Keith to stop until he regained the attention of all his listeners.

Sound familiar? We hope not, but we suspect that you and some of your instructors have had similar experiences. Unfortunately, examples of disrespectful and discourteous communication occur not only in classrooms but also in politics, in workplaces, in meetings, on blogs, and on Internet message boards. The Institute for Civility in Government laments "the lack of civility in our society in general and our public discourse in particular."[8] Communication professors Rod Troester and Cathy Sargent Mester define **civility** as a "set of verbal and nonverbal behaviors reflecting fundamental respect for others and generating harmonious and productive relationships."[9] Sometimes equated with courtesy and etiquette, civility is a more complex pattern of behavior that involves attitudes, such as respect, and behaviors, including providing classmates feedback on their speeches.

We have argued that your public speaking class is a community of learners. You will be a part of that community for the rest of the semester or quarter, and the population will function best if all members exhibit respect and mutual support. The following guidelines, discussed more fully in subsequent chapters, will contribute to your enjoyment and success in this class as both a speaker and a listener.

civility
Communication behaviors that reflect respect for others and foster harmonious and productive relationships.

Speaking with Civility

- *Have good motives.* Select topics that benefit your listeners and the communities to which they belong.
- *Prepare and assess what you will say.* Support your ideas with quality evidence and examples.
- *Respect your listeners.* Appreciate the diversity of your audience and adapt your messages to all your listeners.
- *Speak with conviction.* Believe in your topic and convey that commitment as you speak.
- *Encourage the other side to be heard.* Value public discussion and debate, and answer questions others may have about your topic.
- *Welcome feedback.* Appreciate and act on suggestions and criticisms to improve your speaking competence.

Listening with Civility

- *Give speakers your full attention.* Observe classroom courtesy. Don't text, check Facebook, eat a sandwich, or walk into class when another student is speaking. And, of course, don't sleep or study for another class when your instructor or a classmate is speaking.
- *Expect to learn something.* Don't prejudge speakers or their ideas. Value and learn from people's differences, believing with Malcolm Forbes that "education's purpose is to replace an empty mind with an open one."
- *Evaluate the merits of the speaker's ideas and supporting materials.* Take responsibility for how you act on the information a speaker has presented.
- *Provide the speaker constructive feedback.* Contribute to the learning of others.

The civil classroom doesn't just happen; civility is a choice. It requires work on the part of the instructor and each student, but the results surely include more effective and enjoyable learning. Some advocates even assert that civility "reduces the literal and figurative costs of stress and leads to greater productivity, better health, and more happiness."[10]

Civility grows from mutual respect; it connects us with others. The attitudes and behaviors you develop and practice in this class can serve you well into the future. Civility is "the glue that holds us together and allows us as citizens of a representative democracy to dialogue with each other."[11]

Journal: Civility in the Classroom

Suppose a speaker in your class says something in a speech that you find offensive. How might you form a civil and constructive comment to give the speaker? What would *not* be a civil, constructive approach?

Plagiarism and Copyright Law

2.6 Conduct secondary research in accordance with antiplagiarism and fair use principles.

Not only do ethical speakers carefully craft their own words to express their ideas, but they also care about how they use the words and ideas of others. Thus, three important aspects of ethics are crediting sources, paraphrasing appropriately, and understanding fair use guidelines. But first, you must have a better understanding of what plagiarism is—in its many forms—so that you may work diligently to avoid it.

Recognizing Plagiarism

The word *plagiarize* comes from a Latin word meaning "to kidnap," so in a sense a plagiarist is a kidnapper of ideas and words. A modern definition of **plagiarism** is "literary—or artistic or musical—theft. It is the false assumption of authorship: the wrongful act of taking the product of another person's mind, and presenting it as one's own."[12]

plagiarism
The unattributed use of another's ideas, words, or pattern of organization.

When you write a paper and submit it to a teacher, you are in effect publishing that work. If, in that paper, you copy something from another source and pass it off as your own work, you are plagiarizing. This act is such a serious offense that in most colleges and universities it is grounds for failing the course or dismissal from the school. Yet recent history has shown us numerous examples of politicians, educators, historians, and other public figures caught plagiarizing materials, either consciously or unconsciously. Plagiarism is an offense serious enough to derail a candidate's campaign for office, to force the resignation of a corporate officer, or to end a student's academic career.

Plagiarism applies to more than simply the copying of another's words. You may also plagiarize another's ideas and organization of material. For example, if you presented a speech organized around the five stages of grief (denial, anger, bargaining, depression, and acceptance) and did not give credit to Elisabeth Kübler-Ross, you would be guilty of plagiarism. On the other hand, if your speech analyzed the political, economic, and social implications of a pending piece of legislation, you would probably not be guilty of plagiarism. Kübler-Ross developed, explained, and published her framework, or model, in her book *On Death and Dying*, whereas the second example relies on a commonly accepted pattern of analyzing public policy initiatives. The line between legitimate appropriation of material and plagiarism is sometimes unclear. As a speaker, you must always be on guard to credit the source of your ideas and their structure.

Plagiarism is often categorized as intentional or unintentional. **Intentional plagiarism** occurs when speakers or writers knowingly present another person's words, ideas, or organization as their own. A related ethical issue is sometimes referred to as *double dipping*, *dual submission*, or *self-plagiarism*. This involves recycling your own work. Revisiting earlier research and extending, elaborating, rethinking, or updating it can be beneficial. But no one hearing you deliver a speech on "major themes in Thomas

intentional plagiarism
The deliberate, unattributed use of another's ideas, words, or pattern of organization.

Pynchon's novel *Gravity's Rainbow*" is going to be tricked. You're recycling work you did for another class, and many schools have written policies prohibiting this practice. Check with your instructor about her or his policy regarding use of previous work or research you plan to use in a speech and for an assignment in another class.

unintentional plagiarism

The careless or unconscious unattributed use of another's ideas, words, or pattern of organization.

Unintentional plagiarism is "the careless paraphrasing and citing of source material such that improper or misleading credit is given."[13] Intentional plagiarism is considered the more serious offense. Widespread use of the Internet for research may be blurring the distinction between deliberate and accidental plagiarism, however. Web pages are ephemeral; page content and design can change from one day to the next. That quality, together with the ease of browsing numerous sites in a short time, lets readers pick up phrases, ideas, or even organizational patterns almost unconsciously. If a researcher has not printed, bookmarked, or jotted down the URLs for key sites, retracing steps and finding those sites again may be difficult. Unintentional plagiarism may be committed due to ignorance or sloppy research methods, but the effect is still the same: One person is taking credit for the work of another.

global plagiarism

Plagiarism that occurs when someone presents an entire speech or paper created by someone else as his or her own.

patchwork plagiarism

Plagiarism that occurs when someone presents parts of various speeches or papers as his or her own.

incremental plagiarism

Plagiarism that occurs when someone fails to cite his or her sources when presenting information.

Depending on how, and the extent to which a person plagiarizes the work of others, the offense may be considered *global*, *patchwork*, or *incremental* plagiarism. **Global plagiarism** occurs when someone presents an entire speech or paper created by someone else as his or her own original work. **Patchwork plagiarism**, as implied by its name, occurs when someone presents parts or segments of various speeches or papers as his or her own original work. Finally, **incremental plagiarism** occurs when people fail to cite their sources when presenting information.[14] Regardless of the type of plagiarism one commits, it is a serious offense—even if unintentional. Therefore, you should take precautions to avoid plagiarism by giving credit where credit is due.

Crediting Sources and Paraphrasing Appropriately

Luckily, avoiding plagiarism is not a challenge if you are a careful and diligent speaker. Simply tell your listeners when you are using someone else's words, ideas, or organization. If you want to share a photo you found on Instagram, be sure to cite the source and the date you accessed it. For information from an online reference work, newspaper, journal, magazine, or blog, simply cite the source and report when the information was posted or when you accessed it. Please refer to Chapter 9, Learning Objective 9.4, for a discussion about how to cite your sources correctly.

While global plagiarism and incremental plagiarism are clear to most students, patchwork plagiarism can be more challenging to understand as students sometimes think that they have created something "new" out of several different ideas. If each patch represents an unattributed idea, then your speech lacks ethical cohesiveness and you are guilty of plagiarism.

In addition, ethical speakers must use caution to **paraphrase** appropriately. Unintentional plagiarism sometimes occurs because of a common misconception that by simply changing a few words of another's writing, you have paraphrased the statement and need not cite it. Michael O'Neill refers to this "hybrid of half textual source, half original writing" as a **paraplage**.[15] Note the differences and similarities in the original and adapted passages of the following statement.

paraphrase

To express the meaning of another person's work (written or spoken) using different words.

STATEMENT BY ERIK VANCE

In the mid-1940s, Norman Borlaug started the Green Revolution on a small farm in southern Mexico. His idea was simple. As the human population skyrocketed, he would grow a new kind of wheat with a thicker stem and bigger seed heads, thus increasing its yield and allowing farmers to grow more wheat—and feed more people—per acre.

The results were staggering. Within two decades, Mexico's wheat harvest had swollen six-fold, thanks to crops descended from Borlaug's original modified wheat. Borlaug then turned his talents toward rice in the Philippines, and high-yield crops spread into almost every major food staple. In all, Borlaug's revolution helped feed millions of people in poor and developing countries who would otherwise have starved—an achievement that earned him the 1970 Nobel Peace Prize.[16]

SPEAKER'S PARAPLAGE OF ERIK VANCE

The Green Revolution started back in the 1940s as the human population skyrocketed. Working on a small farm in Mexico, Norman Borlaug developed a strain of wheat with thick stems and bigger seeds. As a result, farmers could increase their yields and feed more people.

Just two decades later, the Mexican wheat harvest had increased to six times what it was previously. Borlaug turned to genetically modifying rice, helping to feed millions of people. For his efforts, Borlaug earned the Nobel Peace Prize in 1970.

SPEAKER'S APPROPRIATE CITATION OF ERIK VANCE

As suspicious as some people are of "genetically modified" foods, the first such foods saved millions of lives. Freelance science writer Erik Vance tells the story of Norman Borlaug's experiments in the July/September 2010 issue of *Conservation Magazine*. Borlaug grew a new kind of wheat with thicker stems and bigger seed heads, which was therefore resistant to the effects of wind and water.

Vance calls the results "staggering" and says that, "Within two decades, Mexico's wheat harvest had swollen six-fold." After Borlaug turned his attention to rice, he saved millions of people.

Notice that the appropriate citation in this example tells the listener something about Vance's credentials and explains exactly where his words appeared. With that information, any listener wanting to read the entire article could find it quickly.

paraplage

Plagiarism consisting of half original writing and half quotation from an unattributed source.

The ability to paraphrase effectively tests your critical thinking skills of analyzing, integrating, and generating. To improve your paraphrasing, consider the following guidelines from the Purdue University Online Writing Lab:

1. Reread the original passage until you understand it fully.
2. Set the original aside; write your paraphrase on a notecard or on paper or type it into a file.
3. Below your paraphrase, write a few words to remind you later how you might use this material in your speech. Near your paraphrase, write a key word or phrase in all capital letters to indicate its subject.

Theory into Practice (TIP)

HOW TO AVOID PLAGIARISM

To avoid plagiarizing, let the following five simple rules guide you:

- *Take clear and consistent notes while researching.* As you review your notes, you should be able to discern which words, ideas, examples, and organizational structures belong to which authors.

- *Record complete source citations.* Each sheet of notes, each photocopied article, and each printed page of a document you have accessed should indicate its source(s).

- *Clearly indicate in your speech any words, ideas, examples, or organizational structures that are not your own.* If you cite a source early in your speech and then use another idea from that author later, you must again give that author

credit. You do not need to repeat the complete citation, however. Use an abbreviated citation, such as "Vance says that" in our earlier example, if you have provided the full citation earlier in your speech.

- *Use your own words, language style, and thought structure when paraphrasing.* Remember that both content and structure distinguish another person's statements. When paraphrasing what another person has written or said, you should use not just your own words but also your own language style and thought structure. Otherwise, you are "paraplaging."

- *When in doubt, cite the source.* If you are unsure whether you really need to acknowledge a source, it's always wise to err on the side of caution.

---

4. Check your version against the original to make sure that your paraphrase accurately expresses all the essential information in a new form.

5. Use quotation marks to identify any unique terms or phrases you have borrowed exactly from the source.

6. Record the source on your notecard so that you can credit it easily if you incorporate the material in your speech.[17]

We have discussed some of the dangers of hiding the true authorship of words and ideas. There are also at least two benefits of crediting sources. First, speakers who cite their sources increase their credibility, or believability, with the audience. When you quote from a book, an article, or an interview and name the author or speaker of those words, you show the audience that you have researched the topic and that you know what you are talking about. Second, and far more important, acknowledging your sources is the right thing to do. It is honest. Good ideas and memorably worded thoughts are rare enough that the original writer or speaker deserves credit. For a handy list of tips to avoid plagiarism in your upcoming speech, see "Theory into Practice: How to Avoid Plagiarism."

Fair Use Guidelines

If the person behind the counter in a copy shop has ever made you feel like a criminal for asking to copy a magazine or journal article—never mind a few pages or photographs from a book—you have experienced one of the quirks of copyright law. The copy shop operates to make a profit; you probably don't have any commercial use for the material in mind. As a result, the copy shop employee may direct you to a self-service copy machine, where you assume full responsibility for respecting copyright law.

Copyright law applies to both print and electronic sources, including audio and video works. The "same copyright protections exist . . . regardless of whether the work is in a database, on CD-ROM, on a bulletin board, or on the Internet."[18] However, section 107 of the Copyright Law of the United States, commonly called the **fair use provision**, says that "the fair use of a copyrighted work . . . is not an infringement of copyright."[19]

Georgia Harper, copyright expert and Scholarly Communications Advisor for the University of Texas at Austin Libraries, has translated these four factors into rules of

fair use provision

Section 107 of U.S. copyright law allowing limited noncommercial use of copyrighted materials for teaching, criticism, scholarship, research, or commentary.

thumb that "describe a 'safe harbor' within the bounds of fair use."[20] If you plan to use any copyrighted material in a speech, ask the following four questions:

- *What is the purpose and character of the use?* If your intended use is personal, educational, or nonprofit, chances are it is fair use. Use of copyrighted material for purposes of research, scholarship, teaching, commentary, and news reporting usually falls under fair use.

- *What is the nature of the work to be used?* Use of published sources that report news and factual information weighs in favor of fair use. Fair use favors published works more than unpublished works, reinforcing the rationale "that authors should be able to decide when to publish their work."[21]

- *How much of the work will you use?* Noncommercial use of a small portion, excerpt, or clip of a copyrighted work likely qualifies as fair use. Commercial uses that exceed strict length limits, however, require permission.

- *What effect would your use have on the market value of the work?* Information from published sources for class speeches and papers are usually considered fair use. Class assignments fall into the category of "one-time use;" speeches are seldom recorded and distributed.[22]

These guidelines seem to suggest that most copyrighted sources for classroom speeches and papers are covered by fair use. However, what if you publish your work beyond the classroom? What if you post your speech online, and it includes a clip from a popular movie? What if you conduct a problem-solving workshop for an on-campus or off-campus organization and you draw heavily from suggestions in a copyrighted source? What if you get paid for the workshop? Be careful. You may be leaving that "safe harbor" of fair use.

We reiterate one final point. The fair use provision does *not* give you the right to use another's work without crediting that person, agency, or organization. Unattributed use—even fair use—of someone else's work leaves you open to charges of plagiarism, an issue that seems to grow more important in these days of cut-and-paste Internet research.

Journal: Practice Paraphrasing

Paraphrase the following sentences from your textbook's discussion of fair use and include a citation: "We reiterate one final point. The fair use provision does *not* give you the right to use another's work without crediting that person, agency, or organization. Unattributed use—even fair use—of someone else's work leaves you open to charges of plagiarism."

› SUMMARY

The Ethics of Public Speaking

Definition of Ethics

2.1 Define ethics.

Ethics refers to fundamental questions of right and wrong in thought and behavior.

Principles of Ethics

2.2 Describe how ethical principles should guide your actions as a speaker and a listener.

- Both speakers and listeners have ethical responsibilities.
- Ethical speakers and listeners possess attitudes and standards that pervade their character and guide their actions before, during, and after their speaking and listening.

Ethical Speaking

2.3 Apply the six common ethical speaking guidelines.

- Ethical speakers speak to benefit their listeners, not merely to fulfill their own needs.
- Ethical speakers choose topics and issues they consider important as well as topics that promote positive ethical values. They present audiences with ideas backed by logical reasoning and authentic, up-to-date supporting materials.
- Ethical speakers care about the consequences their words and actions may have for their listeners, and they seek to improve their public speaking.

Ethical Listening

2.4 Apply the four common ethical listening guidelines.

- Ethical listeners welcome challenges to their beliefs, just as they embrace learning.
- Ethical listeners listen openly, without prejudging the speaker or the speaker's ideas.

- Ethical listeners evaluate the speaker's ideas before acting on them.
- Ethical listeners care about and accept responsibility for the consequences of their listening.

Civility in the Classroom

2.5 Apply the principles of civility to your behavior in the classroom.

- Civility in the classroom is a two-way street. Speakers should have good motives, prepare and assess what they will say, respect their listeners, speak with conviction, encourage the other side to be heard, and finally, welcome feedback.
- Listeners should give speakers their full attention, expect to learn something, evaluate the merits of the speaker's ideas and supporting materials, and, finally, provide the speaker constructive feedback.

Plagiarism and Copyright Law

2.6 Conduct secondary research in accordance with antiplagiarism and fair use principles.

- Both speakers and listeners need to be aware of *plagiarism*, the unattributed use of another's ideas, words, or organization. Plagiarism may be either *intentional* or *unintentional*. Depending on how, and the extent to which a person plagiarizes the work of others, the offense may be considered *global, patchwork,* or *incremental* plagiarism.
- Speakers planning to use copyrighted materials in their speeches need to be aware of the *fair use provision* of copyright law. Factors that determine whether a particular use is fair are the speakers' purposes, the nature of the works used, the proportion of the entire work that speakers want to use, and the effect that widespread use such as the speakers intend would have on the market value of the original work.

SPEAKING WITH CONFIDENCE

⟶ LEARNING OBJECTIVES

After studying this chapter, you should be able to

3.1 Explain public speaking anxiety and why it is a normal experience.

3.2 Describe the seven public speaking skills that can help you manage your nervousness and build confidence.

3.3 Describe the six physical and psychological strategies that can help you manage your nervousness and build confidence.

3.4 Apply the seven guidelines to help you develop a successful first speech.

Nancy Daniels, an experienced public speaking instructor who writes about speech anxiety, once stated:

> It never ceases to amaze me how many people want to get rid of their nervousness in public speaking. In truth, they should embrace that wonderful rush of adrenaline. If you're not nervous when presenting, then I am because being overly confident is never a good thing in public speaking or any live venue for that matter.[1]

Daniels argues further that nervousness should be viewed positively because it can actually enhance the quality of your speech.

Perhaps you experience some apprehension as you think about the speeches you will present in academic, professional, or celebratory settings. This chapter and this class are designed to build your speaking confidence. First, you will learn what public speaking apprehension is and that it is completely normal. (Most of your classmates are also nervous.) Then, you will examine strategies that can help you manage your nervous energy before learning calming guidelines for preparing and presenting your first speech.

Recognize That Speaker Nervousness Is Normal

3.1 Explain public speaking anxiety and why it is a normal experience.

communication apprehension

The fear or anxiety associated with real or anticipated communication with another person or persons.

Communication apprehension is the "fear or anxiety associated with either real or anticipated communication with another person or persons."[2] This apprehension can be experienced in various situations, such as in interpersonal communication situations, when communicating in small groups, or when communicating during meetings.

public speaking anxiety

A fear of speaking to an audience when delivering a speech.

But, more commonly, people experience a fear of speaking to an audience when delivering a speech. This is known as **public speaking anxiety**, sometimes called platform panic or stage fright. It can stem from a fear of making mistakes (like mispronouncing a word or stumbling over a presentational aid) and a concern about receiving negative performance evaluations.[3]

How does public speaking anxiety affect us? Chemically and physiologically, we all experience stage fright in the same way. Adrenaline is suddenly pumped into the bloodstream. Respiration increases dramatically, as do heart rate and perspiration. Have you ever heard a story of a 135-pound person lifting the front of a car to help rescue someone pinned underneath? Such incidents happen because adrenaline mobilizes the body to do what must be done. Yet the body can be similarly mobilized in stressful situations that are not life threatening. Athletes waiting for a game to begin, actors for the curtain to go up, and speakers for their call to the lectern often feel their bodies marshaling all their resources either to perform to capacity or to get away from the threatening situation. This phenomenon is appropriately called the *fight-or-flight syndrome*.

As the time approaches for your first speech, you may experience any of several symptoms to varying degrees. Students tell us that their symptoms include blushing or redness, accelerated heart rate, perspiring, dry mouth, shaking, churning stomach, increased rate of speech, forgetfulness and broken speech, and nervous mannerisms such as playing with jewelry, tapping fingers, and clutching the lectern. Other negative effects include lower levels of self-esteem,[4] cognitive flexibility,[5] self-perceived communication competence, and willingness to communicate in general.[6]

These symptoms are unpleasant, but here is what we want you to understand: *They are perfectly normal.*

A 2012 study by Kevin Dwyer and Marlina Davidson "found that public speaking anxiety was selected by college students more often as a common fear than any other fear, including death."[7] Our experience as well as the research of many other scholars confirms the prevalence of public speaking anxiety among college students. When asked to list their communication weaknesses, a clear majority of students rank speaking before a group as their primary issue. The late James McCroskey of the University of Alabama–Birmingham studied public speaking anxiety extensively. His well-known Personal Report of Public Speaking Anxiety (PRPSA) assesses the degree of nervousness or anxiety college students have about giving speeches. McCroskey collected data from several thousand students just like you and he confirmed that public speaking generates greater anxiety than other forms of communication:

- 40 percent experience high anxiety.
- 30 percent experience moderately high anxiety.
- 20 percent experience moderate anxiety.
- 5 percent experience moderately low anxiety.
- 5 percent experience low anxiety.

Note that nearly three-fourths of college students fall into the moderately high to high anxiety range. This means that the person who always has the quick response, who can make others laugh, and who always looks "together" is probably just as worried as you are about giving a speech. McCroskey and coauthor Virginia Richmond concluded,

> What this suggests, then, is that it is "normal" to experience a fairly high degree of anxiety about public speaking. Most people do. If you are highly anxious about public speaking, then you are "normal."[8]

At this point you may think that taking this course is a terrible mistake. We assure you that it is not! In fact, it's quite the opposite. Research indicates that students' communication apprehension and public speaking anxiety decrease throughout the course as you learn new and beneficial skills. So, by applying the strategies presented in this chapter, you will be able to reduce and manage your nervousness. This also means that your self-esteem, self-perceived communication competence, cognitive flexibility, and other aspects of your psychological well-being are likely to improve throughout this course.

Apply Public Speaking Skills to Manage Speaker Nervousness

3.2 Describe the seven public speaking skills that can help you manage your nervousness and build confidence.

Before discussing what your goal should be regarding speaker nervousness, it is important to note what it should not be. Do *not* make it your goal to eliminate nervousness. Such a goal is counterproductive for at least two reasons. First, as we discussed, nervousness is natural; attempting to eliminate it is unrealistic. Second, some anxiety can actually benefit you as a speaker. Nervousness is energy, and it shows that you care about performing well. Use that nervous energy to drive you to prepare well, to enliven your delivery, and to give your ideas impact.

Your goal, then, is to *manage* and *reduce* your nervousness. The skills we suggest in this section—and further develop throughout this book—will enable you to control the symptoms of nervousness and to channel that energy into dynamic, effective vocal and physical delivery. (See also Chapter 13, Learning Objectives 13.3 and 13.4.)

James Belasco, professor and consultant to major corporations, describes how he uses nervousness as a transforming agent:

> Fear is a wonderful stimulant. It quickens the mind, sharpens the senses, and heightens performance. I've learned to focus the stimulant on doing better, rather than worrying about doing worse. When fear runs through my system, I ask myself, "What can I do to remove the potential cause of failure?" "What can I do to ensure success?" I've evolved rituals to answer these questions constructively.[10]

Journal: Taking the PRPSA

We encourage you to complete the PRPSA at the beginning of the course, before you begin researching and writing your first speech. Where do you fall on the scale? Why do you think you received the particular score that you did? Be sure to retake the PRPSA again at the end of the term to examine whether your public speaking anxiety has decreased as a result of your studies.

Even those whose jobs rely on speaking in front of others experience anxiety. Award-winning actress Meryl Streep once stated, "It's odd. I have this career that spans continents, but . . . I can't get up in front of people and speak. I get really, really nervous."[9]

Nervous energy is a sign that you care about your speech performance. Try to channel that energy into gestures, body movements, and your vocal delivery that will enhance your message.

One of the best ways to ensure success is to increase your knowledge of and comfort level with public speaking skills. The following seven suggestions offer an introduction to skills that you will continue to fine tune throughout this course.

Assess Your Strengths and Weaknesses

Surgeons spend many hours learning to use the equipment they need to perform operations. Each surgeon knows just what each instrument is capable of doing and strives to use it effectively. As a public speaker, your instruments are your voice, body, mind, and personality. Get to know these instruments, and you can use them effectively to create and communicate messages.

To know yourself, you must honestly assess both your strengths and your weaknesses. Use your strengths to communicate your message with force and impact. If you are a lively and enthusiastic person, channel that energy to reinforce your speech physically and enliven your delivery. If you have a talent for creating memorable phrases, use that creativity to help your listeners attend to and remember your ideas. Just as you can tap your strengths in these ways, you can minimize or avoid your weaknesses if you know them. If your friends have told you that you're not exactly a comedian, don't begin your speech with a joke. To do so would risk awkwardness at this critical point in the speech, and that would make you even more nervous.

The more you understand your strengths and weaknesses, the better you will be able to craft your speech to your abilities. The more confident you are that you can accomplish what you set out to do, the less nervous you will be. One note of caution, however: Don't be too critical of yourself and construct a "safe" speech because you have exaggerated your weaknesses. Instead, expand your abilities by incorporating new strategies into your speech making. Only through thoughtful, measured risk taking will you develop as a public speaker.

Master the Speech Principles

If you are confident that you have constructed an effective speech, you will be more confident as you step to the lectern. This textbook and your instructor will assist you in learning and using speech principles. For example, what are the five functions of an effective speech introduction? What strategies help you conclude your speech? (For both, see Chapter 10.) How can you ensure that you have the most relevant, up-to-date, and worthwhile sources and examples? (See Chapters 7 and 9.) How should you construct the body of your speech, and how should you develop each key idea? (See Chapter 8.) What strategies help you word ideas correctly, clearly, and vividly? (See Chapter 12.) How can you use your voice and body to communicate your ideas dynamically? (See Chapter 13.) We address all these questions, and many others, in this book. As you begin to apply what you learn and deeply develop your skill set, you will feel more confident about the content, organization, and delivery of your ideas.

Believe in Your Topic

The public speaking process begins by selecting a topic appropriate for the speaker, the audience, and the occasion. If you are giving an informative speech, you must believe that what you say will benefit your listeners. If you are giving a persuasive speech, be committed to your intended audience influence (attitudes, beliefs, values, or behaviors). Convincing your audience that they should listen to your speech is easier if you believe that the topic is important. The more you believe in your topic, the more

Journal: What Should I Do about My Strengths and Weaknesses?

Identify your strengths and weaknesses as a public speaker. (If you aren't sure what they are, you can speak with a friend who will be honest, a trusted classmate, or your instructor.) For each strength, write a sentence or two about how you can take advantage of this strength in your speeches. Then, for each weakness, write a sentence or two about how you can minimize or eliminate this weakness in your speeches.

If you choose a subject you love, whether it is a favorite hobby, job, class, or poet, you will become deeply involved in developing your speech. This involvement, in turn, may reduce your nervousness about speaking in public.

earnestly you will want to inform or influence your listeners. In short, if you doubt the importance of your topic, you will feel and seem tentative. So, take your time when analyzing your audience and selecting your topic. (See Chapters 5 and 6.)

Study Your Outline

Believing in your topic gains you little if you are not very familiar and comfortable with your speech. You certainly don't need to memorize the entire speech. Rather, to be well prepared, you should carefully craft and study the outline of your major points and the order in which you want to present them. If you forget your notes or drop them and cannot get them back into proper order, you should still be able to deliver your speech because you've taken the time to become comfortable and familiar with what you want to tell your listeners. (Nonetheless, take a minute to number your notecards, and you have one less worry on the day you speak.)

Test Your Message

As a speaker, you can test your message by practicing your speech in front of friends. Can they restate your key ideas after listening to you? Do they find your supporting material believable? Does your delivery detract from or reinforce your message? Answers to these questions will guide your subsequent practice sessions. The more confident you are that your message will achieve the desired effect on your audience, the less nervous you will be.

Project Confidence

Daryl Bem's theory of self-perception states that if you perceive yourself acting a particular way, you will assume that you feel that way.[11] Thus, if you want to feel confident, act confident. Begin by identifying characteristics of speakers who seem confident; then incorporate those behaviors into your speeches. For example, instead of walking tentatively to the lectern, approach it with your head held high and shoulders back. Instead of avoiding eye contact with your listeners, look directly at them, focusing perhaps on a few friendly faces. Instead of leaning on the lectern or shifting your weight from foot to foot, stand erect and still. Instead of tapping your fingers on the lectern or jingling change in your pocket, use your hands to gesture emphatically. Displaying confident behaviors such as these will make you *appear* and *feel* more confident. (See Chapter 13 for a discussion about using gestures in your speeches.)

Practice Your Delivery

The previous coping strategies have implied the importance of practice. However, practicing your speech is so important that it deserves an overt discussion. The late Jack Valenti, former presidential speechwriter, correctly observed, "The most effective antidote to stage fright and other calamities of speech making is total, slavish, and monkish preparation."[12]

Your approach to practice sessions will vary, depending on how your presentation develops. Sometimes you may practice specific sections of your speech that give you difficulty. But you should also practice your speech several times from start to finish without stopping. Too often when students make mistakes while practicing, they stop and begin again. This is not a luxury you have when you address an audience. As you rehearse your speech, you should practice recovering from mistakes. Knowing that you can make it through your speech despite mistakes should make you more confident.

You should also occasionally practice your speech in an environment laden with distractions. Students who practice only in silence may not be prepared for distractions that arise when they actually deliver their speeches, such as a student coming into the classroom during the speech, a lawn mower passing by the window, or two students talking in the back of the room. These distractions, especially those stemming from rudeness, should not occur; in reality, though, they sometimes do. Practicing with the television on in the background or in your room with noise in the hallway forces you to concentrate on what you are saying, not on what you are hearing. You develop poise as a speaker only through practice.

> **Key Points: Public Speaking Skills to Manage Nervousness**
>
> 1. Assess your strengths and weaknesses.
> 2. Master the speech principles.
> 3. Believe in your topic.
> 4. Study your outline.
> 5. Test your message.
> 6. Project confidence.
> 7. Practice your delivery.

Apply Physical and Psychological Strategies to Manage Speaker Nervousness

3.3 Describe the six physical and psychological strategies that can help you manage your nervousness and build confidence.

In the previous section, we offered an overview of specific public speaking skills that increase confidence and reduce anxiety as you learn, practice, and master them. In addition, we offer an overview of strategies from other fields and arenas that can be easily

SPEAKING WITH CONFIDENCE

I love to talk, so I never thought that speaking in front of a crowd, big or small, could place my nerves on a roller coaster. However, I found myself breathing so hard even before I arrived at my public speaking class. It was such a relief to learn that nervousness is quite common and that others are just as nervous as I am. Some methods I use to boost my public speaking confidence are to prepare (practicing in front of a mirror helps me), to take deep breaths before I get up to speak, and, finally, to just do it! When I stood in front of my classmates and began to speak, I scanned the audience and became familiar with some friendly faces, and this put me more at ease. Also, moving my hands for appropriate gestures helped me relax. With practice, you can keep nervousness from having a negative effect on your speech. All of these techniques have helped me build confidence in my public speaking ability.

Mariely Sanchez-Moronta
Marymount Manhattan College

applied to public speaking anxiety (and other forms of communication apprehension). These strategies help you understand how your mind and body experience stress, and how you can use your mind and body to manage your nerves.

Know How You React to Stress

Nervousness affects people differently. Although nervousness is purely psychological, it affects us physically. Perhaps you experience a dry mouth when you approach a prospective romantic partner or speak with a potential employer. In the public speaking arena, your hands or knees might shake. The person sitting next to you may not experience those symptoms of nervousness but may have difficulty breathing comfortably or feel that his voice is shaky in any of those communication scenarios. Whatever your individual responses to stress are, don't wait until you are delivering a public speech (or having a job interview) to discover them.

Knowing your reactions to stressful situations helps you in two ways. First, it lets you predict and cope with these physical conditions. Therefore, your dry mouth or sweaty palms will not surprise you. Second, because you are anticipating these physical conditions, you will be better at masking them from the audience. How do you do this? Try these techniques.

If you know that your hands shake when you are nervous, don't hold a sheet of paper during the speech; the shaking paper will only amplify the movement of your hands and telegraph your anxiety to your audience. If your voice is likely to be thin and quivery as you begin speaking, take several deep, slow breaths. If you get tense before speaking, try some muscle relaxation techniques: Tense your hands, arms, and shoulders, and then slowly relax them. If you get flustered before speaking, make sure you arrive on time or even a little early—never late. If looking at an audience intimidates you, talk to audience members beforehand, and when you speak, look for friendly faces.

Realize That It Always Looks Worse from the Inside

Remember that your audience cannot see your internal state, nor can they read your mind. Many times students have lamented their nervousness after concluding a speech, only to learn that classmates envied them for seeming so confident. In fact, a recent study indicated that the association between speakers' self-reported nervousness and audience members' perceived speaker nervousness is weak.[13] This means that even if you feel very nervous when speaking, the audience members are unlikely to perceive you that way. Realizing and acknowledging this should make you more secure and lessen your anxiety.

One student, Susan, wrote the following in her self-evaluation of her first graded classroom speech: "Too fast, too rushed. I forgot half of it. Yuck! Yuck! Yuck!" Yet here are a few of the comments from her classmates:

- "Wow! You seemed really relaxed! Your speech was organized, informative, and interesting."
- "She seemed to know what she was talking about."
- "Definitely the best speech given so far."

Susan obviously perceived and experienced her speech in a radically different way than her classmates and instructor. When asked about her listeners' written comments, Susan responded, "What you said is definitely true. It does look worse from the inside."

If Susan had not received feedback from her audience, she would probably have retained her high level of public speaking anxiety, perhaps even avoiding future opportunities to share her ideas with others. By offering honest evaluation, her classmates let

Susan see her speech from "the other side," lessened her anxiety, and motivated her to continue improving her public speaking skills.

View Speech Making Positively

cognitive restructuring
A strategy for reducing communication anxiety by replacing negative thoughts and statements with positive ones.

More and more we are discovering and investigating the mind's ability to affect behavior. Doctors have learned, for example, that patients' attitudes about their illnesses significantly affect their speeds of recuperation or their chances for recovery. One method for reducing communication anxiety is called **cognitive restructuring**. This approach recognizes that nervousness is, in part, caused by illogical beliefs. If speakers can restructure their thinking and focus on positive rather than negative self-statements, they reduce their anxiety. Cognitive restructuring involves two steps. First, identify your negative self-statements ("Everyone will laugh at me when I give my speech"). Second, replace the negative thoughts with positive ones ("My classmates understand what it's like to be nervous and will support my speaking efforts").

If you view public speaking as a tedious chore, your audience will sense it from your vocal and physical delivery and perhaps even from your choice of speech topic. On the other hand, if you look at public speaking as an opportunity, your positive attitude will help you manage your nervousness. Table 3.1 illustrates how you can replace negative thoughts with positive ones.

Thinking positively can help turn anxiety into anticipation. Genuine enthusiasm about the chance to speak in public will guide your choice of topic and will reveal itself to the audience through your lively delivery. Seek out opportunities to test and develop your communication skills. Volunteer for oral reports in classes, speak up at organizational meetings, or offer to introduce a guest speaker at your club's banquets. This positive attitude, coupled with practice and experience, will help make you less apprehensive and more confident.

TABLE 3.1   Turn Negative Thoughts into Positive Thoughts

Replace the Negative Thought . . .	With a Positive Thought.
"My audience will probably be bored with my speech."	"I found the topic of how music affects our moods interesting, and my audience will, too."
"When I get up to speak, my mind will probably go blank, and I'll have nothing to say."	"I've rehearsed my speech, and I have a good set of speaking notes. If I momentarily forget a point, I'll just look at my notecards and then continue."

Visualize Success

If you have ever watched golf on television, you may have seen a player taking a practice swing before a shot and then looking down the fairway or toward the green for several seconds. During that time, the player is visualizing the golf ball flying and landing perfectly as intended. As the player mentally watches the ball end up in the desired place, he or she hears the applause from the audience members in recognition of the perfect shot. This process enhances the player's confidence and likelihood of executing the shot as planned.

visualization
A strategy for reducing communication anxiety by picturing yourself delivering a successful speech.

Like athletes, public speakers can also use **visualization** to reduce their nervousness and improve their performance. A study of 430 college speech students revealed lowered speech anxiety among those who visualized themselves delivering an effective presentation.[14] Rodney describes how he used positive visualization to build his confidence:

The week before I gave my speech, I found quiet spots where I could relax. I closed my eyes and visualized myself giving an effective presentation. I saw myself arriving at my classroom on the day I was to speak. Calmly, I would walk to my seat. I'd sit down, check my speaking notes to see that they were in order, and collect my thoughts. When Dr. Conner called my name, I got up from my seat and walked confidently to the front of the room. I put my notes on the lectern, looked at my classmates, and smiled. I paused, took a breath, and then began. I visualized myself being relaxed and delivering my speech as I had planned, with clarity and poise. I felt good talking about a topic that was so important to me. I visualized my classmates smiling at my humor and nodding in agreement as I explained my ideas. I concluded with a dramatic story that really drove home my point. I paused, then walked to my seat. My classmates applauded, and one of them even whispered to me, "Great speech, Rod!"

Burn the Extra Energy

As we have discussed (and as you have likely experienced at some point in your life), anxiety often leads to an adrenaline boost in our bodies, making us more prepared to survive a dangerous situation. Giving a speech is not a life-threatening event that necessitates being able to run quickly to safety, but we still benefit from letting that anxious energy "out." One simple suggestion is to tighten major muscles, such as the legs, stomach, and arms for 10 to 15 seconds at the time, then relax for 10 to 15 seconds. Repeat this process while you wait for your turn to speak; it will burn off some of that extra energy and no one will be able to tell that you're moving your body.

Similarly, consider how much more relaxed you feel after exercising. Your energy levels are lower and your body is at rest. Therefore, you could consider going for a walk before class, making sure to focus on your breathing and on your immediate surroundings (the feel of the wind on your face, the sound of the birds, the chill of the air or the warmth of the sun), rather than speaking scenarios you may have created in your head. This combination of physical movement and focusing on the present may help you to feel less nervous as you enter the classroom.

Take Care of Your Body

Our final piece of advice applies to all sorts of situations, from taking a test to preparing to run a marathon. Be kind to your body to keep it strong and healthy. Get enough sleep to feel well-rested in the days leading up to your speech. (For some that might be 6 hours, for others it might be 10 hours. Only you know the right amount.) Eat a

Journal: Relaxing before, during, and after Your Speech

In this section, we've provided six helpful strategies to help you relax and manage your public speaking anxiety. However, this is by no means an exhaustive list. Are there any strategies or tips that you would add to this section? If so, what are they and why do they help you? Consider sharing your ideas with your classmates.

Stretching, taking a walk, and focusing on your breath can help you reduce the sensation of adrenaline coursing through your body before an event that causes you anxiety—such as giving a speech.

Key Points: Apply Physical and Psychological Strategies to Manage Speaker Nervousness

1. Know how you react to stress.
2. Realize that it always looks worse from the inside.
3. View speech making positively.
4. Visualize success.
5. Burn the extra energy.
6. Take care of your body.

well-balanced diet and try to avoid high-sugar foods in the hours before your speech, which could make you jittery. You may want to avoid caffeinated beverages for the same reason, in addition to the fact that they can increase perspiration if that's a concern you have. If you're worried about your stomach growling in the middle of your speech (a common fear), try to eat something high in protein—like eggs or a piece of toast with peanut butter—that will stave off hunger a bit longer than other foods. You might also eat a few crackers before entering the classroom to settle your stomach, or have water available to hydrate and to address dry mouth. By the time speech day arrives, you will have worked diligently to prepare, so treat your body with the respect it deserves.

The coping strategies we've discussed will help you channel your nervous energy into dynamic confident delivery. After each speech, reflect on the experience and gauge your success using the suggestions in "Theory into Practice: Gaining Perspective." In addition, the "Speaking with Confidence" boxes throughout this book reveal how other public speaking students developed their self-assurance using some of these principles. (For example, see page 34.) For now, however, you can begin training those butterflies to fly in formation as you prepare your first speech in this class.

Prepare Your First Speech

3.4 Apply the seven guidelines to help you develop a successful first speech.

This class may require you to give your first speech before you have read much of this textbook. What is absolutely necessary to know, then, in order to deliver that first speech successfully? Preparing your first speech will be easier if you keep in mind two principles of public speaking. First, the more effectively you prepare, the better the speech you will deliver and the more confident you will feel. Only then can you recognize what you already do competently and begin to identify skills you want to improve.

Second, every public speech is a blend of *content*, *organization*, and *delivery*. Each of these aspects affects the others. The more you know about these principles, the

Theory into Practice (TIP)

GAINING PERSPECTIVE

In this chapter, we present strategies for building your speaking confidence. You incorporate these suggestions as you prepare and deliver your speeches. But what should you do *after* your speech? You've heard the expression, "Experience is the best teacher." Well, there's some truth in that folk wisdom; you can use your public speaking experiences to build confidence.

After each speech, assess your performance by asking and answering important questions. Your instructor will give you feedback for some of these questions; others you will need to answer for yourself because you alone know the true answers.

- How did you react when you walked to the front of the room, turned, and looked at the audience looking at you?
- Did you remember what you planned to say?
- Did you have trouble finding your place in your notes?
- What techniques did you try in your speech that worked? What didn't work?
- Did you get less or more nervous as the speech progressed?

- How did your audience respond to your speech? What did their nonverbal communication convey as you delivered your speech? What feedback did you receive from your classmates and instructor following the speech?

Remember, don't be too critical as you evaluate your performance. You will do some things well, and this should build your confidence. Focus on other aspects of your speech that you can improve.

Suppose that you encounter a serious problem: You lose your place, your mind goes blank, and you bury your head in your notes and race to the end of your speech. Use this as a learning experience. Ask yourself *why* you forgot: Did you try to memorize your speech instead of speaking from notes? Were your notes disorganized, or did they contain too little or too much information? Did you focus too little on the audience?

Once you face a problem and determine its cause, you will be better able to plan so that it does not occur again. You don't *discover* confidence; you build it. Each public speech provides an opportunity to improve and enhance your confidence for your next speech.

better your speech will be. The following seven guidelines will help you toward that goal.

Understand the Assignment

An essential requirement for preparing any speech is to know exactly what you are expected to do. The following questions can help you identify your goals for the speech:

- What am I supposed to do in this speech: inform, persuade, or entertain?
- What are my minimum and maximum time limits for the speech?
- Are there are special requirements for the organization of the speech? If so, what are they?
- Are there special requirements for the content of the speech? If so, what are they?
- Are there special requirements for the delivery of the speech? If so, what are they?

Develop Your Speech Content

If your assignment is to introduce yourself, begin by jotting down as many aspects of your life as you can. Audit your history, assess your current circumstances, and project your future goals. Among others, topics that apply to your life and the lives of all your listeners include accomplishments, aspirations, career plans, educational backgrounds, heroes, hobbies, personal values, pet peeves, prized possessions, skills, special interests, and unusual life events. You could decide to limit your speech to one of the preceding areas or to combine several that you think your listeners will find most interesting.

If your first speech topic is not assigned, brainstorm for topics that interest you and those that you think would benefit or interest your audience. If you generate many possible topics and spend some time reflecting on them, the subject you finally choose will probably be more satisfying for you and more interesting to your listeners.

To ensure you have a clear grasp of your speech topic, answer questions such as these:

- What is my speech topic, and why have I chosen this topic?
- Who are the people in my audience?
- What do I want my listeners to know or remember when I'm finished speaking?

Limit the number of key ideas (main points) to give you enough time to develop them with adequate supporting material. Once you have done this preliminary work, you are ready to assess your speech content by asking questions such as the following:

- Have I selected a few key ideas that I can develop in the time allowed?
- Is everything that I say relevant to my topic?
- Do I use a variety of specific supporting materials, such as examples and stories, to develop my key ideas?
- Will my supporting materials be clear and interesting to my audience?
- Do I acknowledge sources for everything I quote or paraphrase from other speakers or writers?

Organize Your Speech

A coherent speech has three divisions: an introduction, a body, and a conclusion. To determine whether your ideas are clearly organized and easy to follow, you must consider the organization of each of these three parts of your speech.

Organize Your Speech Introduction   Though usually brief, your speech introduction serves five vital functions. First, it focuses the audience's attention on your message. You might, for example, question your audience, arouse their curiosity about your subject, or stimulate their imaginations. (See also Chapter 10, Learning Objective 10.1)

Second, your introduction should clarify your topic or your purpose in speaking. State your purpose clearly in a well-worded sentence. A third function is to establish the relevance of your topic so that your listeners know why they should pay attention. Fourth, use your introduction to establish your credibility on that topic. Reveal any special qualifications you have for speaking on the topic, and use your words, voice, and body to instill confidence in your listeners that you have prepared thoroughly. Finally, your introduction should highlight or preview the aspects of your subject that you will discuss in the body of your speech.

Well-planned and well-delivered opening remarks will make the audience want to listen and will prepare them for what comes next. To check the integrity of your speech introduction, answer the following questions:

What are the parts of my introduction?

- What is my attention getter?
- What is my statement of purpose?
- What rationale do I provide for speaking about this topic?
- How do I establish my credibility to speak on this topic?
- What are the key ideas I will cover in my speech?

Organize the Body of Your Speech The body of your speech is its longest, most substantial section. Though it follows your introduction, you should prepare the body of your speech first. Your organizational goal in the body is to structure your key ideas so clearly that they are both distinct and unmistakable to your listeners.

We recommend a four-step sequence—the 4 S's—for organizing each of your key ideas. First, *signpost* each key idea. Typical signposts are numbers ("first" or "one") and words such as *initially* and *finally*. Second, *state* the idea clearly. Third, *support*, or explain, the idea; this step will take you the most time. Finally, *summarize* the idea before transitioning to your next key idea. These four steps will help you highlight and develop each of your key ideas in a logical, orderly way. The following questions should help you determine whether the body of your speech is well organized. (See also Chapter 8.)

Have I organized the body of my speech clearly?

- What are my key ideas?
- What will I say about each key idea?
- How will I summarize each key idea?

Organize Your Speech Conclusion Your speech conclusion is a brief final step with four main functions. The first is to restate the topic or purpose of your speech before moving on to the second function: to restate your key ideas, a final review of the main points you have covered.

The conclusion's third function is to activate an audience response by letting your listeners know whether you want them to accept, use, believe, or act on the content of your speech. This is your last opportunity to highlight what you want your listeners to take away from your speech.

Finally, your conclusion should provide your speech with a strong sense of closure. To do this, end on a positive, forceful note. You can use many of the same techniques here that you used to get the audience's attention at the speech's beginning. Ask and answer these questions to test your speech conclusion:

What are the parts of my conclusion?

- How do I clearly remind the audience of my topic and purpose?
- How do I restate the key ideas?
- What am I asking my audience to remember or do?
- Does my conclusion offer a strong sense of closure?

If you were able to answer each of the questions we've posed so far, you should have an interesting, well-developed speech that is easy to follow.

So far, you have spent most of your time thinking about the speech and jotting down ideas. Now you have to word those ideas and practice getting them across to your audience through your vocal and physical delivery.

Word Your Speech

Unless your instructor requests that you do so, avoid writing out your first speech word for word. Even though having the text of your speech in front of you may make you feel more secure, students who deliver speeches from manuscripts often sound mechanical and struggle to make sufficient eye contact with the audience. Therefore, if you have a choice, speak from just a few notes with key words or phrases to jog your memory.

The language of your speech should be correct, clear, and vivid. Vividness in particular helps your audience experience your ideas. For example, it would be correct and clear to say, "I've traveled to other countries" in a speech of introduction, but it's also bland. Instead, suppose you said:

> When I was seven, my father worked in the booming oil business, and my family got a chance to live in Venezuela. Instruction in Spanish started in the first grade, and by the time we returned to the States, I was bilingual. I have vivid memories of picking mangoes and papayas off the trees and swimming outdoors on Christmas day.

The second statement is more vivid than the first. The language is personal, conversational, and crisp. The following questions should help you test the language of your speech:

- Does my speech sound conversational?
- Do I use language correctly?
- Will the language of my speech be clear to my listeners?
- Will the language of my speech be vivid for my listeners?

Practice Your Speech

Mental rehearsal will never adequately ready you to deliver a prepared speech. As we said earlier in this chapter, speech making is an active process. You gain a heightened knowledge of what you plan to say and increased confidence in your abilities just by practicing your speech out loud. Before you can do that, however, you must create the notes you will use to practice and deliver the speech.

Preparing thoroughly, practicing often, and wanting to communicate with your audience are keys to any successful speech.

Prepare Your Notes Make certain that your speaking notes are in the form of key words or phrases, rather than complete sentences. Remember, you want your listeners to recall your key ideas, not necessarily your exact wording. Make sure that your notes are easy to read. If your speaking notes are on notecards, be certain to number the cards and have them in the correct order before each practice session. We discuss outlines and speaking notes in Chapter 11.

Practice Productively Practice any way that will help you, being sure to stand as you rehearse. Visualize your audience, and gesture to them as you hope to when giving your speech. You may even want to record your practice session on your phone

in order to watch and listen to it. Give yourself the opportunity to stop for intensive practice of rough spots. but make sure that you also practice the speech from beginning to end without stopping.

Be sure to try your speech out on at least a few friends or family members, if possible. Your rehearsal audience can tell you if there are parts of your speech that are too complex and difficult to grasp and they may be able to suggest clearer, more colorful, or more powerful ways of wording certain statements. A practice audience can point out strengths of your delivery and help you eliminate distractions. Most important, serious practice in front of others should focus your attention on the important interaction involved in delivering a speech to an audience. The following questions make up a checklist for your speech practice:

- Have I practiced my speech as I intend to deliver it in class?
- Have I made my speaking notes concise and easy to use and read?
- Have I recorded my speech and made changes after listening to or viewing it?
- How many times have others listened to my speech, and what suggestions have they offered for improvements?
- Have I timed my speech? Is the average time within my overall time limit?
- What adjustments can I make if my speech is too long or too short?

Deliver Your Speech

Your speech delivery is made up of your language, your voice, and your body. You want to be conversational and to talk *with* your listeners, not *at* them.

Effective vocal delivery is energetic, easily heard, and understandable. Your voice should also show that you are thinking about what you are saying as you deliver your speech. With practice, your voice can communicate humor, seriousness, sarcasm, anger, and a range of other possible emotions. Check your vocal delivery by answering the following questions:

- Do I speak with enough volume to be heard easily?
- Do I change the pitch of my voice enough to create a lively vocal delivery?
- Do I vary my speaking rate to match my audience's comprehension of what I am saying?

Effective physical delivery is direct and immediate. You demonstrate your involvement in your topic and in the speaking situation by interacting with your audience. If you are concentrating on your message and your audience's nonverbal feedback, your physical delivery will most likely seem natural. To gauge your directness, immediacy, and involvement, answer the following questions about your physical delivery:

- Are my clothing and other elements of my appearance appropriate for my topic, my audience, and the speaking occasion?
- Do I look at members of my audience most of the time I am speaking? Do I look at listeners in all parts of the room?
- Do my gestures add emphasis to appropriate parts of the speech? Do my gestures look and feel natural and spontaneous?
- Do my facial expressions show that I am thinking about what I am saying rather than about how I look or sound?
- If I include place-to-place movement, does it serve a purpose?

Your goal should be delivery that looks and sounds effortless. Yet ironically, that will require significant practice and attention to the vocal and physical elements of your delivery.

Evaluate Your Speech

Don't forget your speech as soon as you deliver your final words and return to your seat! While the experience is fresh in your memory, evaluate your content, your organization, and your delivery. What sorts of feedback did you get from your listeners? To evaluate the kind of speaker you are now and the kind of speaker you can become, answer the following questions:

- What did I do well?
- What areas can I target for improvement in this class?
- What specific efforts do I need to make in order to improve my next speech?

No matter what your level of public speaking experience, you will benefit from recognizing two concerns that you probably share with everyone in class. First, as we have discussed throughout this chapter, most of your classmates are probably as apprehensive as you are about their first speech. Your nervousness is natural, typical, and healthy. In fact, your anxiety is a sign that you have reasonably high expectations of yourself and that you care about doing well.

Second, you should know that public speaking is a teachable skill, much like math, reading, and writing. (Assuming that some people are born "good" speakers is a myth.) We, as the authors of this book, share responsibility for part of that learning with your instructor. You are also responsible for much of your learning through your own effort and initiative.

We began this chapter by focusing on speaker nervousness, because we know that it is a real worry for most people. We have suggested some techniques to help manage and channel your anxiety into a lively, enthusiastic speech. We have also sketched in broad strokes the process of developing and delivering an effective speech. Your audience is made up of peers. They are pulling for you. Use this friendly atmosphere as a training ground to become a more effective speaker.

ETHICAL DECISIONS

THE DAY BEFORE YOUR SPEECH

It is the day before your first speech, but you haven't had much time to prepare because you have been genuinely ill with a virus. You don't want to miss your speech (as it's more work to make up later), but you also realize that you will have to use your time wisely if you're going to pull this off. Your two primary concerns are (1) not embarrassing yourself, and (2) not misinforming your classmates.

Based on the objectives you identified, which of the seven guidelines for preparing your first speech would you emphasize and which would you deemphasize? What are some potential ethical consequences to you and to your audience members based on your selected guidelines? Or is it more ethical to ask for an extension, even if you're concerned about making up the work? Why or why not?

❯ SUMMARY

Speaking with Confidence

Recognize That Speaker Nervousness Is Normal

3.1 Explain public speaking anxiety and why it is a normal experience.

- Public speaking anxiety is a particularly common form of communication apprehension. Most of your classmates feel some level of nervousness about giving a speech.
- This anxiety can manifest in a variety of physical and psychological symptoms, from dry mouth to lowered self-esteem.
- Your goal should be not to eliminate, but to manage, your nervousness.

Apply Public Speaking Skills to Manage Speaker Nervousness

3.2 Describe the seven public speaking skills that can help you manage your nervousness and build confidence.

To manage nervousness: (1) assess your strengths and weaknesses, (2) master speech principles, (3) believe in your topic, (4) study your outline, (5) test your message, (6) project confidence, and (7) practice your delivery.

Apply Physical and Psychological Strategies to Manage Speaker Nervousness

3.3 Describe six physical and psychological strategies that can help you manage your nervousness and build confidence.

To further manage nervousness: (1) know how you react to stress, (2) realize that it always looks worse from the inside, (3) view speech making positively, (4) visualize success, (5) burn the extra energy, and (6) take care of your body.

Prepare Your First Speech

3.4 Apply the seven guidelines to help you develop a successful first speech.

Prepare thoroughly for your first speech by (1) understanding the speaking assignment, (2) developing adequate content on a narrow topic, (3) organizing the various sections of the speech, (4) wording your ideas effectively, (5) practicing productively, (6) delivering the speech, and (7) evaluating your performance.

LISTENING

→ **LEARNING OBJECTIVES**

After studying this chapter, you should be able to

4.1 Explain the importance of listening, using examples.

4.2 Distinguish between listening and hearing.

4.3 Apply the six steps of the listening process.

4.4 Describe the five common obstacles to effective listening, using examples.

4.5 Apply the eight strategies to improve your ability to listen effectively.

I n Joel and Ethan Coen's 1998 cult film, *The Big Lebowski,* the main character (the Dude) is lectured by the Malibu chief of police. At the end of the conversation, the chief of police asks, "Do I make myself clear?" After an extended pause, the Dude says, "I'm sorry, I wasn't listening." The

chief of police becomes so enraged that he throws his coffee mug at the Dude.

It's unlikely that someone will throw a mug at you in speech class (or elsewhere) if you're not listening carefully. Nonetheless, ethical listeners should listen openly and critically; they should also provide feedback to assist speakers' thinking on the topic and to help them improve as public speakers. Mutual speaker and listener respect as well as civility are essential components to the process of communication. In this chapter, we examine the importance of listening, the difference between listening and hearing, the process of listening, common listening barriers, and strategies to improve your listening skills.

The Importance of Listening

4.1 Explain the importance of listening, using examples.

You are probably quite familiar with the campus rumor mill that spreads information about campus life. Regardless of the topic, the information relayed through the rumor mill is likely to change slightly as it spreads from one person to another. In fact, most rumors are exaggerated over time. For instance, one student may say that she "saw a bear on campus yesterday." The receiver (listener) of that message may pass it on and say, "There was a family of bears on campus yesterday." The next person may exaggerate the message further: "We have a bear problem on campus." If the rumor continues to spread, it may ultimately suggest that "There are many aggressive bears on campus that have tried to attack students."[1] The end message bares little resemblance to the original message; in most instances, these distorted messages are a direct result of ineffective listening skills.

Each day, you send and receive both oral and written messages. Of the four roles you perform—speaker, listener, writer, and reader—you spend the most time as a listener. College students, for example, spend approximately 53 percent of their communication time listening.[2] Yet while you have taken several courses teaching you to read and write, you have probably never taken one in listening. In short, you have received the least training in what you do the most, despite the clear advantages that strong listening skills have on all aspects of our lives (see Table 4.1).

Sadly, most of us are inefficient listeners. This doesn't surprise listening expert Robert Montgomery, who says:

> Listening is the most neglected and the least understood of the communication arts. It has become the weakest link in today's communications system. Poor listening is a result of bad habits that develop because we haven't been trained to listen.

Journal: The Rumor Mill

Consider the breakdown of the message about bears on campus in our example. It's likely that you have experienced something similar. Describe a time when a message you sent or received was very different from the original, intended message. What happened? To what extent do you feel that poor listening was responsible for this breakdown?

TABLE 4.1   Benefits of Strong Listening Skills

Academic	• Increased learning and comprehension
	• Continued education
	• Completed assignments
	• On-time graduation
Personal & Relational	• Increased opportunity for connection with others
	• More intimate relationships
	• Improved conflict management
	• Fewer relational misunderstandings
Professional	• Safety on the job
	• Increased career opportunity and advancement
	• Monetary gain
	• Compliance with organizational policies
	• Efficient use of time
Social & Legal	• Avoidance of stereotyping
	• Increased appreciation for diversity
	• Compliance with the law

But there is good news, as Montgomery adds, "Fortunately, it is a skill that can be learned."[3]

The first step is to understand that listening is not an automatic process (like hearing), but rather a skill to develop.

Listening versus Hearing

4.2 Distinguish between listening and hearing.

Does the following situation sound familiar? You're watching *The Daily Show* with Trevor Noah, listening to Spotify, or doing economics homework when your friend walks by and tells you she will be back to give you a ride to work. Twenty minutes later, she walks in and finds you still preoccupied with television, music, or homework, and not ready to go. She asks, "Didn't you hear me?" Well, of course you did. You heard her just as you heard Trevor Noah joking with Ellie Kemper, Stevie Ray Vaughan playing a riff, and the air conditioner clicking on in the hall. You *heard* all these things, but you might not have been *listening* to any of them.

What is the difference between **listening** and **hearing**? The two activities differ in at least four important ways.

Listening Is Intermittent

Listening is not a continuous activity but occurs only from time to time when we choose to focus and respond to stimuli around us. Hearing, on the other hand, is a continuous function for a person with normal hearing.

Listening Is a Learned Skill

Hearing means simply receiving an aural stimulus. Unless you have a hearing loss, you don't need training to hear. We hear sounds before we are born, and continue hearing throughout our lives—even as we sleep. Listening, however, is a learned skill that can be developed and improved through training.

Listening Is Active

The act of hearing is passive; it requires no work. Listening, in contrast, is active. It requires you to concentrate, interpret, and respond—in short, to be involved. You can hear the sound of a fire engine as you sit at your desk working on your psychology paper. You listen to the sound of the fire engine if you concentrate on it, identify it as a fire engine rather than an ambulance, wonder if it is coming in your direction, and then turn back to your work as you hear the sound fade away.

Listening Implies Using the Message Received

We choose to listen for various reasons, such as to gain new information; to learn new uses for existing information; to discover arguments for beliefs or actions; to laugh and be entertained; to celebrate a person, place, object, or idea; and to be inspired. There are unlimited topics you could listen to—for example, the history of blue jeans, crimes of ethnic intimidation, preparing lemongrass chicken, and the life of Corrie ten Boom. Some of these topics might induce you to listen carefully. Others might not interest you, so you choose not to listen. The perceived relevance of the topic helps determine how actively you will listen to a speaker. Listening implies a choice; you must choose to participate in the process of listening.

If Trevor Noah and your friend are speaking at the same time, you may hear them both, but you can't listen to both.

listening
The intermittent, learned, and active process of giving attention to aural stimuli.

hearing
The continuous, natural, and passive process of receiving aural stimuli.

Journal: Just Listen

Have you ever been told to "just listen" by a relational partner (perhaps a parent, significant other, manager, etc.)? Describe the situation. What made it difficult to listen—rather than simply hear—in that situation?

The Process of Listening

4.3 Apply the six steps of the listening process.

Any time two people communicate, two messages are involved: the one the sender intends and the one the listener actually receives. These messages will never be identical because people operate from different frames of reference and with different perceptions. Recall our discussion about the Triangle of Meaning in Chapter 1, Learning Objective 1.2. To better understand this concept, examine the six steps in the process of listening shown in Figure 4.1.

Figure 4.1 The Process of Listening

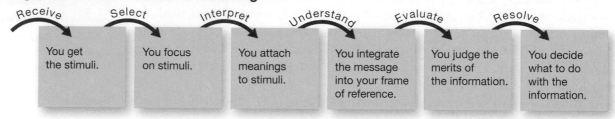

Receive	Select	Interpret	Understand	Evaluate	Resolve
You get the stimuli.	You focus on stimuli.	You attach meanings to stimuli.	You integrate the message into your frame of reference.	You judge the merits of the information.	You decide what to do with the information.

Receive

receive
Getting auditory stimuli.

The first step in listening is to **receive** sounds, the auditory stimuli. In other words, hearing is the first step toward effective listening. Some people, such as those with a hearing loss, unintentionally filter or leave out part of the stimulus. Whenever we filter, parts of the messages available to us will be lost.

Select

select
Choosing which stimuli to focus on.

People **select** different stimuli from those competing for their attention, a phenomenon sometimes called *selective perception*. Imagine that you and two of your friends (Alejandro and Kim) are enjoying a quiet night, watching episodes of *The Walking Dead*. Alejandro is showing off his new Google Pixel phone. You're not a huge fan of zombies, but you do like new gadgets, so you select to listen to Alejandro instead of the show. Kim, on the other hand, is a huge fan of *The Walking Dead* and doesn't care about Alejandro's new device. Therefore, she selects to listen to the television. When Alejandro switches the topic of conversation to his student teaching placement, Kim—a fellow education major—shifts her attention and selects to listen to Alejandro. You, however, are not in the education field and feel that you have little to offer the conversation, so you reluctantly tune back to the show. At the end of the evening, the three of you will likely have different perceptions about the conversation and what happened on television because you selected to listen to different messages.

In public speaking situations, the audience reacts in a similar way. One person may focus primarily on what the speaker is saying, another person focuses on the speaker's voice or accent, and still another person focuses on what the speaker is wearing. You may be distracted by psychological noise, such as worrying about an upcoming exam or trying to resolve a conflict with a friend. Our perception of a speech is shaped by what messages we select to process.

Journal: Selective Perception

Think of a time when you were exposed to two messages at the same time, such as listening to your instructor in class while overhearing a conversation between two students in the row behind you. Identify the situation, what the two messages were, which message you selected to process, and why.

Interpret

interpret
Decoding, or attaching meanings to the stimuli.

People not only select to focus on different stimuli competing for their attention, they also **interpret** those stimuli differently. Interpreting is the process of decoding the message. When you interpret, you attach meanings to the cluster of verbal and nonverbal symbols the speaker provides—words, tone of voice, and facial expressions, for example. The speaker's knowledge and experience must be similar to the listener's if communication is to be clear and effective. (See Figure 1.1 in Chapter 1, Learning Objective 1.2.)

Understand

Once you have decoded, or attached meanings to, a speaker's symbols, you begin fitting the message into your framework of knowledge and beliefs. To **understand** a speaker, you must consider both the content and context of a message. Is the speaker attempting to inform or persuade you? Is the speaker serious or joking? In short, what is the speaker trying to do? As you learn more about speakers, you can understand their messages more accurately.

understand
A sense-making process in which you integrate the stimuli into your frame of reference by considering both the content and context of the stimuli.

Evaluate

Before acting on the message you have decoded and understood, you **evaluate** it. Evaluating is the process of assessing the speaker's credibility and the quality and consistency of her or his information. Is the speaker making eye contact with you? Does he or she speak fluently, without unnecessary pauses or filler words? Do the speaker's gestures and other nonverbal behaviors seem relaxed and spontaneous? In short, does the person seem well prepared, confident, and sincere? If the answer to any of these questions is no, you may wonder whether the speaker has ulterior motives. As you evaluate the speaker's message, you decide whether you believe the data presented and whether you agree or disagree with the position the speaker advocates.

evaluate
Assessing the merits of the stimuli you received.

Resolve

The final step in listening, resolving, involves deciding what to do with the information you have received. As listeners, you can **resolve** to accept the information, reject it, take action on it, investigate it further, or just try to remember the information so that you can resolve it later.

resolve
Deciding what to do with the stimuli you received or how to respond.

Obviously, we do not consciously think about each of these six steps every time we listen to someone. As the significance of the message increases for us, we become more involved in the process of listening—a point every speaker should remember.

> **Key Points: The Process of Listening**
>
> 1. Receive
> 2. Select
> 3. Interpret
> 4. Understand
> 5. Evaluate
> 6. Resolve

Obstacles to Effective Listening

4.4 Describe the five common obstacles to effective listening, using examples.

Speakers and audience members should recognize some of the reasons why effective listening is so difficult. Learning to listen better is easier if you know what you're up against. For this reason, you need to identify the major obstacles (or distractions) to effective listening. We list and discuss five of them in this section.

Physical Noise

Have you ever asked someone in a movie theater to stop talking so that you could hear the actors on screen? If so, you experienced a physical distraction or physical noise. **Physical noise** is a distraction originating in the physical environment: two classmates talking in class, a glare from a sunny window, chill from an air conditioner vent, or the smell of formaldehyde in your anatomy and physiology lab. You may have trouble focusing on the message of a speech if you concentrate on the speaker's outlandish clothing, on a vigorous game of touch football outside, or on the overpowering smell of cologne on the person near you.

physical noise
Distractions originating in the physical environment.

Physiological Noise

physiological noise
Distractions originating in the bodies of communicators.

If you've ever tried to listen to your significant other complain about his or her day while your body wages a sneezing war against pollen, then you have experienced a physiological distraction or noise. **Physiological noise** originates in the body. Any illness or unusual physiological condition is a potential distraction to effective listening. A sore throat, a painful earache, a sprained ankle, fatigue after a sleepless night, or those pesky seasonal allergies will place limitations on your ability to listen.

Psychological Noise

psychological noise
Distractions originating in the thoughts of communicators.

Students who are concerned about their academic performance often find it difficult to retain new knowledge because they focus on their academic concerns rather than their instructors' lectures.[4] Your attitudes also affect your listening behavior in nonacademic settings as well. **Psychological noise**, such as a negative attitude toward the speaker or the topic, or your reason for attending a speech, can affect how you listen. If you are antagonistic toward the speaker or the point of view he or she is advocating, you may resist or mentally debate the statements you hear. If you are coerced to be in the audience, you may also be more critical and less open minded about what is being said. In short, if you are concentrating on thoughts unrelated to what the speaker is saying, you will receive less of the intended message.

Factual Distractions

factual distractions
Listening disturbances caused by attempts to recall minute details of what is being communicated.

College students are often hampered by **factual distractions**, listening disturbances caused by the flood of facts presented to them in lectures. You may be tempted to treat each fact as a potential test question, but this way of listening can pose problems. For example, have you ever taken detailed notes in one of your classes only to realize later that, although you have lots of facts listed, you missed the main points and overarching principles? Similarly, you might find yourself overwhelmed by a speaker's extensive use of statics about childhood obesity and miss his larger point to persuade you that elementary schools should require no less than 1 hour of physical activity per day. Victims of factual distractions sometimes listen for details but miss the speaker's overall point.

Semantic Distractions

semantic distractions
Listening disturbances caused by confusion over the meanings of words.

Semantic distractions are those caused by confusion over the meanings of words. Listeners may be confused by a word that they have never heard before or that is mispronounced. If a student gave a speech about her native country, Eritrea, without showing that word on a visual aid, many listeners would probably begin wondering, "How do I spell that?" "Have I ever seen that country on a map before?" "Is this a new name for

ETHICAL DECISIONS

GIVING IN TO DISTRACTIONS?

It's the beginning of the semester and you are taking the second of your two required chemistry classes for general education. Your instructor tells you that she will explain safety procedures in class today. However, you had the exact same lecture in the exact same lab space by the same professor in your previous chemistry course. Your professor even begins her lecture with the exact same joke she told last semester. You're not sure it's worth your time to pay attention. Besides, you're coming down with a cold and are actively worrying about balancing your current course load with your job.

Do you have an ethical responsibility as a listener in this scenario? Can you safely "tune out" your instructor's explanation to divert attention to physical and psychological noise you might find more pressing? Why or why not?

an established country?" "Is the speaker pronouncing correctly a word I've always heard mispronounced?" These thoughts divert them from the serious business of listening to a speech filled with new and interesting information.

Promoting Better Listening

4.5 Apply the eight strategies to improve your ability to listen effectively.

Promoting better listening should be a goal of both the senders and the receivers of the message, as both have a responsibility to promote effective communication. So, how can you encourage better listening in yourself (as an audience member) and also in others when you are giving a speech?

As a speaker (sender), you can enhance your audience's retention when you select your ideas carefully, organize them clearly, support them convincingly, word them vividly, and deliver them dynamically. As a listener (receiver), you must work hard to understand and remember the speaker's message. The following eight suggestions will help you become a more effective listener. As you master these suggestions, you will find yourself understanding and remembering more of what you hear.

Desire to Listen

Your attitude will determine, in part, your listening effectiveness. Good listeners begin by assuming that each speech might be relevant to them. As a first- or second-year student, you may not be particularly interested in an informative speech on how to apply to graduate school. However, when you are a senior considering additional education, you may be happy that you listened.

Good listeners can learn something from any speech, even if it is poorly prepared and awkwardly delivered. For example, you can determine what the speaker could have done to improve the speech, thus enabling you to apply speech principles you have learned and improve your own speaking. You may also have the opportunity to offer helpful suggestions to speakers. Listen carefully so that you can offer specific and detailed feedback to help them improve.

Speakers can promote better listening by demonstrating early in their speeches how the information is relevant to their listeners. In Chapter 10, Learning Objective 10.1, you will learn more about how to establish the relevance of your topic in the introduction of your speech.

Key Points: Obstacles to Effective Listening

1. Physical noise
2. Physiological noise
3. Psychological noise
4. Factual distractions
5. Semantic distractions

SPEAKING WITH CONFIDENCE

While preparing my persuasive speech to convince my classmates to use lower viscosity synthetic motor oil, I realized the topic would challenge their listening skills. Although I could do very little to control physical and physiological distractions my audience might experience, I considered ways to address other possible distractions. I tried to overcome psychological distractions by stressing the importance of the topic: They would save money on fuel costs and car repairs. To minimize semantic noise, I defined viscosity as oil thickness and explained how oil flows through motor parts. To reduce factual distractions, I supported my ideas with key facts and expert opinions that I cited in my speech. As I spoke, I could see audience members becoming involved in my topic. I had helped make it easier for them to listen to my speech, and I was rewarded with a stronger feeling of confidence as a speaker with an intrigued—dare I say persuaded—audience.

Jodie Moody
Radford University

Focus on the Message

Your first responsibility as a listener is to pay attention to the speaker's message. Yet a speaker's message competes with other, often quite powerful, stimuli for your attention (as in our example about Alejandro vs. *The Walking Dead*). In fact, speakers themselves create distractions. They may play with change or keys in their pockets, dress inappropriately, sway nervously from side to side, use offensive language, or say "um" throughout their speeches. These quirks can be distracting. Nonetheless, listeners should be disciplined and select to listen to the speech at hand in order to be polite, to learn more about the topic and the speaking process, and to provide useful feedback. For specific suggestions on how to focus, see "Theory into Practice: Focusing on the Message."

Listen for Key Ideas

You are familiar with the cliché that sometimes you can't see the forest for the trees; well, that saying applies to listening. A person who listens for facts often misses the main point of the message. While it is important to attend to the supporting material of a speech, you should be able to relate it to the major point being developed. (See Chapter 9, Learning Objective 9.2, for a discussion about supporting materials.)

Theory into Practice (TIP)

FOCUSING ON THE MESSAGE

Most Americans speak at rates between 125 and 190 words per minute. Yet as listeners, we can process 400 to 500 words per minute.[5] This means that, depending on the situation, we can listen at a rate up to four times faster than a person speaks. As a result, we may get bored and move our attention back and forth between what the speaker is saying and some extraneous message, perhaps a personal problem that concerns us. Sometimes, the unrelated thought takes over and psychological noise overpowers the speaker's message. Or sometimes, we tune out because the speaker's presentation is distracting or boring. To be a better listener, you should focus and increase your retention by mentally repeating, paraphrasing, and summarizing what the speaker is saying.

Repeat the Message

You use repetition when you state exactly what the speaker has said. Consider, for example, a speaker who argues that a tuition increase is necessary to preserve educational excellence at your college or university. The first reason she offers is this: "A tuition increase will enable us to expand our library." If, after the speaker makes this claim, you mentally repeat her argument, you are using repetition to help you remember her message.

Paraphrase the Message

Paraphrasing is a second way to help remember the message. By putting the speaker's ideas into your own words, you become actively involved in message transmission. Suppose the same speaker offers the following statement to justify one benefit of a tuition increase:

> A tuition increase would generate funds that could be used to enhance our library facilities and resources. In the chancellor's budget proposal, one-third of the tuition increase would go directly to the library. The chancellor estimates that this would enable us to increase our database subscriptions and electronic resources by 10 percent. Also, projected construction would create at least 12 new study rooms.

Obviously, it would be difficult to restate the speaker's explanation word for word. Yet you could paraphrase and summarize her message this way: "A tuition hike would increase our library holdings by 10 percent and expand the number of study rooms by 12."

Summarize the Message

You summarize when you condense what a speaker says. The previous paraphrase includes a summary, as it leaves out some of the specific information the speaker presented. As a speaker concludes her or his message, you should recollect the key points of the speech. Your summary might be, for example, "A tuition increase will help us expand the library, increase the number of faculty, and renovate some of the older dormitories."

By getting you actively involved in the communication process, repetition, paraphrase, and summary increase your focus, which improves your chances of understanding and remembering the message.

Good listeners recognize that every speech presents an opportunity to learn something new and potentially useful.

When listening to a speech, pay close attention to the speaker's organization. The structure of a speech provides a framework for both speakers and listeners to organize the supporting points and materials. Speakers who clearly enumerate key ideas and repeat them at several points in their speeches give their audience a better opportunity to listen attentively. (We discuss organizational techniques in Chapters 8 and 10.)

Understand the Speaker's Perspective

Each of us has different referents for the words we hear or speak because we have different life experiences that affect how we view our world.

Speaking in favor of agricultural programs that would preserve the family farm, Cathy tried to involve her audience in her speech by tapping their memories. She asked her classmates to think of the houses they grew up in and the memories created there.

> Think of Thanksgiving and family gatherings. Think of slumber parties and birthday celebrations. Of how you changed your room as you moved from child to teenager to young adult. Think of your feelings as you left home to come to college, and of your feelings when you return to those comfortable confines.

After the speech, several students said they were moved by Cathy's eloquence and passion. She had sparked memories that were important to them. Others in the audience, however, said they were unable to relate to the topic in the way Cathy intended. Several had grown up in more than one house. Some were in military families and had moved often. Still others said they had lived in rented townhomes or apartments. And a few commented that their childhood memories were not fond ones. Both speakers and listeners need to remember that different experiences shape and limit our understanding of another's message.

When speakers and listeners come from different cultures, the risks of misunderstanding increase. Differences in language, education, and cultural norms challenge listeners to work especially diligently at understanding the speaker's message and intent. These differences are often evident in today's multicultural classrooms. Some foreign students, for example, come from educational environments that are more structured and formal than the typical American college classroom. They may interpret a speaker's casual dress and use of humor as an indication that the speaker is not serious about the speech. On the other hand, some American students may perceive the

What are some of the listening skills these travelers can use to make the communication experience a positive one for both the speaker and audience?

ethnocentric listeners

Listeners who interpret the speaker's message based on their own lived experiences and cultural background rather than the speaker's experiences and cultural background.

cultural relativism

With regard to listening, interpreting the speaker's message based on the speaker's lived experiences and cultural norms, enhancing the listeners' ability to understand the speaker's perspective.

more formal presentations of some of their foreign classmates as stiff and indicating a lack of interest in the topic. Understanding one another's frame of reference minimizes this distortion.

As a listener, your ability to understand the speaker's perspective depends on your degree of ethnocentrism and cultural relativism. **Ethnocentric listeners** interpret the speaker's message based on their own lived experiences and cultural background rather than the speaker's experiences and cultural background. For example, if a Burmese student talks about neck rings (jewellery worn to push the collar bone down to "elongate" the neck) as a beautification technique in her culture, it may sound strange or cruel to her American classmates because this is not a part of their culture. **Cultural relativism** on the other hand means that the listeners interpret the speaker's message based on the speaker's lived experiences and cultural norms rather than their own, which enhances the listeners' ability to understand the speaker's perspective.

Provide Feedback

A listener can enhance the communication process by providing the speaker with meaningful feedback. Although there is greater opportunity for *verbal* feedback in interpersonal and group environments, it is nevertheless also possible in public speaking contexts. The effective speaker will especially read the audience's *nonverbal* cues to assist in the speech's presentation. If listeners understand and accept the speaker's point and nod in agreement, the speaker can move to the next idea. If listeners appear perplexed, that signal should prompt the speaker to explain the idea fully before moving to the next point.

Listen with the Body

We listen with more than our ears. In a sense, we listen with our entire bodies. If, as your instructor lectures, you lean back, stretch your legs, cross your arms, and glance at a fellow classmate, you detract from your listening effectiveness. Part of listening is simply being physically ready to listen.

You can ready yourself for listening by using the S.O.L.E.R. method of effective listening. First, *squarely face* the speaker. Second, ensure you have an *open posture*. Third, *lean forward* toward the speaker. Fourth, maintain *eye contact* with the speaker. Lastly, *relax* as you process the speaker's message.[6] Effective listeners also pay close attention to the speaker's nonverbal cues. What do the speaker's gestures mean? Do the speaker's facial expressions reflect the content of the message? For example, by looking at a person who gestures while giving directions, you are more likely to remember the directions. Similarly, focusing on the speaker's facial expressions may provide information about how the speaker really feels. Remember, you want to detect any nonverbal messages that intensify or contradict the speaker's verbal message.

Withhold Judgment

You filter what you hear through your own set of beliefs and values. Many of us find it challenging to withhold judgment; we hear something and immediately label it as right or wrong, good or bad. The problem is that once we do that, we cease to listen objectively to the rest of the message.

It is difficult to withhold judgment, of course, when you listen to a speech advocating a position you strongly oppose. During the 2016 presidential election campaigns, for example, we heard speeches about gun control, environmental regulations, and immigration policies, to name a few. Because many people hold strong opinions on these issues, they may begin listening to the candidate with either a favorable or unfavorable attitude, depending on the candidate's position. However, this behavior decreases listening effectiveness. Instead, try to suspend your judgments until after the speaker has presented and supported her or his arguments; it will make you a more effective and ethical listener.

Listen Critically

Even though listeners should understand a speaker's point of view and withhold judgment, listeners should nevertheless test the merits of what they hear. If you accept ideas and information without questioning them, you are in part responsible for the consequences. If the speaker advocating a tuition increase quotes from the chancellor's budget proposal before it has even been submitted, you have every right to be skeptical. "Will the final budget actually earmark one-third of the tuition increase for library use? Will the board of regents accept the chancellor's proposal? Or, is this all speculation?" Decisions based on incorrect or incomplete data are seldom prudent and are sometimes disastrous.

Critical listeners examine what they hear by asking several questions: Is the speech factually correct? Are sources clearly identified, and are they unbiased and credible? Does the speaker draw logical conclusions from the data presented? Has the speaker overlooked or omitted important information? Speakers help listeners answer those questions by presenting credible information, identifying their sources, and using valid reasoning.

John Marshall, chief justice of the United States from 1801 to 1835, once stated, "To listen well is as powerful a means of communication and influence as to talk well." If you use these eight suggestions, you will become a better listener.

Key Points: Guidelines to Promote Better Listening

1. Desire to listen.
2. Focus on the message.
3. Listen for key ideas.
4. Understand the speaker's perspective.
5. Provide feedback.
6. Listen with the body.
7. Withhold judgment.
8. Listen critically.

Journal: Improving Your Listening Skills

List what you perceive to be your top three listening weaknesses. For example, do you particularly struggle to withhold judgment if the speaker holds a different view on a controversial issue? For each weakness, indicate one specific strategy that could minimize this problem and help you listen more ethically and effectively.

› SUMMARY

Listening

The Importance of Listening

4.1 Explain the importance of listening, using examples.

- Most of us have received little to no formal training in listening, despite the fact that we engage in it more than reading, writing, or speaking.
- The benefits of listening well can be seen in all areas of life including academics, personal relationships, the professional realm, and social and legal environments.

Listening versus Hearing

4.2 Distinguish between listening and hearing.

Listening differs from *hearing* in four ways: (1) Listening is intermittent, while hearing is continuous; (2) listening is a learned behavior, while hearing is natural for most people; (3) listening is active while hearing is passive; and (4) listening implies doing something with the message received.

The Process of Listening

4.3 Apply the six steps of the listening process.

Listening involves six steps. The listener *receives* sound stimuli, *selects* particular parts of the total stimulus field for attention, *interprets* or decodes the message, *understands* by matching the speaker's message with the listener's frame of reference, *evaluates* the credibility of the speaker and the speaker's message, and *resolves*, or decides, what to do with the information received.

Obstacles to Effective Listening

4.4 Describe the five common obstacles to effective listening, using examples.

- *Physical noise* is a listening obstacle that originates in the physical environment. *Physiological noise* arises from conditions in the listener's body. *Psychological noise* includes worry, distraction, or preconceived attitudes toward the speaker or the message that originate in the listener's mind.

- *Factual distractions* are caused by our tendency to listen for small supporting details, even when we miss the speaker's main point. *Semantic distractions* are confusion over the meanings of words.

Promoting Better Listening

4.5 Apply the eight strategies to improve your ability to listen effectively.

- Both speakers and listeners can contribute to effective listening.
- Listeners should develop a genuine desire to listen; focus on the speaker's message; listen for the speaker's main ideas; understand the speaker's perspective; provide the speaker with feedback; listen with the whole body; withhold judgment about the speaker and the message until after hearing and considering both; and listen critically.
- Listeners can further focus on a speaker's message by using repetition, paraphrase, and summary.
- Speakers should select their ideas carefully, organize them clearly, support them convincingly, word them vividly, and deliver them forcefully.

ANALYZING YOUR AUDIENCE

→ LEARNING OBJECTIVES

After studying this chapter, you should be able to

5.1 Apply the seven demographic categories to tailor your speech to your audience.

5.2 Apply your knowledge of your listeners' psychographics to tailor your speech to your audience.

5.3 Explain the value of analyzing audience needs before your speech.

5.4 Apply strategies to obtain relevant information about your audience.

5.5 Explain the value of analyzing specific speaking situations before your speech.

5.6 Explain the value of analyzing the audience's attention, understanding, evaluation, and feedback.

arry Reid, a U.S. senator from Nevada, once said that former president Barack Obama possesses "one of the oldest political skills there is: the ability to adjust one's speech, and one's mannerisms, to different audiences."[1] In a speech delivered to a Wall Street audience, Obama "politely but firmly cautioned against dangerous credit-default swaps." During a *60 Minutes* interview 3 months later, Obama used the words "fat cat bankers," a term that would have been highly offensive to the wealthy bankers present for his Wall Street speech.[2] Similarly, Huey Long, a former Louisiana governor, used his thick, Louisiana accent when delivering speeches in the South, but toned down his southern drawl in an effort to connect with his geographically diverse audience members in Washington, D.C.

In politics, the process of changing one's delivery style, use of language, mannerisms, and even the speech content is known as *code shifting, code mixing,* or *style shifting.* Journalist Christopher Beam noted the importance of politicians adapting their speeches depending on the audience members by stating, "Anyone who wants to represent a state or a country composed of different ethnic groups needs to find ways to relate to each of them."[3] As a public speaker, you, like Barack Obama and Huey Long, must analyze your audience. **Audience analysis** is a process of determining who your audience members are, which then shapes the preparation, delivery, and evaluation of your speech.

In this chapter, you will learn techniques to analyze the diverse individuals who constitute your audience so that you may inform and persuade them effectively and ethically. We begin by considering the demographics, psychographics, and needs of your audience members before detailing how to obtain information about them. We end with a consideration of specific speaking situations and how to analyze your audience during (and even after) a speech. With a firm understanding of these ideas and concepts, you can improve your confidence and credibility as a speaker in addition to constructing an **audience profile**, a sketch of relevant characteristics of your listeners, which will assist you in all other areas of research, planning, and delivery.

Analyze Audience Demographics

5.1 Apply the seven demographic categories to tailor your speech to your audience.

Today's college classroom, like most segments of American life, is increasingly diverse. Your classmates may differ from one another in terms of age, ethnicity, religion, and numerous other characteristics. Talking about these differences can also reveal what you have in common and build your sense of community with the people you wish to inform or persuade. Your challenge—as both a speaker and an ethical communicator—is to recognize how your listeners differ from one another and to understand, respect, and adapt to this diversity as you develop and deliver your speeches. Evidence shows that it's a challenge worth taking, as students who interact with diverse peers become more engaged in their learning, improve their critical thinking skills, enhance their interpersonal and social competence, and demonstrate greater acceptance of people from other cultures.[4]

Your first step as a speaker is to discover and evaluate audience demographics. **Demographics** are the aforementioned characteristics of the audience, such as age, sex, sexual orientation, race ethnicity, education, religion, economic status, and group membership. Demographic analysis helps you tailor a message to a specific audience by helping you answer the question, "Who is my target audience?"

Part of your audience analysis will involve discovering what you can about the various divisions or subgroups that constitute your listeners. Advertisers and public relations people call this process **audience segmentation**. You might then choose a topic that you believe can relate to all segments of your audience. However, sometimes speakers choose to address only one or more segments of a larger audience, a strategy

audience analysis

The process of determining the audience members' demographics, psychographics, and needs, which then shapes the preparation, delivery, and evaluation of a speech.

audience profile

A sketch of relevant characteristics of listeners that assists the speaker in researching, planning, and delivering speeches.

demographics

The characteristics of the audience, such as age, sex, sexual orientation, race, ethnicity, education, religion, economic status, and group membership.

audience segmentation

The strategy of dividing an audience into various subgroups based on their demographic and psychographic profiles.

called **audience targeting**. For example, if you know that some of your listeners love to travel but are on tight budgets, you could inform them about the option to couch-surf, or take advantage of a network of people around the world willing to share a spare bedroom. An informative speech on the dangers of heatstroke and heat exhaustion might be appropriate for athletes in your audience or for those who work outdoors. Of course, you must be sure that your target audience does exist and that it is sufficient in size to justify giving them your primary focus.

You will never know everything about your listeners and will therefore make generalizations from what you do know. One note of caution, however: Be careful not to turn these generalizations into stereotypes, like "All older individuals struggle with technology" or "All engineering majors are video game fanatics." This will undermine your speech-making efforts. However, the more you know, the better prepared you will be to present a successful speech. Let's examine some particularly salient demographic categories.

Age

One of the most obvious concerns you have is the age of your listeners. Your public speaking class may primarily include 18- to 22-year-old students, but also people returning to college in order to change careers in midlife, and others pursuing interests after retirement. People of different generations often have different cultural frames of reference. For example, let's say that a classmate in her mid-60s is giving an informative speech on the history of computers. It could be very interesting to share with the class about the 1946 ENIAC (Electronic Numerical Integrator and Computer), which took up 1,500 square feet and weighed 30 tons.[5] The speaker might also share her personal experience of obtaining her first AOL email address in the mid-1990s. However, the speaker must keep the generational context in mind by remembering that her 18- to 22-year-old classmates do not remember a time when the Internet did not exist. She must work to include them in her topic by making comparisons to things that are familiar to them (e.g., comparing the process of checking e-mail in the 90s to checking email via a smartphone app) and showing how the topic is relevant to all audience members.

Sex and Sexual Orientation

"I'm going to inform you girls about the rules of football." "This recipe is so easy that even you guys should be able to make it."

You might balk at the idea that a classroom speaker would make such statements, but—as seasoned instructors—we've experienced it. When preparing your speech, remember that you cannot generalize about men and women. In fact, both men and women can be—and are—assertive, aggressive, competitive, independent, nurturing, emotional, sensitive, and supportive.

Some speech topics may seem to resonate more with listeners of one sex. For example, an informative speech on the risks of estrogen replacement therapy has more immediate interest for women than men; a speech on prostate cancer has more obvious importance for men than women. But couldn't either of these topics benefit both female and male listeners? Rather than using sex to select or eliminate topics, approach any topic so that everyone can benefit from your speech. For example, a few years ago, a male student asked to give an informative speech about "how to be a perfect gentleman." When his instructor told him that his topic seemed to focus primarily on the male audience members, the student said:

> Not really, because by listening to my speech, the female students will know how to encourage the men in their lives to act like gentlemen—whether romantic partners, sons, or a goofy friend.

When establishing the relevance of his topic in the introduction, the student specifically noted that both female and male audience members could benefit from his speech.

audience targeting
The strategy of directing a speech primarily toward one or more portions of the entire audience.

Similarly, you should be careful not to use language that alienates your listeners who identify as LGBT. For example, had the student in the previous example stated that women benefit from his speech on "perfect gentlemen" because it will help them to find a great love interest, he would have risked alienating a lesbian classmate who now feels that she has no reason to devote 5 minutes to listen to his speech. You can go a long way toward inclusion by not assuming that your audience members are all heterosexual or that they all grew up in heterosexual family situations. For example, you might ask your audience to reflect on a childhood memory about their "family" rather than one about "their mom and dad."

Race and Ethnicity

Ethnicity is the classification of a subgroup of people who have a common cultural heritage with shared customs, characteristics, language, history, and so on. It should not be confused with *race*, which refers to the physical characteristics of a group—like skin color. You may have three classmates who are racially black, but ethnically very dissimilar. One may be an African American who grew up in the midwestern United States; another may be an exchange student from Nigeria; yet another might be a native Spanish speaker who grew up in the Dominican Republic.

As with sex, use caution when considering your audience members' race and ethnicity. Do not assume that all the members of any race have the same opinions, particularly if you are delivering a speech on a topic like police brutality or affirmative action—two racially charged topics in the United States today. Similarly, avoid ethnic stereotypes. If you run with statistics stating that your Latino classmates are likely to be politically liberal, you may risk alienating more conservative Latino classmates. For example, some older Cuban American classmates may have more conservative political views.

Education

Your audience's educational level and experience affects what subjects you choose, how you approach them, and the language you use in your speech. Students in the same speech class may have attended private boarding schools, been homeschooled, or earned graduate equivalency degrees after interruptions in their high school educations. Others may have lived and studied overseas due to parental military service or through a study abroad program.

In addition, your audience members likely have different educational interests. If you are at a technical or fine arts school, you may be able to assume some familiarity with disciplinary language and examples. But if you are at a community college or a large university, you're likely speaking with a room full of English, psychology, communication, nursing, and engineering majors. If you're giving a speech to this group on how to change your car's oil or about the history of Cubism, you should avoid complex language with which your audience may not be familiar.

Also remember that education can be informal as well as formal. Listeners who have not completed high school or college are not necessarily uneducated. They may have a wealth of specialized, practical knowledge and training. If you can, find out what your audience members know about a potential speech topic and whether they have experience relevant to your topic. Then tailor your speech to build upon the knowledge they already have.

Religion

Your audience may include agnostics, atheists, and members of various religious groups. Your classmates may practice religions you do not know about, or they may

You might assume the audience in the first photo is more diverse than the audience in the second photo. However, this is not always true. Remember that visible similarities—such as race and sex—do not solely define individuals. Religion, sexual orientation, group memberships, and other demographic factors also matter.

practice familiar religions in a different way. Religion will be very important to some listeners and relatively unimportant to others.

As always, remember the diversity that comes along with religious beliefs. You can't assume that an Episcopalian and a Mennonite will agree on all things simply because they are both Christians. Similarly, an atheist and a person committed to a particular faith can have plenty of things in common.

As a speaker, try to determine whether or not your audience's religious beliefs will be relevant to a topic you are considering. If so, then you should plan for how to be considerate and respectful, and how to make sure your audience members feel included. For example, we advise that students giving demonstration speeches on a culinary topic not pass out samples to the class. There are logistical reasons for this—like the amount of classroom time it takes up and concerns for students with allergies—but some religions (e.g. Judaism and Islam) have strict rules about foods that are not appropriate to consume. A speaker who includes and shares such food risks alienating members of some religious groups.

Economic Status

Economic status is another key factor affecting audience attitudes and behaviors. However, since you're unlikely to find out detailed information about your individual audience members' current financial status, be realistic, fair, and sensitive when choosing topics dealing with economic issues.

For example, it's probably not safe to assume that your listeners will all value learning about the benefits of unpaid internships when many do not have the option to go for a long period of time without paid employment. However, we have observed student speakers generate lively audience interest on topics such as summer employment opportunities at national parks and historic sites and how to negotiate the price of a new or used car. Although money may be of greater concern to some people than to others, few people want to spend money needlessly.

Group Membership

We join groups in order to spend time with others who enjoy our hobbies and pastimes, to learn more about subjects that can help us, or to further our educational, political, and social goals. Many of these groups are voluntary, such as clubs, honor societies, political parties, environmental groups, and social fraternities or sororities. We may also be required to belong to professional associations and labor unions in order to get or keep jobs or special licenses.

Journal: Ignoring Demographics

Think of a situation in which someone (perhaps an instructor, a marketer, or a politician) conveying a message made assumptions about the audience members. What demographic factors should the speaker have considered to ensure all audience members would have felt included in the speech?

Key Points: Audience Demographics

1. Age
2. Sex and sexual orientation
3. Race and ethnicity
4. Education
5. Religion
6. Economic status
7. Group memberships

Knowing your listeners' group membership can be particularly helpful as you prepare persuasive speeches. How you develop your persuasive appeal and select supporting materials will reflect assumptions you have made about your audience. For example, if you are persuading a student environmental group to get involved in a cleanup effort at a local park, you can safely assume that they're already on your side, although you should certainly research the nature of the group as thoroughly as you can before speaking. As always, use caution when using group memberships to make sweeping generalizations about your audience. For example, in current U.S. culture, we make a lot of assumptions about people's political affiliations. Do not assume that all "Democrats" have the same values. Two people can have different opinions on specific social issues and still claim the label "Democrat."

Analyze Audience Psychographics

5.2 Apply your knowledge of your listeners' psychographics to tailor your speech to your audience.

Just as you should develop a useful demographic profile of your audience, you should also generate a psychological profile. **Psychographics** is a term for audience characteristics such as values, beliefs, and attitudes, which often influence our behaviors. These elements help you understand how your listeners think, feel, and behave. Figure 5.1 illustrates how our behaviors are typically shaped by our attitudes, which are based on beliefs, which are validated by values. To better understand the interaction among these elements, we will look at each level of the pyramid, beginning with values and moving upward.

psychographics

Characteristics of the audience, such as values, beliefs, and attitudes, which influence behaviors.

Values

A **value** expresses a judgment of what is important and unimportant, desirable and undesirable, right and wrong, or good and evil. Values are usually stated in the form of a word or phrase. For example, most of us probably share the values of equality, freedom, fairness, justice, good health, and family. These values compose the principles or standards we use to judge and develop our beliefs, attitudes, and behaviors.

If we value equality and fairness, we will no doubt oppose employment practices that discriminate on the basis of sex, sexual orientation, ethnicity, religion, or age. While our actions may not always be consistent with our values, those standards guide what we believe and how we act. When we act contrary to our values, we may experience

value

Judgment of what is right or wrong, desirable or undesirable, usually expressed as words or phrases.

Figure 5.1   Levels of Influence

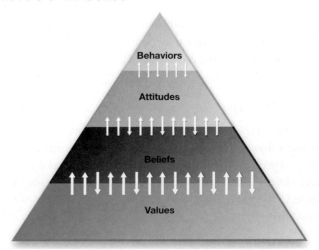

conflict or even guilt (sometimes called dissonance). That dissonance often motivates us either to change our behavior to match our beliefs and values, or to change our beliefs and values by rationalizing our behavior.

Our student Dominic valued honesty. He assumed that his classmates also valued honesty, but wanted to intensify this value among his peers. Dominic delivered a speech with three key ideas: (1) What is honesty? (2) What are the effects of dishonesty? (3) What behaviors boost our perceived honesty? As we listened to Dominic's speech, we realized that honesty was becoming a more important value to us and most likely to Dominic's fellow students as well. Of course, Dominic's personal examples of how a former friend's dishonesty affected him really nailed his point. Honesty is essential in all relationships.

Beliefs

A **belief** is something we accept as true, and it can usually be stated as a declarative sentence. We probably do not think about many of our beliefs because they are seldom challenged. For example:

- College graduates make more money than high school graduates.
- Wearing a seatbelt while driving can save your life.
- Coffee and red wine stain your teeth.

Other beliefs are more controversial, and we often find ourselves defending them. Each of the following statements is debatable:

- College athletes should be paid.
- Facebook is the best way to stay in touch with geographically distant friends.
- Use of the Internet improves the quality of student research.

Those statements you accept as true are part of your personal beliefs.

A few years ago, a former student gave a persuasive speech with the specific purpose: "To convince my classmates that artificial sweeteners aren't a good substitute for real sugar as a means to manage body weight." Because artificial sweeteners have zero calories, many people believe that consuming them positively benefits weight loss; our student assumed her classmates held this belief. After her speech, we reviewed her peer evaluations and learned that her listeners already knew that artificial sweeteners often lead to weight gains rather than weight loss.

If our student had taken the time to analyse her classmates' beliefs, she would have realized that they already agreed with her and her time would have been better spent on another topic.

Attitudes

An **attitude** is an expression of approval or disapproval, our likes and dislikes. A statement of an attitude makes a judgment about the desirability of an individual, object, idea, or action. Examples include the following:

- I prefer morning classes over evening classes.
- I favor a pass–fail grading system.
- I prefer to drink tea over coffee.

Attitudes usually evolve from our values and beliefs. When two values or beliefs collide, the stronger one will generally predominate and determine attitudes. You may value your ability to use your smartphone to monitor the score in your favorite team's game at any time; you may also value your education. So, you may choose to keep your phone in your bag during class because you value learning more than knowing your team's score (and you realize that you can check the scores immediately after

belief
A statement that people accept as true.

attitude
A statement expressing an individual's approval or disapproval, like or dislike.

Key Points: Audience Psychographics

1. Values
2. Beliefs
3. Attitudes
4. Behaviors

Journal: Psychographic Persuasion

At some point in your public speaking course, you will likely be assigned to give a persuasive speech (if you haven't been already). When you consider both your topic and goal for that speech, are you more comfortable analyzing and influencing your audience's values, beliefs, attitudes, or behaviors? Explain your answer.

behavior
An individual's observable action.

Maslow's hierarchy
A model of five basic human needs—physiological, safety, belongingness and love, esteem, and self-actualization—in an ordered arrangement.

It will be difficult to speak about self-actualization needs—like informing your audience on how to graduate a semester early—if their basic needs—like shelter and safety—are not met.

class). Thus, a single belief by itself is not a reliable predictor of a person's attitude or behaviors.

Catharine, a student in her mid-50s, wanted to change her younger classmates' attitudes toward singer and songwriter Bruce Springsteen. She noticed that her instructor referenced Bruce Springsteen in class, but her classmates seemed dismissive because "Bruce is old." Growing up listening to Bruce, Catharine loved his music so she delivered a persuasive speech that focused on (1) Bruce as a storyteller, (2) Bruce as an educator, and (3) Bruce as a political change agent. As part of her first point, she mentioned that Bruce's songs were stories about the struggles of growing up, something we all experience. After class, several students approached Catharine to tell her that they planned to add some of Bruce's songs to their playlists. What a success story! Her peers now had a more favorable attitude toward this American legend they only knew as "an old guy" before Catharine's speech.

Behaviors

A **behavior** is an overt action; it is how we act. Unlike values, beliefs, and attitudes, which are all psychological principles, behaviors are observable. You may feel that maintaining your grandparental relationships is important (attitude) because both grandparents and grandchildren benefit from their relationships (belief) and because you respect your grandparents (value). Your behavior to call your grandparents is a logical and observable extension of your outlook. As such, people's attitudes, values, and beliefs are intertwined, which often influence behavior.

Persuasive speeches frequently seek to alter behaviors. For example, a persuasive speech might encourage you to stop texting and driving, to consume green tea for its many health benefits, to vote for a particular candidate, to take a "screen Sabbath" every week, or to get control over your finances.

Analyze Audience Needs

5.3 Explain the value of analyzing audience needs before your speech.

Once you have considered your audience's demographic and psychographic profiles, you will be in a better position to determine their needs or what motivates them. One particular model, Maslow's hierarchy, will get you thinking about audience needs in an organized way.

Sociologist and psychologist Abraham Maslow is best remembered for a model of human needs commonly referred to as **Maslow's hierarchy**.[6] A hierarchy is an arrangement of items according to their importance, power, or dominance. Maslow's thesis was that all human needs can be grouped into five categories, based on the order in which they are ordinarily filled.[7] (See Figure 5.2.) As a public speaker, you should be aware of the needs dominating any particular audience you address. Maslow's categories are as follows:

1. *Physiological, or physical, needs*—basic human requirements, such as water, food, and sleep. As Maslow and others have observed, hungry people don't play.
2. *Safety needs*—everything that contributes to the "safe, orderly, predictable, lawful, organized world" on which we depend.[8] Feeling safe in our homes and in our cars while driving are typical safety needs.
3. *Belongingness and love needs*—our relationships with people around us. Giving affection to and receiving affection from other people provides us a sense of community.

Figure 5.2   Maslow's Hierarchy of Needs

SOURCE: From *Motivation and Personality*, 1st ed., by Abraham H. Maslow, © 1954. Electronically reproduced by permission of Pearson Education, Inc., Upper Saddle River, New Jersey.

4. *Esteem needs*—feelings of individual self-worth and reasonably high self-evaluation that other people confirm and validate as they recognize what we do well. Everyone has certain talents, and we all need a pat on the back from time to time.

5. *Self-actualization needs*—goals we must achieve in order to feel we have reached our potential or fulfilled our destiny. Our cluster of highly individual self-actualization needs can change at different points in our lives.

Note that we all fill our physiological needs in the same way (when it's possible to get those needs met): by taking nutrition and getting rest. The needs at the top of Maslow's model, in contrast, can be both personally distinctive and temporary. The physical needs also are different from the other needs in that the absence of physical needs (e.g., food, water, air) has an immediate negative impact on us. However, if we don't have time to socialize with our friends one week, we will not suffer any immediate and serious consequences.

Successful speakers identify the unmet needs of their listeners and respond appropriately in informative and persuasive speeches. See "Theory into Practice: Applying Maslow's Hierarchy of Needs" for specific examples.

Gather Information about Your Audience

5.4 Apply strategies to obtain relevant information about your audience.

You are now well aware of the types of information you'll need to learn about your audience. In this section, you will consider how to go about learning this information. There are several helpful ways to go about this, some which require you to directly communicate with your audience members, while others are more passive. Consider the following options:

- *Use your power of observation.* What types of topics are your classmates discussing? If you're in an online class, what do people post about? What happens before, during, and after class? For example, you might notice that a majority of students are fiddling with their phones during lecture. Therefore, a speech on screen addiction or the dangers of multitasking could be relevant. If students are frequently complaining about a lack of weekend activities on campus, a speech persuading them to join a particular campus organization could be of interest.

Key Points: Audience Needs

1. Physiological and physical needs
2. Safety needs
3. Belongingness and love needs
4. Esteem needs
5. Self-actualization needs

Journal: What Are Your Needs?

If you feel overwhelmed thinking about how to determine your audience members' needs, it can be helpful to consider your own. List one unmet need in each of Maslow's five categories (if applicable, as your physical needs may all be met, for example). Choose one. What are two speech topics you could develop based on your selected need?

Theory into Practice (TIP)

APPLYING MASLOW'S HIERARCHY OF NEEDS

What does Maslow's hierarchy mean for you in public speaking? Does this model apply to your listeners, and if so, how? We suggest several ways to make the hierarchy work for you.

- *Physiological and physical needs.* It's likely that most of your classmates have access to adequate food and shelter; it would be very difficult to attend college and succeed without these basic needs met first. However, this doesn't mean that physiological and physical needs aren't relevant to them. For example, many students will move to a new city after graduation and will need to find housing. A speech on a first apartment hunt could be of interest.

- *Safety needs.* Even if the basic safety needs of your classmates are met, this topic is still relevant to anyone who lives and breathes in the world at large. If you alert listeners to the harms of distracted driving, dangerous food additives, or potentially deadly drug interactions, for example, you move them to focus on basic issues of survival. In addition, you cannot assume that all of your audience members live in safe situations. Some may commute from a dangerous neighborhood or have an unsafe home situation. Try to be mindful of this point as you consider safety needs.

- *Belongingness and love needs.* Students—particularly first year or transfer students—are probably interested in being well liked, fitting in, and developing new friendships. In other words, Maslow's third category, belongingness and love needs, is extremely important at this stage. If many or most of the people in your class are in their first year of college, their academic success depends, in part, on how well they integrate themselves into the academic community. Thus, a persuasive speech encouraging your classmates to join a campus or local group is appropriate.

- *Esteem needs.* Take a moment to consider activities you find rewarding and satisfying. Perhaps you volunteer at your local animal shelter or help a family member with daily chores. You may donate money to various charities, work in your campus's tutoring center, or lead a religious organization. A dental technician friend once said, "The best paycheck I've ever received was the smile on a 10-year-old Estonian girl's face after I made her a new set of teeth, free of charge." This statement shows that we often feel good about ourselves after having done a good deed. So, consider some different speech topics in which you inform your listeners about opportunities to volunteer or encourage them to engage in a personally fulfilling activity. After all, we all want to feel good about ourselves.

- *Self-actualization needs.* Although many college students are unsure of the careers they will undertake after graduation, most people have formed, or are forming, self-actualization needs by the time they are in their teens or 20s. Older students may be reassessing and reformulating their self-actualization needs. Those goals are changeable and will adapt as individuals discover new talents, interests, and abilities. For that reason, a college audience is likely to be quite receptive to speeches showing how various pursuits can provide personal rewards or self-fulfillment.

It is important to understand that you cannot easily assign all your listeners a specific set of needs. In fact, as Maslow admits, all of us probably have unmet needs at each of the five levels of his hierarchy. We move from one level to another more frequently than we suspect. Your challenge as a speaker is to identify and emphasize audience needs that are relevant to your topic.

For example, if you feel secure in your surroundings, you may take your safety needs for granted. However, if you read in your school newspaper reports of several attacks on campus, your concern for your own and others' safety will increase. If you choose to address this issue in a persuasive speech, you will want to stress this need for safety, bringing it to the front of your listeners' awareness. Once the situation is evident to them, you can point out ways to satisfy that need. You might advocate for better campus lighting, more security patrols, or personal escort services.

- *Survey your audience.* You can also ask your audience questions by using a questionnaire. If you want to know if they are familiar with Benazir Bhutto (the first female prime minister of Pakistan), you can ask them a dichotomous (yes/no) question; if you're wondering how strongly they feel for or against the idea of a single payer health care system, you can ask a scaled question that measures the intensity of their response. For more information on questionnaires and question types, see Appendix B and Chapter 7, Learning Objective 7.5.

- *Interview your audience.* You can also use the question types discussed in Appendix B and in Chapter 7, Learning Objective 7.5 to conduct an interview with audience members. The interview could be formal (you arrange a time to sit down in the student lounge to talk) or informal (you text each other or post questions in an online forum).

• *Research your audience.* Sometimes, it can be inappropriate or awkward to ask the types of questions you might include in a survey or interview. For example, it would be inappropriate to ask your fellow students how much money they currently have out in student loans. However, you can probably locate or construct general profiles of the typical students at your college. Your school's Office of Institutional Research or Office of Student Life may compile and publish student fact books on their websites.

Your audience analysis is not complete once you have used these techniques to learn about your audience. You must still consider specific speaking scenarios and situations that affect your listeners, a topic we discuss next.

Journal: Asking Questions

Questions are at the heart of interviewing and surveying your audience members in order to learn more about them. (See Appendix B and Chapter 7, Learning Objective 7.5.) Think of a speech topic you are currently researching. Which types of questions are most relevant? Why?

Analyze Specific Speaking Situations

5.5 Explain the value of analyzing specific speaking situations before your speech.

Demographic and psychographic analyses—as well as an assessment of audience needs—give you an arm's-length view of the people who will make up your audience. But who, specifically, are the audience members you will face? What types of conditions will they actually be sitting in? Finding this out requires you to analyze your listeners' dispositions, the size of your audience, the occasion, the physical environment, and the time of day that your speech will occur.

Key Points: Gathering Audience Information

1. Observe your audience.
2. Survey your audience.
3. Interview your audience.
4. Research your audience.

Audience Disposition

Audience disposition describes how listeners are inclined to react to speakers and their ideas. After gathering information regarding audience beliefs and attitudes, you must assess if your listeners are favorable, unfavorable, or neutral toward you and your topic.

The first component of audience disposition is your listeners' attitudes toward you, personally. Do they perceive you as credible, meaning do your listeners believe you are competent, trustworthy, and caring? (In Chapter 16, Learning Objective 16.4, we discuss speaker credibility and its three components in greater detail.) The more credible your

audience disposition

Listeners' feelings of like, dislike, or neutrality toward a speaker, the speaker's topic, or the occasion for a speech.

SPEAKING WITH CONFIDENCE

For me, one of the most daunting tasks of developing a speech was finding an appropriate topic. Don't get me wrong; there are plenty of topics I'm interested in, but I worried that they wouldn't matter to my classmates. My confidence increased tremendously once I learned how to analyze my audience. So, for example, I listened to some of my peers complaining about website and app passwords and how annoying it is to keep track of them and avoid using the same ones over and over again. I enjoy technology and realized that I could give an enjoyable and effective speech on the importance of a good password that would also benefit my listeners. For my second speech, I analyzed my audience members' needs and realized that I could benefit them (and myself) by delivering a speech about test-taking skills. Thanks to my analysis, I felt confident and prepared for both speeches; I wasn't worried about boring my audience.

Alexander Vary
Penn State Hazleton

listeners perceive you to be, the more likely they are to believe you. Thus, if some of your listeners have a neutral or even unfavorable view of you, you will need to work to enhance your speaker credibility.

The second component of audience disposition is your listeners' attitudes toward your topic. Your audience can be slightly, moderately, or strongly favorable or unfavorable toward your topic, and you should try to determine this level of intensity. A listener who only slightly opposes your position will probably be easier to persuade than one who strongly opposes it.

If you sense that some of your listeners are neutral toward your topic, try to uncover the reasons for their neutrality. Some may be *uninterested*, and you will want to convince these listeners of the topic's importance. Other listeners may be *uninformed*, and your strategy should be to introduce them to the data they need to understand and believe your ideas. Still other listeners may simply be *undecided* about your topic. They may be interested, informed, and aware of the pros and cons of your position. However, they may not have decided which position they support. Your strategy in this instance should be to bolster your arguments and point out weaknesses in the opposition's case.

As you can see, evaluating your audience's disposition is a complex activity. The more you know about your listeners, the easier this process becomes.

Size of the Audience

When speaking to a small group, a speaker may be frequently interrupted with questions. The situation may be so informal that the speaker sits in a chair or on the edge of a table during the presentation. A speaker in such a situation may use jargon and colloquial language, presentational aids, and a conversational style of delivery.

As the audience grows larger, however, the speaker must make adjustments. The language of the speech may become more formal, especially if the speaker knows that the speech will be published or recorded. As the distance between the speaker and the last row of audience members increases, the speaker's volume must increase, gestures and facial expressions must be exaggerated slightly, and presentational aids must be projected in order to be seen. (This point is also true of speeches delivered in online, mediated environments.) In very large settings, you may be required to use a lectern with a microphone, which will limit your movements. Unless the audience is encouraged to ask questions after the speech, they will likely remain silent. As you can see, the size of your audience affects both the type of speech you deliver and your manner of presentation.

Occasion

The occasion—or the reason for the speaking event—is a critical factor in determining what type of audience you will face. You need to ask yourself (and maybe even some members of the group), "Why is this audience gathering? What special circumstances

ETHICAL DECISIONS

GHOSTING 101

Listening to a speaker, we usually expect to hear the authentic thoughts of that individual. That seems to be a basic principle of the speaker–audience contract. Yet politicians often do not write the speeches they deliver. Instead they rely on speechwriters, sometimes called "ghostwriters." Journalist Ari Posner laments this tradition, observing, "If college or high school students relied on ghosts the way most public figures do, they'd be expelled on charges of plagiarism."[9]

Is it ethical for political leaders to deliver speeches they did not write? Why or why not? If so, what principles of audience analysis should guide the use of these speeches?

bring them together?" A class, an annual convention, a banquet, a party, a competition, a reunion, and a regular meeting of an organization are all examples of occasions. These can be formal or informal, serious or fun, planned or spontaneous, closed to the public or open to all.

In addition to a simple description of the occasion, speakers may need to know about the history of the occasion or about the recent history of the group they will address. Say, for example, that the officers of an organization have invited you to speak to their entire membership. If there has been recent conflict between the members and the officers, the majority of your audience may look upon you and your speech skeptically. To understand any occasion, you must know both the purpose and the circumstances of the gathering.

Physical Environment

The physical environment or setting can affect the messages sent by the speaker and received by the audience. You may be speaking to a large audience through an inadequate or defective public address system. Or, you may compete with a variety of physical noise sources: the sounds of another meeting next door, a room that is too warm, and interruptions from caterers bringing in carts of ice water. Discovering these challenges before you speak will help you prepare your speech and adapt to your audience.

Time

The time at which you deliver your speech is an important part of analyzing the speaking occasion. An address given at 4:00 p.m. on Friday will almost surely find an audience more fatigued and restless than will one given Tuesday at 9:30 a.m. If you are scheduled to speak first in a class that meets at 8:00 a.m., your audience may be half asleep, so you may need to boost your own energy to enliven them.

The placement of your speech in a program may also affect how your audience receives it. If you follow several other speakers, you may need to work harder at getting and keeping your listeners' attention. In short, if your listeners are not at their best, plan on working extra hard to enliven your delivery.

Key Points: Analyze Situational Factors

1. Audience disposition
2. Audience size
3. Occasion
4. Physical environment
5. Time

Analyze the Audience during and after the Speech

5.6 Explain the value of analyzing the audience's attention, understanding, evaluation, and feedback.

Careful audience analysis before your speech will guide your topic selection, how you focus and develop your subject, the language you use, and how you plan to deliver your speech. However, even the most thorough, conscientious audience and situational analysis will not guarantee a compelling, effectively delivered speech. Speakers do not perform for audiences; they interact with them. The physical presence of listeners transforms and shapes each public speaking experience. To make that vital connection with your listeners, your audience analysis must continue during the delivery of your speech. Communication scholars suggest that, as you speak, you must be aware of three characteristics of your listeners—their attention, understanding, and evaluation—and that you should not assume that your audience analysis ends when you finish delivering your speech.

Audience Attention

First, you must be aware of the audience's *attention* or interest. Do their eye contact, posture, and other body language indicate that they are concentrating on you and your message? Are there physical distractions in the speech setting that are competing with you for the audience's attention? Do you seem to have the audience's attention throughout some parts of the speech, only to lose it during other parts? If you are concentrating on your message and on your listeners rather than on how you sound and look, you will know the answers to these questions.

If you detect a lapse of audience attention during your speech, how can you recapture it? You could address some of your listeners by name or make a connection between your speech and another one that the audience has already heard. You can also recapture your audience's attention with statements such as, "The most important point to remember is. . ." You may also be able to simply change some aspect of your delivery: speaking more loudly or softly, for example, or moving from the lectern for part of the speech so that you are closer to the audience, or even incorporating appropriate humor in your speech. Any change in your established pattern of delivery will likely rekindle audience attention and interest. In addition, changing your usual style of delivery may be essential to overcome the distractions of a stuffy room, a noisy heater, or audience noise.

Audience Understanding

A second characteristic of your audience that you must try to assess is their *understanding* or comprehension of your message. If you have ever produced a false laugh when you didn't really understand a joke, you know how difficult it is to fake comprehension. No matter how hard most of us try to cover up a lack of understanding, something about our voices or our bodies signals to others that we didn't really understand.

Of course, your audience members may not try to hide their incomprehension. Members may deliberately tell you with puzzled expressions and other nonverbal cues that they are confused. The worst thing a speaker can do under such circumstances is to continue as if there were no problems. Clarifying something for the audience may be as simple as repeating or rephrasing the problem statement. If a particular word seems to be the source of confusion, defining the word or displaying it may solve the problem.

Journal: Audience Understanding

Think of a time when one of your instructors covered a complex topic in class. How did you and your classmates react? Did your instructor notice that you and your classmates did not understand? If so, how did your instructor proceed?

Audience Evaluation

The third component of audience analysis during the speech is your listeners' *evaluation* of you and your message. Sensitive speakers attuned to their audiences are able to gauge the reactions of those listeners. Do members of the audience seem to agree with what you are saying? Do they approve of the suggestions you are making? Answers to these questions are particularly important when you are seeking to persuade your audience.

Sometimes the answer to such questions will be no. You may be delivering bad news or taking what you know will be an unpopular stand on an issue. Having the audience disagree with the content of your message doesn't necessarily mean that your speech has been a failure. Simply knowing that many listeners agree or disagree with you at the end of a persuasive speech shows that you are an audience-centered speaker.

Audience Formal and Informal Feedback

Too often, speakers assume that the speech-making process concludes as you utter your final statement and walk to your seat or turn off your video camera. You will certainly want to analyze your own strengths and weaknesses after you speak, and your instructor will offer encouragement and constructive criticism. However, do not discount the feedback from your audience, especially since they will notice things that you will not and they are not subject to the same level of self-scrutiny about your performance.

In this class, that information may come from oral or written critiques from your peers or from comments some of them give you after class. If you deliver a good speech on an interesting topic, one pleasant reward is having audience members ask questions or follow up with you for more information about your topic. Take this as a compliment and incorporate it into your perception of yourself as a speaker. Similarly, graciously accept the critiques of your speech and see them as an opportunity to learn and improve, rather than an indication that you "aren't any good at this." Remember, your audience generally wants you to succeed; their feedback aims to help you achieve that goal as well.

> **Key Points: Analyze the Audience during and after the Speech**
>
> 1. Audience attention
> 2. Audience understanding
> 3. Audience evaluation
> 4. Audience formal and informal feedback

› SUMMARY

Analyzing Your Audience

Analyze Audience Demographics

5.1 Apply the seven demographic categories to tailor your speech to your audience.

- Before the speech, you should consider your audience's demographics, which are characteristics of the audience, such as age, sex, sexual orientation, race, ethnicity, education, religion, economic status, and group membership.

- Be very careful not to stereotype your listeners based on their demographics.

Analyze Audience Psychographics

5.2 Explain how knowledge of your listeners' psychographics can help you tailor your speech to your audience.

- Psychographics is a term for audience psychology and how listeners' thoughts influence their actions.

- Three key components of audience psychology are values, beliefs, and attitudes, which ultimately influence audience members' behavior.

Analyze Audience Needs

5.3 Explain the value of analyzing audience needs before your speech.

- *Maslow's hierarchy* of needs is a useful tool for analyzing audience motivation by ranking five human needs in terms of their predominance: physiological needs, safety needs, belongingness and love needs, esteem needs, and self-actualization needs.

- Prepared speakers will target speeches at audience's unmet needs after careful audience analysis.

Gather Information about Your Audience

5.4 Apply strategies to obtain relevant information about your audience.

- Gathering information about your audience can be formal or informal.

- You can observe their behaviors, survey your listeners, conduct interviews, or research your audience members.

Analyze Specific Speaking Situations

5.5 Explain the value of analyzing specific speaking situations before your speech.

Speakers should analyze specific speaking situations by considering the disposition and size of the audience, the occasion and physical environment for the speech, and when the speech is given.

Analyze the Audience during and after the Speech

5.6 Explain the value of analyzing the audience's attention, understanding, evaluation, and feedback.

- During the speech, you should focus on your listeners' attention, understanding, and evaluation of the speech.

- After delivering the speech you should assess the audience's formal and informal feedback. Anyone who is serious about improving public speaking must be aware of and act on audience feedback.

SELECTING YOUR SPEECH TOPIC

⟶ **LEARNING OBJECTIVES**

After studying this chapter, you should be able to

6.1 Compile a list of possible topics for your speech within the four categories of speech topics.

6.2 Determine the general purpose of your speech.

6.3 Select an appropriately narrow speech topic based on four criteria.

6.4 Construct the three parts of your specific purpose statement.

6.5 Word the central idea of your speech.

The successful writer begins with a blank sheet of paper or a clear screen. The successful director begins with an empty stage or set. To achieve a finished product—a book, play, or movie—both must go through several complicated steps. Directors must study the literary form, understand its dynamics, research the script, generate ideas, focus and organize those ideas, and then translate them into performance. In doing so, directors give the finished product their individual signatures. Writers follow a similar process to complete a project.

As a public speaker, you are both author and director. Therefore, you seek to fill two voids: a blank sheet of paper and an empty space in front of an audience (whether you are physically present with them or presenting online). However, before you can exercise your artistry with language, your persistence as a researcher, or any other talents you possess, you must have a topic. Choosing an excellent speech topic involves five steps, as shown in Figure 6.1. You should (1) generate a list of possible topics, (2) determine your general purpose, (3) select and narrow your topic, (4) formulate your specific purpose, and (5) word your central idea.

Figure 6.1   The Steps in Choosing a Topic for a Speech

1. Generate a list of possible topics.   2. Determine your general purpose.   3. Select and narrow your topic.   4. Formulate your specific purpose.   5. Word your central idea.

Generate Ideas

6.1 Compile a list of possible topics for your speech within the four categories of speech topics.

Many (if not most) speakers in the real world have assigned topics. For example, a human resource manager informs employees about changes to the company's retirement savings plan; the president of the Parent Teacher Association delivers a welcome address to new parents at kindergarten orientation. However, in the context of your speech class, you will most likely have a great deal of freedom in selecting your topic. While this may feel overwhelming, try to reframe this freedom as an opportunity to speak on a topic that is rewarding, interesting, and appropriate. To generate a list of such topics, we advise our students to consider four essential questions:

1. What topics interest *me*?
2. What topics interest my *listeners*?
3. What topics develop from the *occasion*?
4. What topics develop from my *research*?

We will discuss each of these questions as categories of topics. Know that your answers will help you devise a list of many topics from which you can select the most appropriate and appealing topic.

Self-Generated Topics

self-generated topics

Speech topics based on the speaker's interests, experiences, and knowledge.

Self-generated topics come from you—your memory, your thoughts, your notes, your interests, your experiences, your knowledge, your likes and dislikes. Jot down your hobbies, your favorite courses, books you have read, your pet peeves, names of people who intrigue you, current events that concern you, and issues and events that excite you. Review your list and beside each item write possible speech topics.

One technique that can help you move from your own thoughts to a speech topic is **brainstorming**. This involves listing all ideas that come to mind without evaluating or censoring any of them. What may seem silly to you at first (your favorite ice cream flavor) can turn out to be an interesting speech subject with a lot of potential to interest your audience (how to make homemade ice cream). You could also try engaging in **random word association**, in which you jot down a random word (e.g. a word you put your finger on in a book or an object in your sight), and record words, thoughts, or ideas which you associate with the original word. For example, looking at a candle and jotting that word down might get you thinking about indoor air pollution.

Self-generated topics may also include subjects you *need* to know. If, for example, you expect to study abroad in Spain next semester, it may be in your best interest to learn more about the Spanish culture. Are there differences in what is considered polite social manners between Spain and the United States? What are the daily rhythms and routines in the Spanish city where you will be studying? (For example, dinner may be served much later than you are used to.) Researching and delivering a speech on any of these topics will likely serve you well as you prepare for your study abroad adventure.

Consider the following speech topics generated by students based on their personal experiences, interests, and knowledge:

Barack Obama's presidency	Online security
Cyber schooling	Vacationing in the Dominican Republic
Lupus	Vegetarianism
Mindfulness meditation	Water aerobics

Use what you know as a starting point in your selection process. Don't worry that you don't know enough about each topic at this stage to construct a speech. What is important is that you have a list of topics that interest you. Because these topics come from *your* experiences, interests, and knowledge, your commitment to them is usually strong; they will motivate you in preparing your speech. In addition, your enthusiasm for your topic will enliven and enhance your delivery.

One of the most exciting parts of speaking on a topic you love is the opportunity to get your audience members interested in the topic—to share your interest or passion with them. For example, your audience may not initially care about Bruce Springsteen's music. Ask yourself, "Why is this topic relevant to my audience? How can my audience

brainstorming

Noncritical free association to generate as many ideas as possible.

random word association

Recording of words and ideas that come to mind when thinking about a randomly selected word.

TABLE 6.1 Challenges with Self-Generated Speech Topics

Challenge	Explanation and Example
Speech may incorporate technical language or jargon.	When you know a subject well, you know its language. So, while you might be familiar with "coiling" and "dunting" from your many years of pottery making, your listeners probably won't. Ensure you define any subject-specific terms to enhance your listeners' understanding.
Informative topics can become persuasive.	If you feel passionate about a topic, it's difficult not to encourage your audience to love it too. Joe was a passionate snowboarder. He was informing his audience about snowboarding equipment, but encouraged his listeners to try out the sport, thus making his speech persuasive.
Speech can lack objectivity.	If you have very rigid opinions about a topic, you must be careful not to overlook relevant evidence to the contrary. Adika is deeply entrenched in Google's ecosystem, but doesn't address privacy concerns when informing her audience about its benefits.

benefit from my topic?" (In Chapter 10, Learning Objective 10.1, you will learn about the importance of establishing relevance for your topic.) But what if you told them that Bruce Springsteen sings about social and relational issues; he also sings about historical events, such as the Civil War, making his music educational. Even if they don't share your interest, your audience may think it's worthwhile to know this information about a famous and celebrated musician.

Despite their great potential, self-generated topics are not without their pitfalls—all of which can be addressed as you research and plan your speech. Consider the challenges discussed in Table 6.1.

Audience-Generated Topics

audience-generated topics
Speech topics geared to the interests and needs of a speaker's listeners.

Audience-generated topics is a second useful category of speech topics. What topics interest or seem important to your listeners? How can you find out? There are three ways to do this. First, *ask them*. Ask some of your classmates in casual conversation about topics they would like to hear discussed. If possible, you could use a questionnaire to seek topic suggestions from the entire class. (See Appendix B—Using Audience Questionnaires.) If you speak to an organization, ask the person who contacted you about issues of probable interest to the group.

Second, *listen and read*. What do your classmates discuss before and after class? Articles in your campus and local paper or letters to the editor may suggest issues of concern. Finally, *use the audience analysis strategies* to generate topics. Consider your listeners' needs. If your class is composed primarily of students just entering college, a speech on the history of your school could be interesting, informative, and appropriate. If your class is composed primarily of college seniors, a speech on establishing a good credit history may be timely. (See also Chapter 5, Learning Objective 5.2.)

Rituals and special occasions can provide excellent speech topics. Here guests arrive in traditional dress for a Lapp wedding.

If you are lucky enough to be in a diverse class, you can deliver a speech to enhance your classmates' knowledge about various topics. Our student Zoljargal surely had this in mind when she chose to inform her listeners about the clothing and cultural festivals of her native Mongolia. Chantal, a technician at a local blood bank, gave her classmates an insider's view of what happens to blood after donation. Another student older than her classmates informed them about great blues musician Robert Johnson and his influence on guitarists like Eric Clapton. In each case, these students chose topics by considering both their own knowledge and their peers' lack of knowledge.

You may even find that most of your audience members seem to feel one way about a controversial topic while you take the opposite view. You could use this situation to develop and deliver a persuasive speech aimed at winning support for your view of the issue.

Our students generated the following list of topics using an audience-centered approach:

Applying to graduate school	Searching for online scholarships
Controlling test anxiety	Studying abroad
Hazing on college campuses	Supporting campus events
Improving interviewing skills	Taking online classes

Occasion-Generated Topics

Occasion-generated topics are a third source of speech topics. When and where a speech is delivered may guide your selection of an appropriate subject. A speech on setting goals may benefit your classmates more at the beginning of the term, whereas a speech on stress management may have more impact before exams.

If you are scheduled to speak after a bullying case was made public on your campus, it may be suitable to talk about the effects of bullying or how to prevent bullying. If you speak a few weeks before spring break, you may want to inform your classmates about some potential spring break travel destinations or persuade them to enact specific safety standards while traveling. Other students may be scheduled to speak during an election year, so informing the audience members about the Electoral College used in the United States would be a suitable topic. If your campus football team is doing well, you may want to discuss the different bowl games in which top-ranked teams play at the end of the season.

Our students generated the following topics as they focused on different occasions for speeches:

Chinese New Year	Independence Day
Earth Day	MTV Music Awards
First-year seminar	Swedish midsummer celebrations
Graduation ceremonies	Tax preparation

An occasion-generated topic can often lead you to other interesting topics. Drought conditions in your area may make you consider the subjects of cloud seeding or desalting seawater. Unseasonably warm weather may prompt you to talk about global warming. The Syrian refugee crisis may motivate you to persuade your classmates to donate to the World Health Organization in an effort to help the many people in need.

Research-Generated Topics

Research-generated topics require you to explore a variety of sources. First, you could consult some databases and indexes in your library. Look at the list of subjects and jot down those that interest you. A second research strategy is to browse through magazines or journals in your library, at a local newsstand, or online. Just remember that this exploration is the first step in selecting a speech topic. (See Chapter 7, Learning Objective 7.3 for information about accessing databases and other library resources.) Don't leap at the first interesting topic you find. Also, be wary of using social media as a tool to look for news stories because the information presented is not always accurate.

A third research strategy is to peruse book titles at a good bookstore, library, or via an online seller, noting those that interest you. Bookstores are convenient places to discover speech topics because the books are grouped by general subject area and are arranged to catch your eye. By using these three research tools—databases and indexes, magazines and journals, and books—you may not only discover a speech topic but also locate your first source of information.

occasion-generated topics
Speech topics derived from particular circumstances, seasons, holidays, or life events.

Journal: Generating Topic Ideas

In preparation for an upcoming speech, list one topic idea each for self-, audience-, and occasion-generated categories. Does one of these topics stand out to you? If so, why?

research-generated topics
Speech topics discovered by investigating a variety of sources.

SPEAKING WITH CONFIDENCE

Topic selection can be the most important step of the entire speech. When I brainstormed for topics, I would think about things that really interested me. If you choose something that doesn't excite you, you won't be comfortable speaking about it. Interesting topics, however, make the whole experience more enjoyable. During the past election, I really wanted my classmates to register and vote, so I made this my purpose for speaking. My commitment to this topic motivated me to research and practice my speech. I wanted my audience to share my enthusiasm for voting. Public speaking doesn't have to be boring. You can be creative and have fun with your topic. Knowing that I had something important and interesting for my classmates to hear made me feel more confident delivering my speech.

Bryan McClure
Virginia Tech University

Determine Your General Purpose

6.2 Determine the general purpose of your speech.

Despite the dizzying array of potential topics on which you can speak, your speech will have one of three **general purposes**: to inform, to persuade, or to entertain. The general purpose of your speech defines your relationship with the audience. You play the role of a mentor or teacher when you provide information. You are an advocate when you seek to change beliefs, attitudes, values, or behaviors through a persuasive speech. Your speech to entertain is meant to amuse your audience. As the entertainer, you set a mood to relax your audience using your delivery style, tone, and content.

You may sometimes find it difficult to distinguish among these three purposes. Because information may affect both what we believe and how we act, the distinction between informative speaking and persuasive speaking is sometimes blurred. A speech meant to entertain is frequently persuasive because it may make a serious point through the use of humor. Despite the overlap between these general purposes, you must be secure about your primary purpose any time you speak in public. A closer look at the objectives and intended outcomes of each general purpose will help you distinguish them.

general purpose
The broad goal of a speech—to inform, to persuade, or to entertain.

Speeches to Inform

The objective of a **speech to inform** is to impart knowledge to an audience. You convey this information in an objective and unbiased manner. Your goal is not to alter the listeners' attitudes or behaviors but to facilitate their understanding of your subject and their ability to retain this new information or how to enact a certain behavior. A speech on any of the following topics could be informative: Appalachian culture, the history of science-fiction movies, the middle-child syndrome, music software, and vertical ice climbing. (See also Chapter 15 for a discussion about speaking to inform.)

speech to inform
A speech designed to convey new or useful information in a balanced, objective way.

Speeches to Persuade

A **speech to persuade** seeks to influence your listeners' attitudes, beliefs, values, or behaviors. A **speech to convince** focuses on affecting audience attitudes and beliefs, without advocating a specific action. Without suggesting a plan of action, a speaker may argue, for example, that polygraph testing is unreliable. Another speaker may try

speech to persuade
A speech designed to influence listeners' attitudes, beliefs, values, or behaviors.

speech to convince
A persuasive speech focused on influencing audience attitudes and beliefs, without advocating a specific action.

to convince listeners that women have been neglected in medical research without offering a plan to solve the problem.

A **speech to actuate** attempts to change not only the listeners' beliefs and attitudes but also their behavior. Such a speech could move the audience to boycott a controversial art exhibit, to contribute money to a charity, or to urge their elected officials to increase funding for women's health research. In each case, the speaker's goal would be first to intensify or alter the audience's beliefs and then to show how easy and beneficial taking action could be.

A **speech to inspire** is one that attempts to influence how listeners feel. Your audience members may feel negatively about the idea of extending the general education requirements to include a statistics course. Through a well-constructed and dynamically delivered speech to inspire, you may be able to influence your listeners' attitudes toward the new general education requirements so they feel more positive toward general education courses. (We discuss persuasive speeches in Chapter 16 and Chapter 17.)

speech to actuate

A persuasive speech designed to influence audience behaviors.

speech to inspire

A persuasive speech designed to influence listeners' feelings

speech to entertain

A speech designed to make a point through the creative, organized use of amusing supporting materials.

Speeches to Entertain

A third general purpose of a speech is to entertain. To clarify, a *speech to entertain* differs from *speaking to entertain*. The latter includes humorous monologues, standup comedy routines, and storytelling, for example. When you tell your friends jokes or recount a humorous anecdote, you are trying to entertain them. You are probably not trying to develop a key point in an organized, methodical way.

A **speech to entertain** is more formal than speaking to entertain because it is highly organized and its development is more detailed. Speeches to entertain are often delivered on occasions when people are in a festive mood, such as after a banquet or as part of an awards ceremony. Remember that all speeches, including those to entertain, should develop a central idea with organized points and relevant supporting materials. Though the ideas in a speech to entertain will be illustrated and highlighted by humor, a mere collection of jokes does not qualify as a speech to entertain. We agree with the communication scholars who contend that a speech to entertain is actually either a speech to inform or a speech to persuade, usually the latter. For example, when delivering a best man or a maid of honor speech at a wedding, you're entertaining the audience and celebrating the couple, but also persuading listeners to believe that the couple is a wonderful match with a bright future. (We discuss the speech to entertain in more detail in Chapter 18.)

> **Journal: Distinguishing Purposes**
>
> The text notes that it can be difficult to distinguish among the three general purposes (to inform, to persuade, and to entertain). What are some reasons for why this is? Can you offer an example of a topic that could easily fall into more than one category?

> **Key Points: Determine Your General Purpose**
>
> 1. To inform
> 2. To persuade
> 3. To entertain

Select and Narrow Your Topic

6.3 Select an appropriately narrow speech topic based on four criteria.

After you have generated worthwhile ideas and confirmed your general speech purpose, you must select the final subject on which you will speak. Look at your list of general ideas, choose a few, and *focus* them by honing in on a specific aspect of each broad topic. Students often ask us if a topic is too specific or too narrow, but the opposite is more likely to be true. Students tend to choose topics that are far too general to develop in a 5- to 7-minute speech. For example, it's not possible to inform your audience about "salsa dancing" in the allotted amount of time. But you certainly could demonstrate three particular moves common in salsa dancing. Table 6.2 shows how some of our students have taken general topic ideas and made them more specific:

If the task of narrowing your topic seems daunting, you can give **mind mapping** a try. This is a technique that allows you to refine an idea by visually linking more specific ideas that extend from the original idea. For his speech on pet therapy (an extremely general topic), Luis created a mind map and discovered that he might be

mind mapping

A technique for refining an idea by visually linking more specific ideas that extend from the original idea.

TABLE 6.2 From General to Specific Speech Topics

General Topic	Specific Topic
Exercise	Why you should give water aerobics a try
Food Allergies	Why health insurance should cover sublingual immunotherapy for nut-allergic children
Golf	How to hit a perfect bunker shot
Graduate School	How to evaluate graduate programs to find a good match for you
Scuba Diving	How to follow scuba safety procedures
Social Media	Why you should deactivate your Facebook account today
The Amish	How the Amish educate children

interested in speaking about service dogs (more specific) or even the possible benefits for individuals with health issues like cancer, diabetes, and frequent seizures (very specific). See Figure 6.2 to read through Luis's mind map and work through the Theory into Practice to create your own.

A second way to narrow your topic is through research. The more you read about your subject, the more likely it is that you will discover its many aspects. Some may be too narrow for a complete speech, but others may be suitable for an entire speech or may be combined to form a speech. For example, if you are interested in learning about humor in organizations, your research would reveal that there are workshops that teach how to use humor to improve workplace morale, enthusiasm, and productivity. There are humor coaches and even a Humor University. Any one or a combination of these subjects could provide the topic for an excellent speech.

Once you have generated a list of possible speech topics that are sufficiently specific, you must select the best one. Asking and answering the following four questions will help you make a wise decision.

Figure 6.2   Mind Mapping

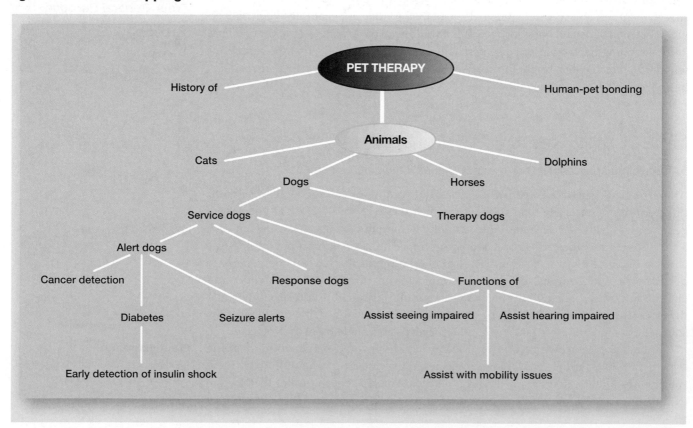

Theory into Practice (TIP)

MIND MAPPING

Mind mapping allows you to break down general topics into more specific and manageable topics. Typically, you'll have a general topic idea in the center and "branch out" like a tree with related topics. This creates clusters of specific speech topics that all relate to the main, central topic in one way or another.

Take out your tablet and stylus or a sheet of paper and pen to begin. (There are also several very highly rated mind mapping apps. Do a search for reviews if you'd prefer to work with a more formal program.) Write your general topic area in the center of the page or screen. Now, think of how you could divide and narrow this topic. It may help you to think of some generic categories such as "causes," "types," and "solutions" that are appropriate to numerous topics. As you think of sub-topics, draw a line from your initial topic areas in any direction and write the narrower topic.

As with brainstorming, try not to judge your ideas as you jot them down. You never know how a seemingly silly idea might lead to a very specific and usable speech topic.

1. *Am I interested in the topic?* The more enthusiastic you are about a topic, the more time and attention you will give to researching, constructing, and practicing your speech. When you enjoy learning, you learn better. As a result, speakers motivated by their topics are almost always more productive than those bored with their topics.

2. *Is the topic of interest or importance to my audience?* This question helps you avoid choosing a topic that you love but that your audience will never care about. Speech making is easier when your listeners are potentially interested in what you have to say. When your audience is attentive and receptive, you can relax and make your delivery livelier. Sometimes topics seem to be of little initial interest to an audience but may, nevertheless, be important to their personal or career success. As long as you can demonstrate the importance and relevance of the topic, you will motivate your audience to listen.

3. *Am I likely to find sufficient authoritative supporting material in the time allotted for researching and developing the speech?* Unless your topic is truly offbeat or brand new, your answer to this question will likely be "yes." Even if the topic is so new that it has not yet appeared in articles, chances are good that you'll find information about it online. In that case, you'll have to judge whether the information you find

Persuading your audience to start a campus community garden is a great persuasive topic that is specific enough to discuss in 5 to 7 minutes and will likely interest your audience if you make it relevant to them. However, if you kill every houseplant you own, this probably isn't the right topic for you.

is authoritative. If your best sources will take you several days or weeks to arrange (like an interview with a professor or outside professional), do you have the time? (This is yet another reason why early preparation benefits you.) Remember the adage that if something can go wrong, it will. Build some flexibility into your schedule so that you can adapt to any crisis that may arise.

4. *Do I understand the topic enough to undertake and interpret my research?* A speaker arguing the merits of a tax increase must understand economics in order to assess research data. When you inform the audience about the benefits of music therapy for children, you need some understanding of psychological treatment techniques and procedures. A speaker may misinterpret the reasons that violent crime in the United States is higher than in Japan if he or she does not understand the Japanese culture. You don't need to know much about your topic as you begin your research, but you must know enough to be able to make sense of the information you gather.

Journal: Eliminating Topic Areas

Of the topic areas you have mind mapped so far, what are two or three that you would eliminate based on the four criteria? Describe how you came to the decision to drop these.

Formulate Your Specific Purpose

6.4 Construct the three parts of your specific purpose statement.

When you are asked to state the general purpose of your speech, you will respond with two words from among the following: *to inform*, *to persuade* (or *to actuate, to convince, to inspire*), or *to entertain*. When asked to state your specific purpose, however, you must be more descriptive. A **specific purpose** statement has three parts.

specific purpose

A statement of the general purpose of the speech, the speaker's intended audience, and the goal or outcome.

First, you begin with the speech's general purpose, stated as an infinitive—for example, "to convince." Second, you name the individuals to whom the speech is addressed, usually phrased simply as "my peers" or "my fellow students" in a public speaking course. (In a professional speech, this might be "the board of directors" or "my colleagues.") Third, you state what you want your speech to accomplish. What should the audience know, believe, or do as a result of your speech? You may want to establish the belief that alcoholism is hereditary. In this case, then, your complete specific purpose statement would be: "To convince my classmates that alcoholism is hereditary." Other examples of specific purpose statements are:

- To inform my fellow students about celebrity worship syndrome
- To actuate my classmates to volunteer in their communities
- To convince my public speaking class that laughter is medically therapeutic
- To entertain my teammates by highlighting Coach Jackson's achievements as head baseball coach

Failure to understand and clearly articulate your specific purpose can be detrimental to your effectiveness as a speaker, both in your public speaking class and outside of the university. Imagine that your goal is to inform your classmates about how to make a sweet potato casserole, but only mention that you will talk about potato casseroles. How will your listeners know what type of potato casserole you are discussing and how will they know that you are simply trying to inform them, not persuade them to make a sweet potato casserole?

While failing to clearly articulate your specific purpose may be a correctable problem in your public speaking class, its effects in the real world may be more serious. A project manager leading a team of structural engineers may intend to give a speech to her colleagues with the specific purpose: "To inform my colleagues about alternative construction approaches." If the lead engineer simply talks about the new construction approaches without specifying she is merely informing the other engineers of these approaches, it is possible that the audience members will assume these new construction approaches should be applied to their current project. If so, the team of engineers may waste valuable time and resources approaching the project incorrectly.

ETHICAL DECISIONS

SHOULD INSTRUCTORS CENSOR?

A colleague of ours had a long and distinguished career teaching communication. After class one day, she returned to her office visibly upset. When questioned by her colleagues, she said one of her students had announced in his speech introduction that his purpose was to teach the class how to make a lethal poison using ingredients people already had in their homes or could easily buy. "Moreover," she said, "to stress the significance of the topic, he assured us that this substance would kill any living animal, certainly even the heaviest human being."

"What did you do?" her colleagues asked. "I sat there thinking of the rash of teenage suicides, even copycat suicides,

we've been hearing about lately, and all the other meanness in the world," she replied. "I wrestled with my conscience for about a minute and a half, and then, for the first time since I started teaching, I interrupted a speaker. I told the student I didn't think we needed to hear this information, and asked him to be seated."

Was this teacher's action justified? Did she violate the student's freedom of speech? Placed in that teacher's position, what would you have done?

Politicians who inform their audiences about other countries' voting procedures without specifying that they are simply *informing* their audiences about voting procedures in other countries could easily be misunderstood. The audience members may assume that the politicians are promoting such voting procedures in their own countries. If the audience members disagree with the discussed voting procedures, they may erroneously discontinue their support of the politicians who discuss voting procedures in other countries because they failed to state their specific purposes.

> **Key Points: Develop Your Specific Purpose Statement**
>
> 1. State your general purpose.
> 2. Name your intended audience.
> 3. State the goal of your speech.

Formulate Your Central Idea

6.5 Word the central idea of your speech.

A **central idea** is a one-sentence statement that specifies the key ideas of your speech. We will discuss developing key ideas (and organizing them) further in Chapter 8, but for now just understand that the speech's "key ideas" are the big picture, main points that you plan to discuss in the body of your speech. For example, the central idea of a persuasive speech on cloth diapering could be the three main benefits you discover in your research: "Cloth diapering is superior to using disposable diapers because it saves money for the family, is healthier for the child, and prevents additional landfill waste."

central idea

A one-sentence synopsis that specifies the speaker's key ideas.

Notice that the process of topic selection has, up to this point, enabled you to focus your subject on something specific and manageable. You are now ready to construct a *working central idea*: a statement that, based on your current research and thinking, summarizes what you will say in your speech.[1] Although a central idea is designed to keep you focused, it may change as you continue to work on and develop your speech. It gives you a handle on your subject and, as you begin to develop your key ideas, will help you determine whether you can support your central idea. When organizing the body of the speech, you may realize that your ideas are not balanced or that two of your key ideas should be collapsed into one. As you research your speech, you may discover additional ideas that are more important than some you had planned to present. That was the experience of our student who spoke on compulsory national service.

Stuart was developing a persuasive speech advocating a system of compulsory national service (CNS). As he began his research, he planned to focus only on the national security that compulsory military service would provide. His working central idea was, "Compulsory national service would benefit the nation by ensuring its military readiness." Yet his research quickly revealed many other benefits of CNS: domestic conservation and recycling, rural health care, and in-home assistance to the elderly.

By the time he had completed his research, Stuart had broadened the focus of his speech and felt he had developed a much stronger case for instituting a CNS program. When he delivered his speech, he presented three key ideas:

I. CNS would promote the national spirit.

II. CNS would promote the national defense.

III. CNS would promote the national welfare.

Stuart then revised his central idea to reflect his new organization.

The following examples illustrate how you can narrow a topic's focus from a general topic area to the speech's central idea:

Topic Area: Sculpture

Topic: Works by Andy Goldsworthy

General Purpose: To inform

Specific Purpose: To inform my classmates about Andy Goldsworthy's sculptures

Central Idea: Andy Goldsworthy sculpts wood, ice, and leaves into intricate works in their natural settings.

Topic Area: Police oversight

Topic: Mandatory videotaping of police

General Purpose: To persuade

Specific Purpose: To persuade my peers that all police actions should be videotaped.

Central Idea: Videotaping all police actions will deter police misconduct, discourage false charges of police misconduct, and restore public confidence in police work.

Journal: The Central Idea

Think of your favorite musician or actor. What is it about this person that draws your admiration? What are some important contributions this person has made to the entertainment industry? Based on your answers to these questions, formulate a central idea.

› SUMMARY

Selecting Your Speech Topic

Generate Ideas

6.1 Compile a list of possible topics for your speech within the four categories of speech topics.

- Appropriate speech topics can be self generated, audience generated, occasion generated, or research generated.
- Great speech topics will be of interest to you and your audience in addition to being appropriate for the occasion.

Determine Your General Purpose

6.2 Determine the general purpose of your speech.

Understand the general purpose of your speech—to inform, to persuade, or to entertain—before moving on to the details of your speech.

Select and Narrow Your Topic

6.3 Select an appropriately narrow speech topic based on four criteria.

- Select your topic and narrow it by mind mapping or researching your topic.

- Ask yourself: (1) Am I interested in this topic? (2) Is the topic of interest or importance to my audience? (3) Am I likely to find sufficient authoritative supporting materials in the time allotted for researching and developing the speech? (4) Do I understand the topic enough to undertake and interpret my research?

Formulate Your Specific Purpose

6.4 Construct the three parts of your specific purpose statement.

To construct your specific purpose, you should identify (1) your general purpose, (2) your intended audience, and (3) what you will accomplish in your speech.

Formulate Your Central Idea

6.5 Word the central idea of your speech.

- In one sentence, describe your key ideas and what you want to accomplish in your speech.
- Your central idea should identify what the audience should know, believe, or do as a result of hearing your speech.

RESEARCHING YOUR SPEECH TOPIC

→ LEARNING OBJECTIVES

After studying this chapter, you should be able to

7.1   Construct a general plan for conducting research on your topic.

7.2   Collect and evaluate information gathered online.

7.3   Collect and evaluate information gathered via the library.

7.4   Record relevant information systematically.

7.5   Collect, analyze, and interpret information gathered through primary research.

R esearch scholar Patricia Breivik summarizes the snowballing accumulation of information as follows:

> The sum total of humankind's knowledge doubled from 1750–1900. It doubled again from 1900–1950. Again from 1960–1965. It has been estimated that the sum of humankind's knowledge has doubled at least once every 5 years since then. . . . It has been further projected that by the year 2020, knowledge will double every 73 days.[1]

In light of these circumstances, it is surely smarter to think of being educated as *knowing how to access and analyze* information, than *possessing* it.

For public speakers, the challenge is selecting from the wide range of available data the information most appropriate for their speeches. That requires knowing how to research—how to scratch "an intellectual itch."[2]

Research is the gathering of evidence and arguments you will need to understand, develop, and explain your subject. Research is not a single step of the speech construction process but should occur throughout the process. First, research can help you select your topic. Once you have chosen a topic, additional research helps you focus and determine your specific purpose. As you begin to construct the body of your speech, you may need to develop some of your ideas further with additional research. Your research continues even as you consult dictionaries, thesauruses, and collections of quotations to help you word your ideas before delivering your speech.

Research is not necessarily a linear process. As a result, you may be exercising and developing a number of critical thinking skills simultaneously. If you have some experience with or knowledge about the topic area, you'll begin by *remembering* and assessing your knowledge. You'll be *gathering information* as you formulate questions you want your research to answer and then collect your data. You'll use your *generating* skills to develop new lines of inquiry based on the research you have completed. Throughout the process, you'll be *analyzing* whether and how information from different sources fits together. As you connect items of information, you'll be *integrating* and *organizing*. As you measure the quality and quantity of your research results, you'll be *evaluating*. And because you will often find more information than you can use, your entire research process will have you *focusing* your speech topic more and more narrowly.

In this chapter, we'll walk you through a solid plan for conducting research to learn more about your topic and support your speech, including developing your research plan, conducting secondary research (online and via the library), and recording the important information you find. We conclude with an overview of conducting primary research.

research

The process of gathering evidence and arguments to understand, develop, and explain a speech topic.

Develop Your Research Plan

7.1 Construct a general plan for conducting research on your topic.

Once you have an idea for a topic, developing your research plan is the first important step in the research process. Your research plan begins as you answer several questions:

1. What do I already know that will help me develop my topic?
2. What information do I need to learn?
3. Where should I obtain information about my topic?
4. How will time constraints affect my research options?

The first question you should ask is, "What do I already know that will help me develop my topic?" Your memory has been shaped by what you have read, heard, observed, and experienced. Use that knowledge as a starting point for researching your topic. For example, a student who spent the summer interning at the city zoo drew from personal and professional experience in his speech on wildlife conservation;

a student who struggled with ADHD drew upon her coping mechanisms and medical intervention to speak about the condition. These speakers used their knowledge and experience as starting points for their research and both developed and delivered interesting speeches.

Your topic and specific purpose clearly help drive the type of information you'll need to learn, particularly if you lack personal experience with your topic. If you are informing your audience about a medical condition, you will want to consult medical materials, or perhaps a medical professional, to learn everything you can. (No one expects you to be as well informed as a medical student, but you should have a solid working knowledge of your topic.) If you are persuading your audience to support women's athletics at your school, you'll probably want to learn about current turnout at events, the history of women's athletics at your school, or even hear about an athlete's or coach's sense of support for a given team.

You'll next want to figure out how to obtain the information you need to learn. There are several strategies that we will discuss in this chapter, including conducting primary research, secondary research, or a combination thereof. **Primary research** is the process of generating new knowledge and information by collecting, analyzing, and interpreting new data (e.g., conducting a focus group, administering a questionnaire). **Secondary research** is the process of gathering, reviewing, and summarizing existing information (e.g., conducting library research, online research). One important note at this point: Don't assume that all relevant information for a given topic can be found online. Different topics demand different research strategies and a good research plan accounts for these variations.

Finally, prepare a timetable for constructing your speech. If you will be speaking in 2 weeks, you still have time for a lot of online or library research. You may even have time to arrange and conduct interviews. However, if your speech is in 2 days, be realistic about what you can accomplish. Two days is not enough time to make an appointment and interview an American literature professor about Flannery O'Connor for your speech on her works. (Yet another reason why starting early really matters.)

primary research

The process of generating new knowledge and information by collecting, analyzing, and interpreting new data (e.g., conducting a focus group, administering a questionnaire).

secondary research

The process of gathering, reviewing, and summarizing existing information (e.g., conducting library research, online research).

Journal: Constructing a General Research Plan

If your upcoming speech is an "informative speech on a different culture" (a culture other than your own), how would you start developing a general plan for conducting research on the culture you select? What steps would you go through to develop your general research plan?

Conduct Internet Research

7.2 Collect and evaluate information gathered online.

Once you have developed a general research plan, you will likely begin by conducting secondary research to find existing sources. The reality is that you will likely begin this search online and move to other secondary sources (e.g., books, magazines, journals) as you proceed. For that reason, we begin with an overview of search engines, the deep Web, and even Wikipedia before moving on to more traditional library resources.

Search Engines

search engine

A tool for locating information on the Internet by matching items in a search string with pages that the engine indexes.

There are a multitude of **search engines** available to conduct online research, such as Yahoo!, Bing, and Ask.com, but the most widely used is Google. In August 2016, Google held 79.88 percent of the market share for search engines, with Bing as the distant second at 9.9 percent.[3] Since you are likely quite accomplished at using these common search engines, we don't need to go into detail here. But we do caution you to be very focused in your search for information. For example, if you are giving an informative speech about the Zika virus's effect on South American tourism and you type "Zika virus" into Google, you will receive (at the time of this writing) 38.2 million results. That's hardly helpful! Rather, you'll want to enter more information to narrow the search. For example, "Zika virus tourism impact" narrows the results considerably and helps you focus more specifically on your topic. In addition, Google helps you narrow the search results further by allowing you to select only news articles, images, maps, or videos. From these options, you can tailor your research to your specific needs. For example, news stories might help you obtain facts and statistics; a map might be a useful visual aid. Or, you might want to watch a video to obtain a quote from a pregnant woman who cancelled a trip to Brazil due to concerns about the virus.

One feature that makes Google such an attractive search engine for research is its Google Scholar search engine, which specifically targets academic resources. This allows you to use a search engine with which you are already familiar without having to go through the library databases. Instead, Google Scholar provides links directly to articles in the school's library databases. However, keep in mind that this feature works best when you are using your school's computers or Internet service on your personal computer. Academic opinions regarding Google Scholar appear to be split, however, with one librarian arguing that Google Scholar "is easy to use, saves them [students] time in writing essays, and links to a vast amount of information,"[4] while one university website cautions students, "It is in no way comprehensive, and has limited field searching."[5]

Academic Search Engines

We encourage our students to use Google Scholar as a starting point into a topic, realizing that the most effective next step is to move to academic search engines for full-text and better searching and indexing capabilities. **Academic search engines** filter the extraneous from the essential and are a key component of serious, targeted searches. Information from academic search engines is more focused and of higher quality than what you may find via general search engines such as Google, Bing, Yahoo!, and others.

> **academic search engines**
> Search engines that are full-text archives of focused, high-quality sources.

Below are three useful academic search engines and their web addresses:

Academic Index	www.academicindex.net
EbscoHost	search.ebscohost.com
LexisNexis	www.lexisnexis.com/hottopics/lnacademic/

The Deep Web

The **deep Web**, sometimes called the *invisible Web*, contains public, government, corporate, and private information. The "content in the deep Web is massive—approximately 500 times greater than that visible to conventional search engines—with much higher quality throughout."[6] Deep Web information often exists in topic-specific databases as multimedia files, graphic files, or in portable document file (PDF) formats.[7] "A full 95 percent of the deep Web is publicly accessible information—not subject to fees or subscriptions."[8] In contrast to static web pages, information in the deep Web is "dynamic"—that is, the pages form only in response to specific research queries.

> **deep Web**
> Huge databases of Internet information posted by public, government, corporate, and private agencies and available only by specific queries.

To explore the deep Web, try the following portals:

- InfoPlease (www.infoplease.com/index.html): a free search engine with access to numerous encyclopedias, almanacs, and atlases.
- DeeperWeb (www.deeperweb.com): a free search engine option that uses tag cloud methods to explore Google search results.
- TurboScout (www.turboscout.com/): a quick and convenient way to get results from several search engines.

ETHICAL DECISIONS

THE PRIVACY OF PUBLIC INFORMATION

Jeanine was researching a speech on the problem of child sexual abuse. While she was searching the Internet, she discovered a series of forums devoted to this topic, including a newsgroup and a live chat group. She found thought-provoking and useful discussions in the newsgroup, but the chat discussions were the most intimate and revealing. There, sexual abuse survivors described their memories of actual incidents and talked about how the trauma affected their adult lives. Jeanine took notes on some of the most remarkable stories and decided to recount one to vivify her speech.

Is this a legitimate way for Jeanine to use her research? Should stories told on the Internet be considered public property, available for anyone to write or speak about? Should Jeanine try to find out whether the source of her information would feel comfortable about having the story repeated in a speech? Should she try to verify that the story is true?

Wikipedia

A discussion of Internet research would not be complete without mentioning the popular resource Wikipedia. You likely already know that your professors have legitimate concerns about the use of Wikipedia as a source in essays and speeches because it operates on an "openly editable" model, allowing anyone with an Internet connection to write or edit its entries. Therefore, we support Wikipedia's statement, "Students should never use information in Wikipedia (or any other online encyclopedia) for formal purposes (such as school essays) until they have verified and evaluated the information based on external sources."[9] This suggestion offered by Wikipedia reinforces the importance of knowing how to critically evaluate the content found on the Internet.

That said, a recent study revealed that students often begin their research on Wikipedia.[10] This can be a useful strategy if you are giving a speech on a topic that interests you, but about which you know very little. Consider this example from Eva.

> When thinking about a topic for my upcoming speech, I considered my interests and things I wish I knew more about. I really enjoy the novels of Amy Tan, particularly *The Joy Luck Club* and *The Kitchen God's Wife*. However, I didn't know much about Tan's life. I used Wikipedia to get an overview, and was fascinated to learn about her family history. However, I was most interested to learn about Tan's struggle with Lyme disease, which went undiagnosed for several years and resulted in medical complications. From there, I was able to reference more reputable sources, including a *New York Times* piece about Tan's personal experiences with Lyme disease. I also visited the webpage for the Lyme Disease Association to research the condition and to learn more about LymeAid 4 Kids, a fund Tan helped to establish to financially assist families with children affected by Lyme disease.

See "Theory into Practice: Evaluating Resources" for recommendations about evaluating information you find online and elsewhere.

Conduct Library Research

7.3 Collect and evaluate information gathered via the library.

Though you may begin your research online, your school or local library contains many resources that you won't find anywhere else. One of the most helpful sources of information is the library staff, particularly reference librarians. A good reference librarian can acquaint you with the library's services and holdings, guide you to particularly helpful sources of information, and instruct you in the use of library equipment. He or she can also guide you to your library's areas of strength, making your research more efficient and your life easier. In this section, we consider magazines and journals, newspapers, government documents, books, reference works, and television/radio

Theory into Practice (TIP)

EVALUATING RESOURCES

When you conduct research, your critical thinking skills may not just get exercise, but a full-tilt workout, because you are likely going to find an abundance of information. So how do you know what information to include and what to exclude? There are five categories (purpose, expertise, objectivity, accuracy, and timeliness) with a series of questions that we recommend you consider as you evaluate your sources.

Purpose

- What seems to be the purpose of this source? To provide information? To promote a position? To sell a product or service?
- If it's an Internet source, what type of site is it? Is it aviation (.aero), commercial (.com, .coop, or .biz), educational (.edu), governmental (.gov), information business (.info), military (.mil), nonprofit organization (.org), personal (.name), or professional (.pro)?
- Is there an institution, agency, or organization identified as sponsoring the source?
- If it's an Internet source, does the site contain advertisements? If so, by whom?
- Who is the author's apparent audience, as reflected by the vocabulary, writing style, and point of view: students, professionals, consumers, or advocates?

Expertise

- If it's an Internet source, is the author, compiler, or webmaster identified?
- Does the author have verifiable expertise on the subject?
- Are the author's credentials provided?
- Do you know the author's occupation?
- Do you know the author's educational background?
- Do you know the author's organizational affiliation?
- If the source is a compilation, are sources and authors of individual works identified?

- If this is a research project, does the author explain data, methodology, and interpretation of results? Does the author refer to other works? Provide notes?
- If it is an Internet source, is the site linked to another site that you already trust or value?
- Are sources or viewpoints missing that you would expect to be present?
- What does this source offer that you could not find elsewhere?

Objectivity

- Does the author's affiliation with an organization, institution, or agency suggest a bias?
- Does the source's sponsorship by an organization or institution suggest an inherent bias?
- Are opposing views represented or acknowledged?
- Are editorial comments or opinions clearly distinguished from facts?

Accuracy

- Can you corroborate the facts using other sources?
- If it's an Internet source, is the site inward-focused (providing links only to other parts of the site) or outward-focused (providing links to other websites)?
- Has the author expended the effort to write well, with correct spelling and proper grammar?
- Does the author solicit comments, inquiries, and/or corrections by email?

Timeliness

- Is the publication date important to this subject matter?
- Can you tell when the source was created (publication year, last updated websites)?
- Does the author cite other recently published sources?
- Are the arguments presented in the source still applicable?[11]

sources. As you discover these sources during your library research, we encourage you to examine the quality of your sources by asking the questions listed in the Theory into Practice.

Magazines and Journals

Magazine and journal articles are probably the most common source of information for student speeches. With hundreds of thousands of magazines from which to choose, it's helpful to use an index to filter useful from extraneous information.[12] Hundreds of excellent indexes of periodicals exist, and many standard indexes are now available online. These can guide you as you focus your search even more.

The true monster trucks of academic research in periodicals today are full-text **databases**. These databases are powerful because each gives you access to articles in hundreds or even thousands of periodicals and scholarly journals. You can print or

database

A large collection of information arranged for quick retrieval by computer using key words entered by a researcher.

College libraries provide computer terminals to help you research your speech topic. With a few keystrokes, you can unlock a wealth of information in and beyond the library.

email yourself useful articles or you can upload them (or photos of printouts) to a cloud service to keep track of them. If you are a registered college or university student, you have already paid to use these research tools from any computer with Internet access through your school's library website.

Some of the general full-text databases likely available to you are listed in Table 7.1. In addition, specialized indexes exist for almost every academic field. Subject-specific computer databases include *Alternative Health Watch, Biography in Context, Contemporary Women's Issues,* and so on. Similar print indexes in the reference section of your library may include titles such as *Education Index, Hispanic American Periodicals Index,* and *Music Index.* Because these indexes are so specialized, the periodicals and journals they lead you to will likely be written for a specific audience; they may use jargon and technical language familiar only to people in that field. Even if you understand these articles easily, you may have to simplify their language and ideas for a more diverse audience.

If you have particular magazines and journals in mind at any stage in your research, you can also check the online versions of these publications. Some magazines provide the full text of current issues along with searchable archives; others give you only sample articles and subscription information. Though browsing individual magazines is not an efficient use of limited research time, searchable online periodicals can be useful and are frequently available via your school's library website. If you have trouble locating these resources, you should speak directly with a reference librarian who will be able to assist you.

TABLE 7.1   Examples of Subscription Databases and Indexes

Database/Index	What It Provides
Academic Search Complete	The world's most comprehensive full-text database for multidisciplinary research, which includes full coverage of multidisciplinary, full-text academic journals, reports, books, and much more.
AccuNet/AP Multimedia Archive	Searchable archive of Associated Press (AP) photos, charts, logos, maps, and other graphics produced for AP, 19th century to the present. Brief stories accompany most photos 48 hours after publication.
Communication & Mass Media Complete (CMMC)	CMMC is the most comprehensive database related to communication and mass media. It includes the content of *CommSearch* (formerly produced by the National Communication Association) and *Mass Media Articles Index* (formerly produced by The Pennsylvania State University) along with numerous other journals in communication, mass media, and closely related fields of study.
ERIC	An online digital library with access to more than 1.3 million bibliographic records of journal articles and other education-related materials.
General OneFile	Approximately 80 million articles and records in refereed journals, general interest magazines, newspapers, National Public Radio transcripts, subject-specific collections, and other sources. From this website you can also access *InfoTrac Student Edition* with access to nearly 9 million articles, updated daily.
LexisNexis Academic	International business, health, law, news, and reference articles, most in full text. Updated continually.
Opposing Viewpoints in Context	Pro–con essays on controversial topics. Includes text of reference works, magazine and newspaper articles, websites, statistics, and images.
Project Muse	Full-text articles from nearly 500 scholarly journals published by scholarly presses in the arts, humanities, social sciences, and mathematics.
ProQuest Education Journals	Includes more than 1,000 educational publications, such as *Childhood Education, College Teaching, Harvard Educational Review, Journal of Athletic Training,* and *Educational Theory.*
Science in Context	Full-text articles from more than 200 magazines, scholarly journals, and links to quality websites. Includes biographies, experiment descriptions, pictures, illustrations, topic overviews, and news of recent scientific discoveries.

Newspapers

Newspapers offer abundant information—local, national, or international in scope. Large newspapers such as the *New York Times*, the *Washington Post*, and the *Christian Science Monitor* have been indexed individually in the past. The computer index to the *New York Times*, for example, provides full text of all articles from 1851 to the present.

Today, however, your campus library is more likely to subscribe to powerful databases such as *LexisNexis Academic* that contain full-text newspaper articles in addition to other sources.

Most newspapers now have websites and provide indexes to their own archives. If you have selected a localized topic, you may want to research specific newspapers using a search engine like Google. If you're unsure about newspaper titles, *Newslink* (http://newslink.org) lets you browse lists of U.S. newspapers by state as well as world newspapers by continent or country; click on links to specific papers.

Government Documents

The most prolific publisher in the United States is the federal government. Much of our bureaucracy is devoted to collecting, cataloguing, and disseminating information. Luckily, most of what's available is accessible online: presidential speeches and transcripts of press conferences, pending legislations, contact information for senators and representatives, agency reports, and ordering information for documents not available online in full text. Online, you can take a virtual tour of the White House, listen to audio files of unedited arguments before the Supreme Court, and see digital photographs of historical documents. In short, almost every federal agency has a website.

Your library probably subscribes to several government databases, among them *LexisNexis Government Periodicals Index*, *Federal Register Online*, and *MarciveWeb DOCS*. Searchable by keyword, these databases save you time.

With just a couple of Web addresses, you can access virtually any area of the government. The Library of Congress maintains THOMAS: Legislative Information on the Internet at http://thomas.loc.gov. The Government Printing Office maintains a list of links to government information products at www.access.gpo.gov. At those two sites, you can get any information you need from the legislative, executive, or judicial branches of the government.

Books

Books are excellent sources of information. Because they are longer than magazine and newspaper articles, books allow authors to discuss topics in greater depth and often provide an index of key terms or concepts discussed in the book along with a list of sources consulted. However, if your speech topic requires the most up-to-date data you can find, information in magazines and newspapers may be more current and accessible than what you find in books. Despite this limitation, books can be an integral part of your research plan. Today the online catalog in most academic libraries permits you to search by subject, title, author, and key words.

Additionally, the books you need may be available as ebooks that you can access—"check out"—in your choice of formats after you establish a library account. On the Internet, full-text literary works are also well represented by *Literature Online* (*LION*, http://lion.chadwyck.com), a searchable subscription database of more than 350,000 British and American works.

Reference Works

Reference works include many types of collections to aid you in your research. Whether you use hard-copy versions in the library, access databases through your library's webpage, or log on to the Internet, a few of the reference works you will find most helpful are dictionaries, encyclopedias, almanacs, and books of quotations.

Dictionaries help you clarify the meanings, spellings, and pronunciations of words. Online dictionaries often provide audio pronunciation of words, terms, and names. For example, search for "mischievous pronunciation," "Alzheimer's pronunciation," and "Ryukyu Islands pronunciation" to hear correct ways to say these words.

Encyclopedias are multivolume sets of books that organize information on many branches of knowledge. Some electronic encyclopedias are free; for others you may have to pay a subscription fee unless you access them from a library or through a library website.

Almanacs contain a wide range of specific and statistical information about topics such as education, politics, sports, entertainment, and significant events of a particular year. Almanacs are excellent sources when you need specific facts and background information.

Books of quotations provide captivating quotes, both serious and funny, which can enliven the language of your speech. Quoting another person also may add credibility to your comments and strengthen the development of your ideas. Fortunately, many excellent *books of quotations* are available. These collections are organized alphabetically by author or subject, with handy indexes or search functions.

Television and Radio

You can find ideas for excellent speech topics and materials to support them among the investigative reports on television and radio. Many programs provide transcripts for purchase; networks now offer transcripts of many of these shows for print or download at their websites. If you require older transcripts, you may have to order them online for a fee. Many National Public Radio programs are archived for downloading as podcasts after their initial broadcast.

Your library may have copies of special televised broadcasts such as the PBS documentary series *Lewis and Clark* or Martin Scorsese's *Bob Dylan: No Direction Home*. Through informational videos, you can research topics such as military battles, McCarthyism, and space exploration, to name just a few. Commercial videos (as well as websites) can take you on tours of museums such as the Louvre or the Museum of Modern Art and of distant places such as Australia and Italy. Instructional videos can teach you how to garden, refinish furniture, and make a sales presentation. While not library services, your Netflix and Amazon video accounts can also provide you with access to documentaries and educational programs.

Journal: Using Library Resources

If you are asked to deliver a persuasive speech in which you should influence your audience members to try your favorite form of exercise, what type of library resource do you think would be most useful to you and why?

Record Your Information

7.4 Record relevant information systematically.

Once you have located information, you must determine what to record and how to record it.

When in doubt, record more rather than less information. Certainly, it is possible to copy too much information. If you find everything potentially important, your topic probably needs better focus. Without focus, you risk becoming so bogged down in research that you leave little time for organizing and practicing your speech. On the other hand, if you are too selective, you may be inefficient. As you research your speech, you may shift the focus of your topic; hence the supporting material you previously thought was irrelevant becomes important. Discarding unnecessary information is easier than trying to remember a source, retracing your steps, hoping that the information is still on the library shelves or that the Internet source is still live, and then recording that information.

Traditional advice to researchers is to record each piece of information (e.g., quotes or paraphrases) on a separate notecard, along with the source citation, as you find it.

With this strategy, you can organize your speech visually and experiment with different structures. The disadvantage of this method is that it consumes a great deal of library time that might be better devoted to searching for other sources.

Another method is to photocopy material at the library or to print articles you find online. You may also be able to upload some of this material to a cloud service giving each entry a clear label (such as the author/title of the material). Later, you can review, evaluate, and select from the materials, deleting or throwing away any that are not worthwhile. Photocopying, printing, and uploading material have two additional advantages over using note cards. First, you may not know what you want to use from an article at the time you first find it. If the focus of your speech changes, a different part of the article may become important (indeed, sometimes your research forces you to refocus the speech topic). Second, if you are quoting from or paraphrasing one specific part of an article, you may need to check to make sure that you are not quoting the author out of context. Having a copy of the book chapter or journal article lets you check the context and the accuracy of your quotation.

It is important to record full citations of sources you cite in your list of works cited at the end of your speech. Note that it is *considerably easier* to keep track of this information all along—even if you ultimately discard several sources—than to go back and figure it out at the end. Most writers' handbooks recommend a particular form, including the forms of the *Publication Manual of the American Psychological Association*, 6th Edition (APA); the *Modern Language Association Handbook for Writers of Research Papers*, 8th Edition (MLA), and the *Chicago Manual of Style*, 17th Edition (CMS). Be sure to check with your instructor, who may prefer one of these or some other bibliographic form.

Copies of the three style manuals we just listed are probably in your library's reference section. College and university libraries often have online guides for citing print and online resources. One of our favorites is the Purdue University Online Writing Lab (OWL). Regardless of which style you use and how you access information about those styles, you will generally need to record and know specific information about your various sources. Note that the information record varies depending on the source, but in general, record as much as possible of the following information:

- Author and/or editor's name
- Journal or book title
- Article or chapter title
- Volume and issue number
- Page numbers
- Publishing company and location
- URL (and date accessed and last updated if available)

We cannot stress enough that the more organized you are in this endeavor, the less stress you will feel as the day of your speech approaches.

Conduct Primary Research

7.5 Collect, analyze, and interpret information gathered through primary research.

If your secondary research online and via the library did not provide adequate information for you to develop your speech, you may need to conduct some primary research. Most primary research is either qualitative or quantitative. **Qualitative research** refers to gathering descriptive, nonnumerical information, which can be done by conducting interviews or focus groups. **Quantitative research**, as the name implies, focuses on numerical information, which can be gathered by administering a questionnaire. (See Appendix B for tips on how to construct and administer a questionnaire.) For the purpose of this public speaking course, we suggest that you conduct interviews and focus groups, or administer a questionnaire (or a combination thereof).

Journal: Recording Relevant Source Information

Grab one of your textbooks for another class from the shelf or pull it up on a screen and record the relevant source information as you would when researching your speech topic.

Key Points: Record Your Information

1. Record more rather than less.
2. Use notecards, photocopies, or archival apps/services.
3. Record full citation information.
4. Consult relevant style manuals.

qualitative research
Research aimed at gathering descriptive, nonnumerical data, in pursuit of new knowledge.

quantitative research
Research aimed at gathering numerical data in pursuit of new knowledge.

Personal Interviews

Depending on your topic, a personal interview may be the best source of firsthand information. Today you can interview people by email, texting, Skype (or a similar service), telephone, or in person. The personal interview can aid you in four ways. First, if published sources are inaccessible, the personal interview may be your only option. The topic you have chosen may be so recent that sufficient information is not yet in print or online. Or, your topic may also be so localized as to receive little or no coverage by area media.

A second advantage is that the interview permits you to adapt your topic to your specific audience. Take the topic of "wasted food." If you interview the director of your school's food and housing services to find out how much food is wasted on campus each day, you give your speech a personal touch. You could take your speech one step further by figuring out how much money your college could save and how much lower the student food and housing fees could be if no food was wasted. This shows your audience how this topic affects them directly.

Third, personal interviews provide opportunities for you to secure expert evaluation of your research and suggestions for further study. The experts you interview may challenge some of your assumptions or data. If this happens, encourage their feedback and don't get defensive. Knowing all the angles can only help you give a more thoughtful speech. Near the end of your interview, ask your interviewee to suggest additional sources that will help you better research and understand your topic.

Finally, personal interviews can enhance your image as a speaker. Listeners are usually impressed that you went beyond library research in preparing your message for them. Therefore, informing your listeners of the interviews you conducted will bolster your perceived speaker credibility.

Prepare for the Interview   Once you decide to conduct a personal interview, you must take several steps in preparation.

1. *Determine whom you want to interview.* Your interviewee should be someone who is both knowledgeable on the topic and willing to speak with you.
2. *Decide on the interview format.* Will you communicate face-to-face, online, by phone, or via email exchanges? A face-to-face or online interview may give you the most information as people tend to open up more when they interact both verbally and nonverbally. A phone interview is another possibility, particularly if your interviewee is uncomfortable with services like Skype or Facetime. A third option, conducting an interview by email, has both advantages and disadvantages. The email interview is time consuming because you must prepare a set of questions, send it to the interviewee, and wait for a response. It has the added disadvantage of not allowing for immediate follow-up questions for clarification. However, the email interview often results in more thoughtful and better worded responses than face-to-face, telephone, or online interviews.
3. *Schedule the interview.* When requesting an interview, identify yourself and the topic on which you seek information. Let the person know how you intend to use that information, the amount of time needed for the interview, and any recording procedures you plan to use. Some people may object to being quoted or recorded. You are likely to discover that most people you seek to interview are flattered that you selected them as experts and are therefore happy to cooperate.
4. *Research the person to be interviewed.* Research the interviewee beforehand. Obviously, your selection of this person suggests that you already know something about her or him. In addition, read any articles the interviewee has published on your topic. This enables you to conduct the interview efficiently. You won't ask questions that the person has already answered in published work, and your prior reading may prompt some specific questions on points you would like clarified.

Also, your research will show that you are prepared. The interviewee will take you and the interview seriously.

5. *Prepare a list of questions.* Always have more questions than you think you will be able to ask, just in case you are mistaken. Mark those that are most important to your research, and ask them first. You may want to have some closed and some open questions, as Joel did when he interviewed a professor of recreation for his speech on how American adults spend their leisure time.

Open questions, such as those that begin with the phrase, "How do you feel about . . .?" can elicit more substantive responses from interviewees than closed questions.

Closed questions are those that can be answered with a yes, a no, or a short answer. For example, Joel asked, "Do American adults have more time for leisure activities today than they did a generation ago?" and "How many hours per week does the typical adult spend watching TV?" The first question can be answered by a yes or a no, the second with a specific figure.

Open questions invite longer answers and can produce a great deal of information. Joel asked this open question: "How do American adults typically spend their leisure time?" When you ask open questions, sit back and prepare to listen for a while. The less time you have for the interview, the fewer open questions you should ask. Open questions can sometimes result in rambling responses. At times, the interviewee's rambling will trigger questions you would not have thought of otherwise. Joel was surprised to learn that American adults spend approximately 2 hours a week in adult education, a venture he had not included on his initial list of adult leisure activities.

Conduct the Interview   The interview is an excellent opportunity to practice your interpersonal communication skills. Specifically, follow these guidelines:

1. *Set the tone.* Introduce yourself when you arrive or connect, thank the person for giving you time, and restate the purpose of the interview.

2. *Conduct the interview in a professional manner.* Make sure you are appropriately dressed. Be ready and able to set up and handle any equipment with a minimum of distractions. Try to relax the interviewee—establish a professional atmosphere, pose questions that are clear and direct, listen actively, take notes efficiently, and follow up when necessary. You should control the interview without appearing to be pushy or abrupt.

3. *Conclude politely.* When you have finished the interview, thank the person again for the interview.

Follow Up on the Interview   After the interview, review your notes or listen to your recording. Do this as soon as possible after the interview, when your memory is still fresh. If you are unclear about something that was said, do not use that information in your speech. You should contact your interviewee to clarify the point if you think it will be important to the audience's understanding of the topic.

As a matter of courtesy, you should write to the people you interviewed, thanking them for the time and help they gave you. You may even want to send them a copy of your finished speech if it is in manuscript form or a link to your speech if it is posted online.

Focus Groups

A focus group is a type of group interview in which you can collect information from multiple people simultaneously by facilitating a group discussion. Generally, it's recommended to have 5 to 10 participants when conducting focus groups.[13] Therefore, focus groups have three primary advantages compared to personal interviews. First, focus groups are time efficient. Instead of conducting multiple personal interviews

SPEAKING WITH CONFIDENCE

Once I choose my speech topic, the fun begins. Sometimes I already know the main points I want to discuss in my speech; sometimes I don't. Either way, what really builds my speech are the interesting and credible supporting materials I find in my research. Of course, it's great to have an informative source like the Internet at my fingertips, but it's also rewarding to use sources that may take a little more time and effort to obtain.

A trip to the library, for example, puts books, newspapers, and journals at my disposal. My favorite source, however, is the interview. Asking an expert specific questions on my topic can yield lots of really helpful information. The person can also direct me to other sources I may not know about. The more I research, the more confident I feel about my speech. So, remember to start researching early and use all the resources available.

Matthew Williams
Radford University

with one person at the time, you can interview several people simultaneously. Second, focus groups may provide more information than personal one-on-one interviews because the interviewees often feed off one another's comments, resulting in deeper and more detailed information. Third, information gathered in a focus group is more reliable than information from a single one-on-one interview. In a personal interview, you cannot be sure that other people have similar experiences. In focus groups, however, you may be able to identify common themes among the participants and you will notice if the participants seem to have similar or different opinions and experiences.[14]

Similar to personal interviews, focus groups can be conducted online, such as using a service like Google Hangouts, or they can be conducted face-to-face. If you do decide to gather information using a focus group, follow the same guidelines for preparing, conducting, and following up as you would in a personal one-on-one interview.

Questionnaires

As discussed in Chapter 5 and in Appendix B, a questionnaire is a series of written questions given to people in order to gather information. When you administer a questionnaire, you engage in *survey research*. As with other research methodologies, there are both advantages and disadvantages to using questionnaires. One advantage is that they are time efficient. You may be able to ask all of your classmates to complete your questionnaire at the end of class. This would give you information from 20 to 25 students in just a few minutes. The main disadvantage is the possibility that the participants' answers are influenced by their own biases. Oftentimes, we inflate our responses to positive questions and deflate our responses to negative questions. For example, as a student you are expected to study hard and not to skip class. So, if asked how many hours per week you study, your answer may be 20 hours even if the true answer is 10 hours. On the other hand, if you are asked how many times per semester you skip class, you may answer two or three times even though the true answer may be four or five times. This is known as *social desirability bias*.[15]

To develop your questionnaire, you should first look for existing questionnaires that can be used. For example, if you want to explore whether female and male students experience different levels of anxiety when speaking in public, the Personal Report of Public Speaking Anxiety would be a suitable questionnaire for you to use. Sometimes, however, you may need to develop your own questionnaire. (See Appendix B for sample questions and guidelines for how to develop your questionnaire.)

With your research complete, you can now begin to support the ideas in your speech, which is the topic of our next chapter.

Journal: Conducting Primary Research

If you are required to conduct primary research as a part of your next major speaking assignment, how would you go about collecting that information from your classmates? Why is the method you selected more suitable for your topic, audience, and occasion than the other methods of collecting primary information?

› SUMMARY

Researching Your Speech Topic

Develop Your Research Plan

7.1   Construct a general plan for conducting secondary research on your topic.

You begin assessing your knowledge and developing a research plan by asking yourself: "What do I already know that will help me develop my topic? What information do I need to learn? Where should I obtain information about my topic? How will time constraints affect my research options?"

Conduct Internet Research

7.2   Collect and evaluate information gathered online.

- Useful Internet sources are search engines, academic search engines, and the deep Web.
- Wikipedia can also be useful as you begin your search on a topic, but should not be trusted as a reliable source.
- As you assemble your information, critically evaluate your sources, considering the purpose of the source, the creator's expertise and objectivity, the source accuracy, and its timeliness.

Conduct Library Research

7.3   Conduct and evaluate information gathered via the library.

- Libraries provide numerous sources, including magazines and journals, newspapers, government documents, books, reference works, and television and radio recordings.
- Evaluate the quality of your library sources in a manner similar to how you evaluate your online sources.

Record Your Information

7.4   Record relevant information systematically.

- The fourth step in research is to record the information you consider important and useful.
- You may choose to take notes, photocopy, print, or upload your information.
- Be sure to record the source of the information using a current bibliography form.

Conduct Primary Research

7.5   Collect, analyze, and interpret information gathered through primary research.

- Gather primary information by conducting interviews and focus groups, or by administering questionnaires.
- Qualitative research is descriptive and nonnumerical, such as conducting personal interviews and focus groups.
- Quantitative research is numerical, such as administering a questionnaire with closed questions.

ORGANIZING THE BODY OF YOUR SPEECH

→ LEARNING OBJECTIVES

After studying this chapter, you should be able to

8.1 Construct an organizing question to identify relevant information and key ideas.

8.2 Select an organizational pattern appropriate for your topic and purpose.

8.3 Develop your key ideas using the 4 S's strategy.

8.4 Construct four types of transitions to connect the key ideas in your speech.

The seventeenth-century mathematician and philosopher Blaise Pascal once wrote to a friend, "I have made this letter longer than usual, because I lack the time to make it short."[1] As Pascal realized, it takes time to organize your thoughts succinctly and coherently, whether you're writing a letter, an essay, or developing a speech. Investing the time to organize simplifies the task in the end, much like organizing your food pantry or your desk allows you to find things and work more effectively. Getting organized will also simplify your speech preparation and make your speech more vivid and memorable for your listeners.

A coherent speech has a beginning, a middle, and an end—what we call the *introduction*, *body*, and *conclusion*. Many speech textbooks and instructors summarize the overall strategy of a speech as follows: "Tell us what you are going to tell us. Tell us. Then, tell us what you told us." Use this organizational perspective in every speech.

In this chapter, we teach you how to organize the body of your speech. Although you deliver it after the introduction, organize the body of your speech first, because in order to "tell us what you are going to tell us," you must first determine what to tell us! In constructing the body of a speech, your best strategy is to formulate an organizing question, divide the speech into key ideas, develop each key idea, and then determine how to best transition between the key ideas.

Formulate an Organizing Question and Key Ideas

8.1 Construct an organizing question to identify relevant information and key ideas.

In Chapter 6, Learning Objectives 6.4 and 6.5, we introduced two important organizational concepts: the specific purpose and the central idea. As you recall, your specific purpose includes three parts: your general purpose (to inform, to persuade, or to entertain), your intended audience (my peers, my classmates, my colleagues), and your speech purpose (what your audience should know, do, think, etc.). For example, an informative speech about freethrows in basketball could have the following specific purpose statement: "To inform my speech class about how to shoot a freethrow in basketball." Note that your specific purpose only provides a general idea of your speech topic and your objective, but it does not specify what your key ideas are.

Your central idea, however, is a one-sentence statement that specifies the **key ideas** of your speech. Using our freethrow example, your possible central idea could be: "Shooting a freethrow in basketball includes five steps, which are (1) the preshot routine, (2) taking your stance, (3) gripping the ball, (4) positioning yourself for the shot, and (5) taking the shot." But how do you determine what your central idea is? How do you move from the specific purpose to the central idea? How do you know what information to include and what to exclude? In other words, how do you know that your central idea is sufficient to achieve your speech purpose? To answer these questions, you must conduct research on your topic and formulate an appropriate organizing question.

An **organizing question** is one that, when answered, indicates the key ideas and information necessary to develop your topic. In the freethrow example, your organizing question might be: "What are the steps involved in shooting a freethrow in basketball?" Through your research, you may have discovered that most coaches and instructional materials suggest that the preshot routine is up to each player and it is therefore not something that is taught. So, you may decide to eliminate the "preshot routine" point because it is up to each player and it does not affect *how* to shoot a freethrow. Thus, by answering your organizing question, you may conclude that shooting a freethrow only involves four steps, not five, and finalize your central idea accordingly: "Shooting a freethrow in basketball includes four steps, which are (1) taking your stance, (2) gripping the ball, (3) positioning yourself for the shot, and (4) taking the shot."

It is important to remember that the way your question is worded will shape the structure of your speech. If your organizing question was "What steps do *professional* basketball players go through when shooting a freethrow?" then you would probably include the "preshot routine" because all professional basketball players have a preshot routine.

As you can see, answering your organizing question will benefit you by helping you identify your key ideas (typically two to five ideas in a 5 to 7-minute classroom speech), which provides the roadmap of *what* to discuss in your speech. Let's consider and break down another example.

key ideas

The two to five main points you will discuss in your speech.

organizing question

A question that, when answered, indicates the ideas and information necessary to develop your topic.

Say you're an avid kayaker, so you would like to inform your audience about the benefits of the sport. Your specific purpose is: "To inform my fellow students about the benefits of kayaking." Through your personal experience, your careful research of sport magazines and journal articles, and an interview with the president of your city's kayak and canoe club, you decide to answer the organizing question: "What are the health benefits of kayaking?" The answer to that question becomes your central idea: "Kayaking improves participants' health, particularly in the realms of cardiovascular fitness, strength, and psychological well-being." Each of those key ideas in your central idea becomes the body of your speech.

> *Key Ideas:*
>
> I. Kayaking improves participants' cardiovascular fitness.
> II. Kayaking improves participants' strength over time.
> III. Kayaking improves participants' psychological well-being.

subpoints

Ideas that support the key idea which, in turn, supports the central idea.

Note that our key ideas could be further broken down into **subpoints**, ideas that support the key idea which, in turn, supports the central idea. For example:

> I. Kayaking improves participants' cardiovascular fitness.
>   A. Kayaking lowers participants' blood pressure.
>   B. Kayaking lowers the participants' oxidative stress levels.
> II. Kayaking improves participants' strength over time.
>   A. Kayaking improves participants' arm and shoulder strength.
>   B. Kayaking improves participants' back and torso strength.
> III. Kayaking improves participants' psychological well-being.
>   A. Kayaking provides participants with time for quiet self-reflection.
>   B. Kayaking provides participants with opportunities to socialize with others.

> ### Journal: Construct an Organizing Question
>
> Choose one of the following topics: pet ownership, Greek organizations, college football, Election Day, the Olympic Games, iPhones, the Pepsi Company, or snowboarding. Write a specific purpose statement for your topic and then construct two different organizing questions that you could use to develop a speech on this topic.

Once you've identified your key ideas, it's time to think about how to organize them, the topic of our next section.

Organize the Key Ideas

8.2 Select an organizational pattern appropriate for your topic and purpose.

Once you have decided what your key ideas are, you need to determine how to organize them. Ask yourself the following question on your topic: "If I heard this information for the first time, in what order would I prefer to hear it so it would make sense to me?" Your answer to that question will most likely indicate that one of the following seven organizational patterns will be most appropriate for your speech: (1) topical, (2) chronological, (3) spatial, (4) causal, (5) pro–con, (6) problem–solution, or (7) need–plan. The first five patterns are appropriate for either informative or persuasive speeches. The last two patterns are appropriate only for persuasive speeches.

As you consider these patterns, keep in mind that no single pattern is best. To be effective, you must select a structure that accomplishes the purpose of *your* speech. In other words, fit the organization to your topic rather than your topic to the organization.

Topical Division

topical division

Organization of a speech according to aspects, or subtopics, of the subject.

Topical division is the most common organizational pattern for public speeches. This is a pattern, not a strategy, because it does not require you to arrange your key ideas in a specific order. Instead, the topical division pattern creates subtopics, or categories, that constitute the larger topic. For example, a speech on graffiti is divided topically if it focuses on graffiti as artistic expression, as political expression, and as vandalism. Note, though, that the order in which these key ideas are presented will not affect the audience members' ability to follow your speech because they do not build on one another; they are simply subtopics, or categories, of the larger topic.

Coffee-lover Rowena organized her informative speech to cover the following points:

Specific Purpose: To inform my speech class about the different types of coffee roasts

Central Idea: Coffee can be categorized into three different types of roasts: light roast, medium roast, and dark roast.

Key Ideas: I. Light roasts
II. Medium roasts
III. Dark roasts

An example of topical division for a persuasive speech is as follows:

Specific Purpose: To persuade my peers to engage in at least 5 hours of outdoor activity each week

Central Idea: Engaging in 5 hours of weekly outdoor activity has psychological, physiological, and social benefits.

Key Ideas: I. Psychological benefits
II. Physiological benefits
III. Social benefits

As these examples suggest, topical organization is particularly appropriate as a method of narrowing broad topics, which may explain its popularity and widespread use.

Chronological Division

Chronological division is considered a strategy because your key ideas are arranged to follow a time sequence. This organization is especially appropriate if you are explaining procedures or processes. A simple and familiar example of chronological organization is a recipe. Any well-written recipe is organized in a time sequence: First, make sure that you have these ingredients; second, preheat the oven; and so forth. Topics that begin with phrases such as "the steps to" or "the history of" may be developed chronologically. Examples of such topics include the history of your university, the biography of author Toni Morrison, the stages of intoxication, steps to getting your first job, and how a product is marketed.

The following ideas are developed chronologically:

Specific Purpose: To inform my classmates about how to hit a perfect tee shot in golf

Central Idea: Hitting a perfect tee shot in golf involves gripping the club, addressing the ball, completing the backswing, and completing the downswing.

Key Ideas: I. How to grip the club
II. How to address the ball
III. How to complete the backswing
IV. How to complete the downswing

chronological division
Organization of a speech according to a time sequence.

Spatial Division

Spatial division is a strategy in which you organize your key ideas according to their physical proximity or geography. This pattern is appropriate for a speech discussing the parts of an object or a place. An example of spatial division is:

Specific Purpose: To inform my peers about the halls and palaces of the Forbidden City in Beijing, China

Central Idea: The halls and palaces of the Forbidden City in Beijing, China, include the Halls of Harmony, the Palace of Heavenly Purity, the Palace of Earthly Tranquility, and the Hall of the Cultivation of the Mind.

spatial division
Organization of a speech according to the geography or physical structure of the subject.

Speakers often use maps and diagrams to organize their topics spatially and to discuss the parts of places.

Key Ideas: I. The Halls of Harmony
   II. The Palace of Heavenly Purity
   III. The Palace of Earthly Tranquility
   IV. The Hall of the Cultivation of the Mind

Causal Division

causal division

Organization of a speech from cause to effect, or from effect to cause.

Causal division is a strategy used to trace a condition or action from its causes to its effects, or from effects back to causes. Medical topics in which a speaker discusses the symptoms and causes of a disease can easily be organized using this method of division. Informative speeches on topics such as hurricanes, lightning, earthquakes, and other natural phenomena may also be organized using this pattern. The following speech outline illustrates the causal pattern:

Specific Purpose: To inform my peers about sports-victory riots

Central Idea: We can trace sports-victory riots back to four primary social causes, which—independently and together—have three primary effects, each of which is costly for communities.

Key Ideas: I. Causes
   A. The competitive nature of sports
   B. Mob psychology
   C. Unfavorable economic conditions
   D. Inadequate police presence
II. Effects
   A. Death and injuries
   B. Vandalism
   C. Law enforcement costs

Because the causal pattern may be used any time a speaker attributes causes for a particular condition, it is suitable for persuasive as well as informative speeches. A speaker could attempt to prove that certain prescription drugs are partly responsible for violent behavior among those who use them; that televising executions would lead to a call for an end to capital punishment; or that new antibiotic-resistant bacteria are promoting the incidence of infections once thought to be under control. For example, consider Andrew's speech on excessive smartphone usage:

Specific Purpose: To persuade my classmates that excessive smartphone use poses risks to our health

Central Idea: The excessive smartphone usage we have come to accept as normal is actually damaging to both our psychological and to our physical well-being.

Key Ideas: I. People are spending significant amounts of time on smartphones.
   A. The reasons people use their smartphones
   B. The addictive qualities of smartphones
II. Excessive smartphone usage is damaging to our psychological well-being.
   A. Social isolation
   B. Lowered self-esteem
III. Excessive smartphone usage is damaging to our physical well-being.
   A. Eye strain
   B. Headaches

Pro–Con Division

Pro–con division is a strategy in which you present the arguments for and against a position. Thus, it informs you specifically of how to arrange your key ideas. Because it is balanced in perspective, this pattern is more appropriate for an informative speech than a persuasive one. After discussing each side of an issue, however, you could choose to defend the stronger position. In this case, your division becomes **pro–con assessment**, a pattern appropriate only for a persuasive speech.

Brian decided to inform his classmates on "snapping." Also known as "cracking," "dissing," and "playing the dozens," this game of insults is part of African American history and culture. In the book *Snaps*, Brian found examples of this war of words, such as Quincy Jones's snap, "Your house is so small, you have to go outside to change your mind."

At first, Brian thought he would use a topical division and discuss (1) the history of snaps, (2) how the game is played, (3) common topics, and (4) sample snaps. As he continued to research his topic, however, he discovered that there is a lively debate as to whether snapping is constructive or destructive. Brian decided to use a pro–con division to tell his listeners about the debate:

Specific Purpose: To inform my classmates about the debate over the value of snapping

Central Idea: Snapping has constructive elements that make it an interesting part of African American culture, but we must not ignore the drawbacks that cause many people to conclude that it is destructive.

Key Ideas: I. Pros of snapping
   A. It reinforces African American history and culture.
   B. It is a nonviolent way of expressing hostility.
   C. It encourages imagination and creative wordplay.
II. Cons of snapping
   A. It is demeaning.
   B. It can provoke violence.
   C. It is not an effective way to express anger.

Note that if Brian took a side on the issue of whether or not snapping should be encouraged or discouraged, his speech would cross over into persuasion.

An advantage of the pro–con pattern is that it places an issue in its broader context and provides balance and objectivity. A disadvantage, however, is the time required to do this. You need plenty of time to discuss both sides of an issue in sufficient detail. Therefore, you will probably want to use this strategy only in one of your longer speeches. If you do not devote sufficient time to each idea, a pro–con or pro–con assessment development may seem simplistic or superficial to your audience.

pro–con division
Organization of a speech according to arguments for and against some policy, position, or action.

pro–con assessment
Organization of a speech according to arguments for and against some policy, position, or action followed by a final key idea in which the speaker supports the strongest position.

Problem–Solution Division

The **problem–solution division** is a simple, rigid, organizational approach for a persuasive speech. In this approach, the major divisions of your speech and their order are predetermined: You first establish a compelling problem and then present a convincing solution. Therefore, the key ideas build on one another (problem–solution), making it a strategy. Because you advocate a plan of action, this pattern is by nature persuasive.

Speeches that call for a law or some action often use a problem–solution format, as in the following example:

Specific Purpose: To persuade my peers to support reform of our national park system

Central Idea: Supporting reform of our national parks is important because they are threatened and because they can be saved by government intervention.

Key Ideas: I. Our national parks are threatened.
  A. Political influence is a threat.
  B. Environmental pollution is a threat.
  C. Inadequate staffing is a threat.
  II. Our national parks can be saved by government intervention.
  A. Environmental laws should be stricter.
  B. Funding should be increased.

A common alternative to the problem–solution division is to divide the speech into a discussion of problems, causes, and solutions, known as the **problem–cause–solution division**. Notice how Matthew uses this approach:

Specific Purpose: To persuade my classmates to support the construction of a campus parking garage

Central Idea: The lack of campus parking spots causes problems for students—problems that will not soon dissipate—but they can be resolved by building a new parking garage.

Key Ideas: I. The current lack of campus parking spots causes problems for students.
  A. Student parking tickets
  B. Late arrival to class
  II. Two factors continue to perpetuate these problems.
  A. Enrollment increases every year.
  B. First year students are now allowed to have parking permits.
  III. To solve this problem, we must build a new parking garage on campus.
  A. The spaces offered by the garage would allow 100% of commuting students to have a guaranteed space.
  B. The spaces offered by the garage would allow 50% of residential students to have a guaranteed space, an increase of 15% over what is currently available.

Need–Plan Division

The **need–plan division** is a variation of the problem–solution division. This fourfold approach (1) establishes a need or deficiency in the present system, (2) presents a proposal to meet the need, (3) demonstrates how the proposal satisfies the need, and (4) suggests a plan for implementing the proposal. Because it requires a specific order of your key ideas, it is considered a strategy.

Salespeople often use the need–plan strategy. They demonstrate or create a need, supply the product or service to meet that need, demonstrate or describe how well it will work, and often even arrange an easy payment plan to help guarantee your purchase. This fundamental sales approach is prevalent for one simple reason: It works!

You can use this strategy when you want to prompt an audience to action. Thus, the need–plan strategy is most suitable for persuasive speech topics.

Specific Purpose: To persuade my fellow congregants that our church should have a dedicated nursery to care for young children

Central Idea: The addition of dedicated nursery space will greatly benefit parents, children, and other members of our congregation and is easy to establish.

Key Ideas: I. Many parents have small children who can disrupt the services.
  A. Young children should not be expected to sit still.
  B. Parents find it difficult to concentrate.
  II. Our church should provide accommodations for parents with young children.
  A. A nursery for children ages 3 and younger
  B. A playroom for children ages 4 to 8-years-old
  III. The nursery and playroom would benefit children and adult congregation members.
  A. Members would be able to focus on the service without minding children.
  B. Children would be provided with an age-appropriate and safe space to have fun.
  IV. The congregation could pitch in to easily create a nursery space.
  A. We could use the empty parlor to the left of the front entrance.
  B. Families could donate used toys and books from their homes.
  C. Adults could take turns volunteering to staff the nursery each week.

As you consider your options for organizing your key ideas, know that most speeches can be effectively organized in several ways. A speech about golf courses, for example, can be organized spatially by talking about the one closest to campus, second closest to campus, and the one farthest away from campus. These three golf courses could also be discussed chronologically by first talking about the most recently built course, the second most recently built course, and finally the oldest course. Additionally, you could organize this speech topically by arranging the three golf courses into different types, such as links, parkland, and resort courses.

Develop the Key Ideas

8.3 Develop your key ideas using the 4 S's strategy.

Assume that your speech is divided into key ideas, that you have selected the most appropriate pattern to organize them, and that you have decided their order in the speech. Now you need to develop each major idea by explaining and supporting each one sufficiently. The organizational strategy we suggest is one we call the 4 S's. (See Figure 8.1.) Your listeners will better comprehend and remember your speech if you *signpost*, *state*, *support*, and *summarize* each key idea.

Figure 8.1 The 4 S's Strategy of Speaking

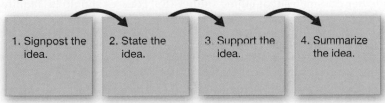

1. Signpost the idea. 2. State the idea. 3. Support the idea. 4. Summarize the idea.

Key Points: Organizing Key Ideas

1. Topical division
2. Chronological division
3. Spatial division
4. Causal division
5. Pro–con division
6. Problem–solution division
7. Need–plan division

Journal: Selecting an Organizational Pattern

Select an organizational pattern you think would be appropriate for a speech with the specific purpose: "To inform my classmates about local restaurants." Could the specific purpose be achieved using other patterns? If so, which ones?

Signpost the Idea

It's Monday morning and you're sitting in your European History class. You take notes as Dr. Jimenez lectures on five events leading up to World War II. In which scenario will you likely understand and remember more of what she says?

1. Dr. Jimenez presents her material using words and phrases such as "also," "another factor," and "additionally."
2. Dr. Jimenez introduces her ideas with statements such as "the first event leading to World War II was . . ." or "the final event leading to World War II was . . ."

If you're like most students, you chose the second scenario. In fact, one experiment tested this and found that "students are able to process information more effectively when lecturers use obvious organizational cues." The researcher's advice to teachers is: "Incorporating organizational cues appears to pay substantial dividends . . ."[2]

That same advice is equally important for public speakers. Because your audience may not consist of note takers, your task is even more challenging. One obvious organizational cue you can use is signposting. A **signpost** is a word such as *initially*, *first*, *second*, and *finally*. Just like the numbering of the chapters in your favorite book tells you how far into the book you are, a signpost in a speech tells the audience where they are in the speaker's message. Signposts help listeners follow your organizational pattern and increase the likelihood that they will remember your key ideas.

Take a look at Austin's speech about chewing gum. (See Appendix E.) Not only did he signpost the two major divisions of the body of his speech, he also used signposts in the substructure to make it easier to understand the specific pros and cons of chewing gum. A signpost serves as a "safety net." Even if your transition from one key idea to another isn't clear, it will become obvious that you are starting a new idea when you signpost the next point.

signpost

Numbers (*one*, *two*, or *three*) or words (*initially*, *second*, or *finally*) that signal to the listener the speaker's place in the speech.

State the Idea

Each key idea needs to be worded precisely and with impact. In order to achieve a clear, concise, and easy-to-follow speech, keep the following suggestions in mind when wording your key ideas:

1. *Key ideas should clearly state the points you will develop.* Your audience will follow along better if they understand where you intend to go.
2. *Key ideas should usually be worded as complete sentences.* Complete, clear sentences help your readers understand each key idea.
3. *Key ideas should be concise.* If you state your key ideas with too much verbiage, you may lose your listeners' attention.
4. *Key ideas should be parallel to other key ideas.* Parallel wording gives your speech rhythm and repetition, two qualities that help listeners remember your points.
5. *Key ideas should summarize the speech.* When you state your key ideas, listeners should see how those key ideas answer the organizing question and achieve your specific purpose.

Let's see how these tips play out in an example. In her persuasive speech, Esperanza argued the benefits of a multicultural college experience. Her specific purpose was to persuade her classmates that ethnic studies (ES) courses should be required for all students. Her organizing question was: "Why should all students be required to take ES courses?"

Based on her research, she found three main benefits of ES courses, which led to the following fine-tuned central idea: "Ethnic studies courses should be required because they promote cultural awareness, reduce ethical and racial conflict, and improve social skills."

She then organized her three key ideas using a topical organization:

I. ES courses promote cultural awareness.

II. ES courses reduce ethnic and racial conflict.

III. ES courses improve social skills.

Each of these key ideas clearly states a distinct point that Esperanza will argue. Each statement is a concise, complete sentence. All three sentences are grammatically parallel. Notice, too, that each of the three key ideas directly answers Esperanza's organizing question.

An alternative to introducing each key idea as a declarative sentence is to ask a question. For example, the specific purpose of Joshua's speech was to inform his fellow students about the positive effects of affectionate communication.

He organized his supporting materials to answer three questions:

I. What effects does affectionate communication have on our psychological well-being?

II. What effects does affectionate communication have on our physiological well-being?

III. What effects does affectionate communication have on our social/relational well-being?

You can usually accomplish the first two S's, signposting and stating your idea, in one sentence. For an informative speech assignment requiring the use of visual aids, our student Jennifer decided to speak about Victorian homes—America's "painted ladies." Using spatial organization, she focused her speech on interior details and decoration, taking her listeners on a virtual tour of a Victorian home she called Conglomeration House. Jennifer introduced her first key idea as follows:

> The first room we will visit on our tour of a Victorian home is the parlor, the woman's domain.

That sentence clearly signposts and states Jennifer's initial main point.

In Austin's speech about chewing gum, he stated each key idea clearly. After his first signpost, he stated the key idea by saying, "Let's uncover the positive effects of chewing gum." Similarly, he stated his second key idea by saying, "Let's discuss the negative implications of chewing gum." (See Appendix E.)

Support the Idea

The third S is the meat of the 4 S's. Once you have signposted and stated the idea, you must support it. Several categories of supporting materials are at your disposal, limited only by the amount of research you have done and by time limits on your speech. (See Chapter 9, Learning Objective 9.2 for a discussion of examples, definitions, narration, comparisons, contrasts, statistics, and testimony.)

In her speech on Victorian homes, Jennifer combined specific language with visual aids to depict a different style of each room. For example, as part of her support for the first room, the parlor, she stated the following:

> The parlor in Conglomeration House is done in the Rococo revival style, which is almost exclusively used in interior design. In their book *The Secret Lives of Victorian Homes*, Elan and Susan Zingman-Leith, who restore Victorian houses, give us this wonderful example of this style. [Jennifer showed an enlarged photograph.] Typical of the Rococo theme, the walls are painted white or a pastel color and are broken into panels decorated with wooden molding or even artwork painted directly onto the wall. Around the windows and ceiling are intricately carved wooden details that are influenced by botanical or seashell designs. These are painted to match the color of the walls, but are heavily accented with gilt, or gold-colored paint. Following the pale color scheme, the mantel is made of marble. It is also intricately carved in a botanically inspired design and has cherubs worked into it as well.

Summarize the Idea

A summary at the end of a key idea reinforces the gist of that idea by drawing attention to the main point discussed within that key idea. These periodic summaries may be as brief as one sentence. Early in the course, our students sometimes summarize a point by saying, "So I've told you a little about. . . ." What you say in these internal summaries within the body needs to be more substantial and more varied than that. An effective summary should reinforce the point you have just developed and also provide a note of closure for that key idea. Keep in mind, however, that your summary statements should only focus on one key idea. Joshua discussed psychological benefits of affectionate communication in his first key idea and physiological benefits in this second idea, so his second summary should only reinforce the gist of physiological benefits without referencing psychological benefits.

If you introduced your idea as a question, your summary should provide the answer. Remember, your point is lost if the audience remembers only your question; they must remember your answer as well.

To summarize his second key idea, Austin stated,

> Researchers are continually attempting to discover connections between chewing gum and maintaining our memory. However, the phenomenon of gum chewing is very robust and it is unclear to determine whether or not chewing gum is actually beneficial.

Jennifer summarized her first key idea with the following statement:

> So the parlor gives us a wonderful example of the Rococo revival architectural style: very feminine, very ornate, and very French.

Such a summary not only clued her audience that she had finished discussing this first room but it also alerted them that they were about to move to the second room on the tour.

We believe that the use of the 4 S's is fundamental to effective organization within the body of any speech. As you begin to master and apply this four-step strategy, it may seem to be a cookie-cutter approach to public speaking. It is exactly that. The 4 S's are to speech organization what the required movements are to gymnastics—basics that you must learn before you can develop your own style or flair. As you master the 4 S's and gain confidence in public speaking, clear organization will become almost a reflex reaction performed without conscious effort. As your ability to organize ideas clearly becomes second nature, you will find that the structure of your thinking, writing, and speaking has greatly improved, as it did for our student Alex (see "Theory into Practice: Applying the 4 S's").

Key Point: The 4 S's

1. Signpost
2. State
3. Support
4. Summarize

ETHICAL DECISIONS

CRUNCH TIME

Rosa has delayed working on her speech until the night before it is due. She goes online and begins downloading articles related to her topic: "How to avoid harming yourself with prescription drugs." The next morning, she sorts through the material, jotting down examples, statistics, and testimony she finds interesting. However, by the time she needs to leave for class, Rosa's speech is still not well organized, and she admits that her listeners may not be able to follow some of the information she plans to present. Rosa is torn between two courses of action. She does not want to get a failing grade on the speech, and she'd like to get some practice speaking in front of a group, so she is tempted to "wing it" and see what happens. "I can always clear up any confusion by answering questions later," she thinks. "After all, I have done the research." However, because she knows that some people in the audience may get lost and even misinterpret the information she presents, Rosa considers telling her instructor that she is not prepared and is willing to accept the consequences of delivering her speech late.

What would you do if you were Rosa? Would she be violating any ethical standards if she were to forge ahead and deliver her speech? Do you think that delivering a disorganized speech is an abuse of the power a speaker wields over an audience?

Theory into Practice (TIP)

APPLYING THE 4 S's

Assigned to deliver an informative speech about something that originated or that exists outside of the United States, our student Alex developed the first key idea in the body of his speech as follows:

First, I'd like to *describe the Itsukushima Shrine's Grand O-Torii Gate* as I experienced it for the first time.

Along the way I'll give you some specific details about the structure. During 1991 and halfway into 1992, I was still in the military and living in Japan. On one of our off weekends, we decided to visit the shrine in Miyajima-guchi, a small town south of the military base where we were stationed. We boarded a train and enjoyed the 30 to 45-minute ride to the small town. From the train station, we walked a short distance to a pier. There we boarded a ferry that took us to Miyajima Island, where the shrine was located. We got off the ferry and walked toward the shrine location, not knowing that it was really close. The tide was in. Suddenly, there appeared this big red Japanese gate in the water about half a football field away from where we were standing near the shore.

I was already excited from the train ride and the ferry ride. Seeing the Grand O-Torii Gate was kind of like seeing Sleeping Beauty's Castle at Disneyland for the first time. You see it in pictures and movies all the time. But seeing it for real, well, if you've been to Disneyland you know the feeling. This is what the Grand O-Torii Gate looks like when the tide is in. It really looks like it's floating in the water, especially if you have never seen it when the tide is out.

I promised you some specific details about the structure and I won't let you down. On the First of March, 2017, I accessed the Miyajima Tourism website (that's the island on which the O-Torii gate is located). The site mentions that the gate is 16.8 meters tall (that's about 55 feet) and that the main pillars are about 13.4 meters tall (about 44 feet) and 9.9 meters around (or 33 feet). The cross beam is 23.3 meters, or close to 77 feet across.

The gate is constructed entirely of wood from the camphor tree, which is native to the area. Concrete beams and pillars support the O-Torii gate, and it's covered with vermillion, or deep red, lacquer. Because it is out at sea, partially submerged in the water, shipworms and barnacles encrust and slowly deteriorate the wood at the base. I've seen the barnacles but I had no clue of the damage that was going on. Fortunately, plastic resin has been found to be effective in preserving the wood.

You can now imagine the impression the Grand O-Torii gate made on me even from a distance, but it can be even more awe-inspiring when you get a chance to stand as close to it as I did.

Japan is, unfortunately, subject to destructive typhoons. That's why governments and organizations have banded together to help preserve this shrine for future generations. So, second, let's examine some of the work required to preserve the gate.

Alex signposts and states his first key idea.

In these sentences, Alex provides support for his key idea, including his narration of the events. He also compares the distance to the gate to a football field, a space his audience is familiar with.

Alex again uses comparison, comparing the experience of seeing the gate to seeing Sleeping Beauty's Castle at Disneyland – something many in his audience will have experienced. In addition, he provides a visual example to support his point by showing a photograph of the Grand O-Torii Gate.

Alex offers an oral footnote so that his audience understands where he obtained these statistics to support his key idea. This also builds his credibility.

Alex summarizes his key idea.

Alex effectively transitions to his second key idea.

To clarify the look of the Grand O-Torii Gate for his listeners, Alex showed them this view he had seen as he stood on the shore of Miyajima Island at high tide looking out at the Sea of Japan.

SPEAKING WITH CONFIDENCE

Before taking a speech class at Penn State, I always had butterflies in my stomach when speaking in front of an audience. Learning how to organize the body of my speech helped to ease those worries by giving me confidence that I developed a speech worth listening to. By utilizing the 4 S's, I was able to stay focused on my purpose while simultaneously keeping the audience engaged. Signposting provided simple indicators of which points I would discuss. Stating my ideas clearly helped me stay focused (and did the same for my audience). Supporting my points with examples and other materials increased my credibility while boosting my confidence in my speech delivery. Summarizing reminded the audience of my idea (and reinforced its importance) while allowing me to transition to the next key idea.

As a current teaching assistant at Penn State, I constantly use this method to organize my thoughts, to effectively help other students learn, and to ease my own nervousness. Knowing that my presentations were, and continue to be, well organized has eased my public speaking anxiety.

Alyssa Bixler
Penn State Hazleton

Connect the Key Ideas

8.4 Construct four types of transitions to connect the key ideas in your speech.

The body of a speech is composed of key ideas—the building blocks of your speech—and you have just seen how to develop each according to the 4 S's approach. For your speech to hang together, you must connect those ideas, just as a mason joins bricks and stones with mortar. A speaker moves from one idea to the next—puts mortar between the units—with the aid of a transition. A **transition** is a statement connecting one key idea to another. If the speaker fails to use transitions between the key ideas, these key ideas will be introduced abruptly. As a result, the speech will lack a smooth flow of ideas and sound choppy.

transition

A statement that connects one key idea of the speech with another key idea.

A transition not only connects two ideas but also indicates the nature of their connection. Transitions are usually indicated by *markers* or *triggers*, which are words or phrases near the beginning of a sentence that indicate how that sentence relates to the previous one.[3] You will use some transitions *within* each of your key ideas to offer illustrations (*for example*), indicate place or position (*above*, *nearby*), or make concessions (*although*, *of course*).[4] However, the transitions you use *between* the key ideas of your

Transitions are the glue that joins your key ideas together, just as a mason uses mortar to join bricks.

speech generally are one of four basic types of connections: complementary, causal, contrasting, and chronological.

A **complementary transition** adds one idea to another, thus reinforcing the major point of the speech. Typical transitional markers for complementary transitions include *also*, *and*, *in addition*, *just as important*, *likewise*, and *not only*. When Joshua transitioned between his first key idea about the benefits of affectionate communication (its psychological value) to his second key idea (its physiological value), he stated: "Not only does affectionate communication benefit our psychological well-being, it also benefits our physiological well-being."

You can also review Austin's speech. He used a complementary transition between the first and second key idea.

> In addition to the positive effects of chewing gum, it should be noted that chewing gum has also been found to have negative effects on people, or even no effects at all.

A **causal transition** emphasizes a cause–effect relationship between two ideas. Words and phrases that mark a causal relationship include *as a result of*, *because of*, *consequently*, *due to*, and *therefore*.

Recall from earlier in the chapter that Andrew documented problems resulting from excessive smartphone usage in his speech. As he shifted his focus from cause to effect, he used the following transition: "Due to our heavy reliance on smartphones in our daily lives, many of us will experience negative effects to our psychological well-being."

A **contrasting transition** shows how two ideas differ. These transitions often use markers such as *although*, *but*, *in contrast*, *in spite of*, *nevertheless*, *on the contrary*, *unlike*, and *on the other hand*.

In her tour of Conglomeration House, Jennifer moved her audience from her first to her second main idea with the following clear contrasting transition:

> In sharp contrast to the parlor is the library, the man's retreat in the home. This is the second room we will visit on our tour.

A **chronological transition** shows the time relationship between ideas and uses words or phrases such as *after*, *as soon as*, *once you have*, and *post completion of*.

Xialing informed her classmates on the SQ3R system of studying and remembering written material. She organized her five main points around five key words: *survey*, *question*, *read*, *recite*, and *review*. Her transitions emphasized the natural sequence of these stages: "After surveying, or overviewing, what you are about to read, you are ready for the second stage of the SQ3R system: to question."

A good transition serves as a bridge, highlighting the idea you have just presented and preparing your listeners for the one to come. It smoothes the rough edges of the speech and enhances the cohesiveness of your ideas. Note, however, that transitions alone cannot impose order on a speech. The key ideas and their natural links must exist before you can underscore their connections with transitions.[5] Developing and pursuing an organizing question can help ensure that you know your key ideas and their connections in the first place.

Effective transitions require more than just inserting a word or phrase between two ideas. If you find yourself always using a single word such as *now*, *next*, or *okay* to introduce your ideas, you need to work on varying the language of your transitions. Avoid using weak and pedestrian phrases as transitions, such as "Moving on to my next point" or "The next thing I would like to discuss." Instead, work on composing smooth, functional transition statements.

If you follow the guidelines and examples in this chapter, the body of your speeches will be well organized. You should now know how to generate an organizing question and use it to determine your useful information and key ideas. You can then select an appropriate organizational pattern. You should also know how to develop each key idea in the body of your speeches according to the 4 S's and how to connect those main ideas with appropriate transitions.

complementary transition
Adds one key idea to another, reinforcing the major point of the speech.

causal transition
Connects one key idea to another by establishing a cause–effect relationship between two key ideas.

contrasting transition
Connects one key idea to another by showing how the two key ideas differ.

chronological transition
Connects one key idea to another by showing how one key idea precedes or follows another in time.

Journal: Assessing Transitions

Consider the following two transitions used in a speech with the specific purpose: "To inform my classmates about how to make a lasagna." (1) "So you have identified and gathered the ingredients you need to make a lasagna; let's discuss some other information you need to know" or (2) "Once you have identified and gathered the ingredients you need to make a lasagna, you are ready to assemble the ingredients." Which transition is most effective and why? What type of transition is it? What problems do you see with the other transition?

Key Points: Transitions

1. Complementary transition
2. Causal transition
3. Contrasting transition
4. Chronological transition

CHAPTER 8

> SUMMARY

Organizing the Body of Your Speech

Formulate an Organizing Question and Key Ideas

8.1 Construct an organizing question to identify relevant information and key ideas.

- Answering an organizing question will help you determine information you need in order to develop your topic and to fine-tune your central idea.
- Your answer to the organizing question should also suggest possible ways of organizing the body of your speech.

Organize the Key Ideas

8.2 Select an organizational pattern appropriate for your topic and purpose.

- There are seven organizational patterns for the body of the speech. Five are appropriate for both informative and persuasive speeches: *topical division, chronological division, spatial division, causal division,* and *pro–con division. (Pro-con assessment division* is an extension of the *pro-con division,* and it's only used in persuasive speeches.)
- Two organizational patterns are appropriate only for persuasive speeches: *problem–solution division* (and, by extension, *problem–cause–solution*) and *need–plan division.*

Develop the Key Ideas

8.3 Develop your key ideas using the 4 S's strategy.

To organize the presentation of each major idea in the body of your speech, we recommend the memory device we call the 4 S's: *signpost* the key idea, *state* the key idea, *support* the key idea, and *summarize* the key idea. Apply these four steps to each key idea in the speech.

Connect the Key Ideas

8.4 Construct four types of transitions to connect the key ideas in your speech.

- Each of the key ideas you develop needs to be connected to the next key idea using a transition.
- Effective transitions indicate the nature of the relation between the ideas: *complementary, causal, contrasting,* or *chronological.*

SUPPORTING YOUR SPEECH

→ LEARNING OBJECTIVES

After studying this chapter, you should be able to

9.1 Explain the four purposes of supporting materials.

9.2 Develop supporting materials that are appropriate to your topic, your audience, and yourself as the speaker.

9.3 Apply the seven guidelines for evaluating the validity and strength of your evidence.

9.4 Cite sources while delivering your speech.

When you think of argument, you likely think of two people trying to persuade each other. In a real sense, however, all public speaking is argument. We should speak and accept ideas only if they are supported with sufficient evidence and reasoning. Speakers must prove what they assert whether they are a politician speaking about tax increases, a teacher delivering a lesson on World War I, or an exercise instructor informing and persuading the class to perform. Listeners should think critically and evaluate the merits of any statement based on evidence the speaker offers for its support.

As you learned in Chapter 8, we recommend applying a formula for structuring each major idea in your speech. This pattern, called the 4 S's strategy, consists of *signposting*, *stating*, *supporting*, and *summarizing* each key idea. In this chapter, we focus on the third of these four S's: *supporting* your major ideas. You will learn more about the purposes of supporting materials, and we will discuss seven types you can use. Finally, we'll suggest ways to evaluate evidence and how to cite it to ensure that you communicate your ideas clearly, memorably, and authoritatively.

Purposes of Supporting Materials

9.1 Explain the four purposes of supporting materials.

You will use supporting materials in your speeches to provide specific points of reference for your audience. Effective supporting materials help you anchor your ideas in the minds of your listeners. They do so by giving your ideas clarity, vividness, relevance, and credibility.

Clarity

On the way to a conference a few years back, we stopped and asked for directions to East Tennessee State University. The person who attempted to give us directions said, "You sort of need to go down this road for a bit, and then take a right, but it's more like a fork, really. . . ." The man continued to use similar language and vague descriptions as he tried to help us get to our destination. Needless to say, we had to stop and ask another person shortly thereafter because the first person's directions lacked clarity.

As a speaker, your first goal is to communicate clearly. *Clarity* refers to the exactness of a message. The clarity of any message you send results partly from your language. In addition, the supporting material you choose should make your message clear. As you develop a speech, ask yourself, "Does my supporting material really explain, amplify, or illustrate the point I'm trying to make?" If it does not, disregard it and continue your search for relevant material. Clear supporting materials help listeners understand your ideas.

Vividness

Which of the following sentences makes a stronger impression?

> An online practice test program is a helpful teaching tool in the classroom.

or

> An online practice test program is a wise and genial tutor, giving immediate feedback and waiting patiently until the student masters the task at hand.

Most people choose the second sentence. The first statement seems flat and generic. The second personalizes the technology, gives it human qualities, and creates an image that remains with you for a while.

In this chapter, we use several excerpts from speeches to illustrate various types of supporting materials. Once you finish reading this chapter, you will no doubt remember some of the examples and forget others. Those you remember will be ones you found particularly vivid. *Vivid* supporting materials are striking, graphic, intense, and memorable. A major purpose of supporting materials, then, is to help your audience remember the key points in your speech. You will accomplish this best by using vivid forms of support chosen with your unique audience in mind.

Relevance

When you listen to your professors in class, you probably appreciate their efforts to make the course content relevant and applicable to you and your career goals or current life situation. Audience members of relevant speakers also develop positive attitudes toward the speakers and they generally follow the speakers' recommendations. So, *relevance* means that speakers structure both their verbal and the nonverbal messages in a way that establishes a connection with the audience.[1]

You can enhance your perceived topic relevance verbally by using examples with which the audience members are familiar. For instance, if you are a Penn State student, you can make a speech about student athletes more relevant to your audience by using examples of athletic teams on your Penn State campus. Nonverbally, you enhance your perceived topic relevance by using illustrators to accompany various types of supporting materials, such as using a definition by visual example. If you are giving a speech about boxing, you can illustrate how a boxer "throws" an uppercut while you orally define that particular method of hitting the opponent. Illustrate how a boxer initiates an uppercut by lowering her or his hand below the waist and then moves it upward rapidly. By doing this, your audience members can see how they can use an uppercut if ever in a boxing match.

Credibility

You gasp as you see the headline "Scientists Discover Microbial Life on Mars." Would it make a difference whether you saw this on the cover of *Scientific American* or the *National Enquirer*? Of course it would. A scientific article reviewed and selected for publication by a panel of experts is significantly more believable than an article from any weekly tabloid. **Credibility** refers to the audience members' perceptions of the speaker's trustworthiness, competence, and caring, which are, in part, functions of (dependent on) the speaker's sources.

Many ideas in the speeches you prepare will require simple supporting materials: short definitions, brief examples, or quick comparisons. In other instances, you may present complex or controversial ideas that require several types of supporting materials. Whether your supporting materials are simple or complex, they must be accurate and their sources should be cited clearly if they are to reinforce your credibility. A speech with all its ideas and support taken from a single source is too limited. Using several sources to corroborate your ideas and facts can be a valuable and persuasive tool. Your main points will be stronger and you will be perceived as more credible if you show that these ideas are shared by several experts.

You establish clarity by explaining your idea so that listeners *understand* it. You establish vividness by presenting your idea so that listeners will *remember* it. You establish topic relevance by *relating* your topic to some aspect of your audience members' lives. Finally, you establish credibility by presenting the idea so that listeners *believe* it. If the supporting materials in your speech make the audience understand, remember, relate to, and believe what you say, you have done a good job selecting them.

Accomplishing these goals will require you to use four critical thinking skills. *Focus* on and *evaluate* specific pieces of information and measure their quality. *Analyze* the different supporting materials to see how they fit together to clarify your message. Finally, *integrate* as you combine and restructure your information in a way that is both appropriate to your listeners and uniquely your own.

Journal: Using Vivid Language

Rewrite the following sentence to make it more vivid: The food at the Cozy Café is very good.

credibility

Listeners' perceptions of a speaker's competence, trustworthiness, and caring.

Key Points: Purposes of Supporting Materials

1. Clarity
2. Vividness
3. Relevance
4. Credibility

Types of Supporting Materials

9.2 Develop supporting materials that are appropriate to your topic, your audience, and yourself as the speaker.

To help you achieve clarity, vividness, relevance, and credibility in your speech, consider seven types of supporting materials available to you: example, definition, narration, comparison, contrast, statistics, and testimony. Keep in mind that there is no best type of support for your ideas. Select what is most appropriate to your topic, your audience, and yourself.

Example

example

A sample or illustration of a category of people, places, objects, actions, experiences, or conditions.

An **example** is a specific illustration of a category of people, places, objects, actions, experiences, or conditions. In other words, examples are specimens or representations of a general group. The sound of the word itself gives perhaps the easiest definition to remember: An *example* is a *sample* of something. Measles, mumps, and chickenpox are examples of common childhood illnesses that have been largely eradicated in the United States. *The Kids are All Right* and *Laurel Canyon* are examples of Lisa Cholodenko movies. Using examples that are familiar to listeners is an excellent way to make your points clear, relevant, and memorable. This, of course, requires you to have done some good audience analysis.

Four specific types of examples for you to consider are brief examples, extended examples, actual examples, and hypothetical examples.

brief example

A short, general point about a specific person, place, object, experience, or condition discussed in a speech.

Brief Examples   **Brief examples** are short, specific instances of the general category you are discussing. They may be used individually but are often grouped together. Notice how Jocelyn combined several brief examples early in her speech on the attractions of New York City:

> Your walking tour of midtown Manhattan could take you to places as diverse as St. Patrick's Cathedral, Rockefeller Center, and the Museum of Modern Art. Try not to gawk as you look at some of the most famous architecture in the world—the Chrysler Building, the Empire State Building, and Grand Central Station. Tired of pounding the pavement? Slip into a chair in the Algonquin Hotel's dim lobby, soak up the literary history, ring the bell on your table, and order something to drink. Hungry? You've got the world's table to choose from—everything from four-star restaurants to little holes-in-the-wall serving the best ethnic dishes: Chinese, Vietnamese, Indian, Mexican, Thai.

extended example

A lengthy and elaborate example that allows for a detailed picture of a person, place, object, experience, or condition discussed in the speech.

Extended Examples   **Extended examples** are lengthier and more elaborate than brief examples. They allow you to create more detailed pictures of a person, place, object, experience, or condition. Later in her speech, Jocelyn developed an extended example of one of her favorite New York City attractions:

> Beginning with my second visit to New York, one of my first stops has usually been the Museum of Modern Art. If you're like me, you'll need to give yourself at least a couple of hours here, because for a small admission price you're going to get a chance to see up close art that you've only seen before as photographs in books. Upstairs on my last visit, I saw works such as Vincent van Gogh's *Starry Night* and Roy Lichtenstein's huge pop art paintings of comic strip panels. On a wall with a number of other paintings was a canvas so small that I almost missed it. I'm glad I didn't. It was Salvador Dali's famous surrealist work, *The Persistence of Memory*, with its melting clock and watch faces. Then over in a corner is a special room that holds only one painting. As you walk in, you see an expanse of gray carpet and several upholstered benches. One wall is glass, two others are white and bare, but the fourth one holds the three panels of Claude Monet's massive painting, *Water Lilies*.

Notice how vividly this extended example suggests a scene and recreates an experience for the listeners.

Actual Examples   An **actual example** is real or true. Each of the examples we've used so far is an actual example. (The Chrysler Building and the Empire State Building are famous New York landmarks.)

Notice how Kyle tells a real story in his speech on the health of 9/11 recovery workers:

> Upon graduating as an NYPD detective, Michael Valentin took an oath to have utmost "loyalty, bravery, and fidelity." So on the morning of 9/11, Valentin could do nothing else than selflessly and heroically put his fears second and head straight to downtown Manhattan. For 2 months he searched for the bodies, but within weeks of working at the site, Valentin began feeling numbness in his hands, coughing up blood, and developed a cancer mass the size of a lemon outside his lung. Now every breath he takes is a choice between a life of pain and no life at all.[2]

Later in this chapter, we'll show how Kyle combined this extended example with statistics, another type of supporting material, to develop a compelling case for helping 9/11 recovery workers.

Hypothetical Examples   **Hypothetical examples** are imaginary or fictitious. A speaker often signals hypothetical examples with phrases such as "Suppose that," "Imagine yourself," or "What if." Hypothetical examples clarify and vivify the point you are making, but they do not prove the point.

Notice how the following introduction mentions actual products but places them in a hypothetical situation. Javier chose this method knowing that not all listeners would have all the products listed, but then generalizes from these examples to support the claim that we live in a digital world.

> Imagine this scenario. You wake up in the morning and listen to soothing music on your iPhone® 7S via the Spotify app. You stumble downstairs, enticed by the aroma of coffee brewed by a preset coffee maker with 24-hour digital clock timer and automatic shut-off function. You zap on your 40-inch smart TV. Nothing of interest on network television? With a click of a button, you can access your Netflix or Amazon video accounts, or search for a video on YouTube. On your way out the door, you put on your Fitbit® which will track your every step as you go about your day and sync that information back to your smartphone. What would our grandparents think? Certainly, we live in a digital world!

Definition

A **definition** tells us the meaning of a word, a phrase, or a concept. Definitions are essential if your audience is unfamiliar with the vocabulary you use or if there are multiple definitions of a particular term. In her speech on the protection of animals, Paris used the terms *animal welfare* and *animal rights* interchangeably. Her speech confused and misled her listeners. You want to clarify terms early in your speech so you don't confuse your listeners and lose their attention. For instance, in one of his key ideas in his speech on Turkish culture, Ashkan noted that in Turkey, the "father is the head of the household, meaning he holds all authority in the house." Note that in the second part of this statement, Ashkan defined what it means to be the "head of the household" in Turkey.

When you define terms in your speech, be aware of four options: definition by synonym, etymology, example, and operation.

---

actual example
An example based on a true instance or illustration.

hypothetical example
An example based on an imaginary or fictitious instance or illustration.

definition
An explanation of the meaning of a word, phrase, or concept.

definition by synonym
Substitution of a word having similar meaning for the word being defined.

Definition by Synonym The first type of definition is **definition by synonym**. Synonyms are words that have similar meanings. Consider these pairs of words:

mendacity and *dishonesty*	*pariah* and *outcast*
obviate and *prevent*	*anathema* and *curse*
mitigate and *lessen*	*surreptitious* and *secret*

Each word is coupled with one of its synonyms. The first word of each pair may not be a part of your listeners' working vocabularies. As a speaker, you would want to use the second word in each pair, because those words are more familiar to your audience and will allow you to communicate more clearly. As the joke goes, never use a big word when a diminutive one will do.

definition by etymology
Explanation of the origin of the word being defined.

Definition by Etymology A second type of definition is **definition by etymology**. Etymology is the study of word origins. Describing how a word has developed may clarify its meaning. You can use this type of definition to highlight the unusual nature of a familiar term. The reference section of your library and a variety of websites have several dictionaries of word origins and histories of word usage that may be useful as you prepare your speeches.

definition by example
Providing an instance or illustration of the word being defined.

Definition by Example An example is a specific instance or illustration of a larger group or classification. **Definition by example** uses a specific instance to clarify a general category or concept. In his informative speech on violent crimes, Jacob presented two definitions to help his audience understand the distinction between "assault" and "battery."

> According to the Chicago Police Department website, accessed last Saturday, "In Illinois, assault is a threat, while battery is an actual attack." The New York Public Library Desk Reference provides a more vivid explanation. Their 2002 calendar draws this distinction: "If you angrily shake your fist at someone, it's legally considered assault. If you follow up your actions by punching the person in the nose, the offense is assault and battery."

Jacob first used definition by synonym and then definition by example to clarify the distinction between these two terms.

You need not confine your definitions by example to language, however. Often audible and visual examples can be the quickest and most vivid ways to define a term or concept.

Audible examples are those you let your audience hear. Speeches on types of music, voice patterns, or speech dialects could define key terms by audible examples. For instance, if you used the word *scat* in a speech on jazz, you could offer a dictionary definition of the term: "jazz singing that uses nonsense syllables."[3] But wouldn't an audio sample be more memorable to your audience?

Visual examples define a term by letting the audience see a form of what you are describing. If you're using the term *krumping* in a speech on contemporary dance, you could construct a definition, using phrases that describe the term, for example: a style of urban street dance that integrates elaborate face painting and facial expressions with exaggerated movements of arms and legs to suggest the expressive style of hip-hop. But a more vivid way to define the term might be to show a video clip of dancers krumping.

Journal: Using Definitions

Discuss a method of definition you could use for each of the following terms:

a. Palpable
b. Ballistic fingerprinting
c. Speed dating

definition by operation
Explanation of how the object or concept being defined works, what it does, or what it was designed to do.

Definition by Operation Sometimes the quickest and liveliest way to define a term is to explain how it is used. **Definition by operation** clarifies a word or phrase by explaining how an object or concept works, what it does, or what it was designed to do. The terms *radar detector*, *media streamer*, and *laser scalpel* are but a few of the physical objects best defined by explaining their operation.

You can also define concepts, actions, or processes by operation. To define *magnetic resonance imaging*, you would have to explain how that technology operates. Notice how the following speaker defines an unfamiliar term by explaining its function:

> Humpback whales feed themselves by the technique of "bubble netting." A group of four or five whales will locate a school of krill or other small fish. The whales dive deep, encircling the fish and releasing a curtain of rising bubbles. The bubbles confuse the krill and force them into a tight column. The humpbacks then surface through the middle of the column with their mouths wide open, enjoying the feast.

Definition by operation is often livelier and clearer than many dictionary definitions. It can also be especially useful in the case of new technologies whose dictionary definitions have yet to be written.

Narration

Narration is storytelling, the process of describing an action or a series of events. If you come to school on Monday and tell a friend about something you did during the weekend, you are narrating those events.

Consider the value of personal and third-person narratives in your speech.

Personal Narrative   As a participant in the events, you will probably speak in first person at least part of the time, using the pronouns *I* or *we*. Such a story is called a **personal narrative**. We have suggested that you draw on your own experiences as you select and develop a speech topic, and personal narratives can be rich and interesting supporting materials.

Henric, an international student from Croatia, delivered a speech to actuate in which he attempted to persuade his audience to visit his native country. To enhance his speech, Henric used a personal narrative by stating, "When I visit Croatia during the summer, I go snorkeling in the clear Adriatic Sea water. I also travel to the many beautiful islands, and I enjoy their amazing pizzas."

Third-Person Narrative   Narratives need not be personal but may relate incidents in the lives of others. When you speak from someone else's point of view and use the pronouns *he*, *she*, or *they*, you are telling a **third-person narrative**.

narration
The process of describing an action or series of occurrences using storytelling.

personal narrative
A story told from the viewpoint of a participant in the action and using the pronouns *I* or *we*.

third-person narrative
A story told from the viewpoint of a witness and using the pronouns *he*, *she*, or *they*.

In the following example, notice how Chiwoneso used third-person narrative to illustrate the need for improved global food aid policies.

> Muna is an eight-year-old girl from Mulonda, Zambia. Every morning she walks to a food distribution point set up by the World Food Program at a nearby hospital. She holds tightly to her battered tin cup as she waits in line for hours to receive the mixture of corn and soy powder, but the stocks are running low and like every other day, she walks home empty-handed. Muna's reality is that she is an AIDS orphan who struggles to stay alive, but she will not die from AIDS; more than likely she will die of hunger.[4]

Comparison

comparison
The process of associating two items by pointing out their similarities.

literal comparison
Associations between two items that share actual similarities.

Comparison is the process of depicting one item—a person, place, object, or concept—by pointing out its similarities to another, more familiar item. Just as examples can be actual or hypothetical, comparisons can be literal or figurative.

A **literal comparison** associates items that share actual similarities. Sai spoke on the need for a national high-speed rail network. He framed his speech using a comparison with the Interstate Highway System, developed in the 1950s through the 1970s. Sai argued that the interstate system significantly promoted economic growth, decreased travel time, and increased travel safety and mobility. The challenge, he noted, was that it required a strong national commitment of vision, patience, and resources. Sai used literal comparison as he presented these same arguments for a high-speed rail system.

figurative comparison
Associations between two items that do not share actual similarities.

contrast
The process of distinguishing two items by pointing out their differences.

When you draw a **figurative comparison**, you associate two items that do not necessarily share actual similarities. The purpose of figurative comparisons is to surprise the listener into seeing or considering one person, place, object, or concept in a new way.

Effective figurative comparisons must contain an element of surprise, as well as a spark of recognition. Katherine highlighted the enormous popularity of the social-networking site Facebook when she quoted from the May 2011 issue of *Success*: "If Facebook were a nation, it would be the world's third largest nation, behind only China and India."

literal contrast
Distinctions between two items that share some actual similarities.

figurative contrast
Distinctions between two items that do not have actual similarities.

Contrast

Contrast links two items by showing their differences. A **literal contrast** distinguishes items that do share some similarities. In a persuasive speech on the dangers of overexposure to the sun, our student Patricia effectively used the following literal contrast:

> Sunblocks are either chemical or physical. Oils, lotions, and creams that claim a certain SPF factor all contain chemical blocks. On the other hand, zinc oxide, the white or colored clay-looking material you see some people wearing, usually on their noses, is a physical block.

On PBS's *Great Performances*, New York City Public Theater Artistic Director, Oskar Eustis, compared playwright Lin Manuel Miranda (best known for the Broadway musical, *Hamilton*) to William Shakespeare, noting that both elevated common language into art.

A **figurative contrast**, on the other hand, distinguishes items that share no actual similarities and are used to emphasize the differences between two objects, ideas, places, etc. For instance, you can use a figurative contrast when discussing the United States and Sweden. The two countries are completely different in terms of size, climate, language, population, political system, social structure, education, and much more.

You can use comparison and contrast together in your speech. If you clarify a term by showing how it is similar to something the audience knows, you can often make the term even clearer by showing how it differs from something the audience also knows.

Another student, Paul, used a variety of supporting materials to document problems of exercise anorexia, an addiction to exercise:

> According to *Psychology Today*, June 2005, this disorder can affect 35 percent of those who work out three to five times a week for more than an hour each time. Specific symptoms can be when someone exercises even when ill, or withdraws from others to exercise, or becomes upset if unable to work out. Just like alcoholics, exercise anorexics are literally addicted to their behavior. But unlike alcoholism, exercise anorexia is an even bigger epidemic because people don't recognize that there is a problem.[5]

Paul explained exercise anorexia by comparing and contrasting it with alcoholism. He also demonstrated the dimension of this problem by using statistics, the next type of supporting material we discuss.

Statistics

Statistics are collections of data. Broadly speaking, any number used as supporting material is a statistic. Think of how much trust politicians and the general public put in preference polls gathered before elections. Statistics can predict certain events in our daily lives, such as price increases or decreases on certain goods and services. Used appropriately, statistics can make your ideas clear and vivid, can increase your credibility, and can prove your point. For instance, in his speech about gum chewers, Austin claimed, "In a survey consisting of American undergraduate students, 'nearly 87 percent confirmed that they chew gum at least occasionally.' " He also stated that chewing gum has "even become a billion-dollar industry." These statements clarify the widespread use of chewing gum.

> **statistics**
> Data collected and presented in the form of numbers.

Used inappropriately, however, statistics may baffle, bore, or even mislead your audience. The following five suggestions should guide you in presenting statistics.

Do Not Rely Exclusively on Statistics   If statistics are your only form of supporting material, your audience will likely feel bombarded by numbers. Since your audience has only one chance to hear and assimilate your statistics, use statistics judiciously and in combination with other forms of support.

Remember Kyle's speech on the health of 9/11 recovery workers? He used a real example, NYPD detective Michael Valentin, to illustrate serious health consequences and to tap listeners' emotions. Kyle then introduced statistics to demonstrate the breadth of this problem:

> But, Valentine is not alone in his illness. A September 5, 2006, CBS News article reveals an astonishing 70 percent of the 40,000 recovery workers who responded to the attack on the World Trade Center are suffering lung problems.[6]

Round Off Statistics   A statistic of 74.6 percent has less impact and is more difficult for your audience to remember than "nearly three-fourths." No one in your audience will remember the statistic of $1,497,568.42; many, however, may be able to remember "approximately a million and a half dollars." Rounding off statistics for your listeners is neither deceptive nor unethical. Instead, it reflects your concern for helping your audience understand and retain key statistical information.

Use Units of Measure That Are Familiar to Your Audience   In her speech on London tourist attractions, Veronica described the London Eye as being "135 meters high—equivalent to 64 red telephone boxes stacked on top of one another." If she had stopped there, listeners unfamiliar with the metric system or with British phone boxes would have had only a vague idea of the height Veronica was describing. However, she wisely converted meters to feet, adding that the London Eye is 443 feet tall.

Supporting materials, such as visual examples, can help make complicated concepts clearer and easier for an audience to grasp.

Use Presentational Aids to Represent or Clarify Relationships among Statistics   In his first informative speech of the semester, Alec discussed U.S. college study-abroad programs. He accessed a report by the Institute of International Education listing the percentages of students studying in various host countries: 20.4 percent in the United Kingdom, 9.7 percent in Spain, 9 percent in Italy, 8.3 percent in France, and so forth. Alec decided that his classmates would remember more of this information if he presented it orally and visually. Therefore, he constructed a chart that ranked these nations according to the percentage of U.S. students studying there. Listeners were able to see the rankings and focus on the particular countries where they would like to study.

Stress the Impact of Large Numbers   Former U.S. surgeon general C. Everett Koop used statistics effectively to make his point that tobacco-related diseases cause significant deaths. Notice how he used repetition and helped his audience visualize the enormity of these deaths:

> Let's start with a factual description of the problem. Based on the calculations of the finest statistical minds in the world and the World Health Organization, they have predicted that by 2025, . . . 500 million people worldwide will die of tobacco-related disease. That's a numbing figure. It is too large to take in, so let me put it in other terms for you. That's a Vietnam War every day for 27 years. That's a Bhopal every 2 hours for 27 years. That's a Titanic every 43 minutes for 27 years.
>
> If we were to build for those tobacco victims a memorial such as the Vietnam Wall, it would stretch from here [Washington, D.C.] 1,000 miles across seven states to Kansas City. And, if you want to put it in terms per minute, there's a death [every] 1.7 seconds, or about 250 to 300 people since I began to speak to you this afternoon.[7]

Testimony

Examples, definition, narration, comparison, contrast, and statistics are discrete types of supporting materials. Each is a different strategy for validating the ideas of a speech. Speakers sometimes generate these types of support themselves. Other times, they glean them from their research, citing their sources but justifying the point in their own words. Still other times, speakers find the words and structure of the original source so compelling that they quote directly or paraphrase the source. This latter strategy is known as **testimony**, or quotation.

testimony

Quotations or paraphrases of an authoritative source to clarify or prove a point.

Testimony is a commonly used supporting material. It is therefore not surprising that both of our students, Ashkan and Austin, used testimony to support their arguments. In his last key idea, Ashkan noted that "Hande Bozdagan, a famous Turkish chef has said, 'Turkish food is amongst the top three greatest cuisines in the world.'" Similarly, in his first key idea, Austin stated, "in 2011, Tucha and Simpson reported that chewing gum has a positive effect on healthy adults' abilities in maintaining focus during extended periods of time."

In his speech "Ribbons: Function or Fashion," Tony discussed how wearing an awareness ribbon can inform and connect communities. To give his ideas credibility, he used the expert testimony of a communication professor and an animal welfare website:

> Dr. Judith Trent, a communication professor at the University of Cincinnati, states in the *Cincinnati Enquirer* of September 18, 2001, that wearing a ribbon "shows you're a part of something that's larger than yourself. It helps to unify and support the cause. It's a public signal about a private thought." By wearing ribbons, people can easily give support and find comfort in people around

SPEAKING WITH CONFIDENCE

Before presenting my speech on how to start a new small business, I began gathering and evaluating the supporting materials I would use to support my key ideas. Like most speakers, I searched online for information. I was careful to be selective and to avoid webpages that were based on personal opinion and bias. I supplemented the examples and statistics I found with my own expert testimony as a successful, self-employed businessman. I cited my sources to establish my credibility and let my listeners assess the quality of my data and documentation. Knowing that I had selected and tested my supporting materials allowed me to minimize my use of qualifiers such as "I think," "this might," and "maybe." I was confident with what I said, and the audience could be confident with what they heard.

Jovan Coker
Radford University

them. The Purple Ribbon Campaign website, last updated July 15, 2003, states, "Wearing a ribbon allows a person to represent their hopes and drive for a better day to come. It also provides support to others in letting them know that they are not suffering alone."[8]

Tony clearly identified two sources and quoted them directly, trusting their credibility and their words to persuade his listeners. Testimony relies largely on the reputation of the source being quoted or paraphrased.

You also use expert testimony when you support your ideas with your own experiences and observations. Many students select a speech topic because they have some special knowledge or experience with the subject. One student, for example, gave a speech comparing retail prices at large supermarkets to those at convenience stores. He was careful to explain his credentials and establish his expertise in the subject. Not only did he wear his store apron and manager's name tag, but he also said early in his introduction, "As a former receiving control manager, I was in charge of purchasing products for the store, so I have some knowledge of how wholesale prices are translated into the retail prices you and I pay." The speaker enhanced his credibility both verbally and nonverbally. Speakers should choose supporting materials carefully and ethically.

> **Key Points: Types of Supporting Materials**
>
> 1. Examples
> 2. Definitions
> 3. Narration
> 4. Comparison
> 5. Contrast
> 6. Statistics
> 7. Testimony

Tests of Evidence

9.3 Apply the seven guidelines for evaluating the validity and strength of your evidence.

The positions you develop in your speech will be only as strong as the evidence supporting them. Seven guidelines will help you evaluate the validity and strength of your supporting materials, a process that you began in Chapter 7 on researching your topic. These suggestions will also help you evaluate evidence you hear others present in their speeches.

Is the Evidence Quoted in Context?

Evidence is quoted *in context* if it accurately reflects the source's statement on the topic. Evidence is quoted *out of context* if it distorts the source's position on the topic. For example, suppose Joyce was preparing a speech on hate crimes on campus. She read in the campus paper the following statement by the president of her college:

> We've been fortunate that our campus has been relatively free of bias-motivated crimes. In fact, last year, only two such incidents were reported—the lowest figure in the past 5 years. Yet no matter how small the number is, any hate crime constitutes a serious problem on this campus. We will not be satisfied until our campus is completely free from all bias-motivated intimidation.

Now, suppose Joyce used the following statement to support her position that hate crimes are prevalent on campus:

> We need to be concerned about a widespread and growing problem on our campus: the prevalence of hate crimes. Just this past week, for example, our president argued that hate crimes constitute, and I quote, "a serious problem on this campus."

The president did say those words, but Joyce failed to mention the president's position that hate crimes on campus are few and decreasing. By omitting this fact, she has distorted the president's message. Joyce has presented the evidence out of context. The evidence you cite in your speech should accurately represent each source's position on the topic.

Is the Source of the Evidence an Expert?

If you delivered a speech advocating the licensing of law clerks to draft wills and conduct other routine legal business, would you rather quote a first-year law student or a senior law partner of a major legal corporation? Of course, it would depend on the specific individuals and what they said, but you would probably place more trust in the more experienced person.

An expert is a person qualified to speak on a particular topic. We trust the opinions and observations of others based on their position, education, training, or experience. The chairperson of a committee that has studied the effects of a community-based sentencing program is knowledgeable about that issue. A person completing graduate study on the effects of a local Head Start program on literacy has also developed an area of expertise. As a speaker, select the most qualified sources to support your position.

Is the Source of the Evidence Unbiased?

When Markdown Marty of Marty's Used Cars tells you he has the best deals in town, do you accept that claim without questioning it? Probably not. Marty may be an expert on used cars, but he's understandably biased. When individuals have a vested interest in a product, a service, or an issue, they are often less objective.

You expect representatives of political parties, special-interest groups, business corporations, labor unions, and so forth to make statements advancing their interests. For example, the supermarket receiving control manager we quoted earlier concluded his speech by stating that it is more economical to shop at large supermarkets than at convenience stores. When you include testimony and quotations in your speeches, try to rely on objective experts who do not have a vested interest in sustaining the positions they voice.

ETHICAL DECISIONS

BIASED SOURCES: TO USE OR NOT TO USE?

You probably wouldn't be surprised that a Gallup study sponsored by Motorola found that people who use cellular phones are more successful in business than those who don't or that a Gallup poll sponsored by the zinc industry revealed that 62 percent of Americans want to keep the penny. These are just two examples that *Wall Street Journal* writer and editor Cynthia Crossen uses in her book *Tainted Truth: The Manipulation of Fact in America* to illustrate the difficulty of distinguishing between neutral research and commercially sponsored studies.

Assume that you are preparing to give a speech about how college students' use of iPads® for note-taking impacts their academic performance. While researching your topic, you find a study that suggests that students who use iPads for note-taking earn higher grades than students who take notes using traditional notebooks. When you look for the source, you see that the study was sponsored by Apple—the iPad manufacturer.

What course of action should you follow? Should you disregard the findings because the study was sponsored by Apple, use the findings without mentioning the study's sponsor, mention the findings and acknowledge that the study was sponsored by Apple, or treat the findings in some other way? Fully support your answer.

Is the Evidence Relevant?

Evidence should relate to the speaker's claim. Sounds pretty obvious, doesn't it? However, both speakers and listeners often fail to apply this guideline in evaluating evidence. A speaker who contends that amateur boxing is dangerous but presents only evidence of injuries to professional boxers has clearly violated the relevance criterion. However, many times irrelevant evidence is difficult to detect.

Ryan's speech called for increased funding of medical trauma centers. Throughout his speech, he cited the need for the specialized care provided in these facilities. Yet when he estimated the demand for this care, he used statistics of emergency room use. Trauma centers are not the same as emergency rooms. Therefore, Ryan's evidence was irrelevant to his argument. As you construct your speech, make certain your evidence relates specifically to your key points.

Is the Evidence Specific?

Which of the following statements is more informative?

> The new convention center will increase tourism a lot.

or

> The new convention center will increase tourism by 40 percent.

What does "a lot" mean in the first statement? 20 percent? 50 percent? 80 percent? We don't know. The second statement is more precise. Because it is specific, we are better able to assess the impact of the new convention center. Words such as *lots*, *many*, *numerous*, and *very* are vague. When possible, replace them with specific or precise words or phrases.

For example, if you are giving a persuasive speech in which you encourage your classmates to adopt a companion animal from a shelter, you could use specific evidence to document your assertion that homeless animals are in need by stating:

> In February 2017, the ASPCA website noted that approximately 2.7 million companion animals are euthanized each year. To put this number in perspective, that is virtually the same number as the population of Chicago, Illinois, which had 2,722,389 people as of July 2014 according to the *Chicago Tribune*.

Is the Evidence Sufficient?

In her speech on rap music, Lea played excerpts from two rap songs, one of which she characterized as antiwoman and the other as antipolice. She encouraged her listeners to boycott rap music because "it demeans women and law enforcement officers." Lea did not apply this sixth guideline to her evidence. Two examples do not justify a blanket indictment of rap music.

In considering the guideline of sufficiency, ask yourself, "Is there enough evidence to prove the point?" Three examples of college athletes graduating without acquiring basic writing skills are insufficient to prove that athletes are failing to get a good education. One example may illustrate a claim, but it will rarely prove it. Make certain you have sufficient evidence to support your points.

Is the Evidence Timely?

If you were preparing a travel budget for a trip overseas, which would you find more helpful: an airline ticket pricing schedule you had from last year or one you found on Kayak or Priceline last night? Of course you would want to rely on more recent information. The timeliness of information is especially important if you are speaking about constantly changing issues, conditions, or events. What you read today may already be dated by the time you give your speech.

Key Points: Tests of Evidence

1. Is the evidence quoted in context?
2. Is the source of the evidence an expert?
3. Is the source of the evidence unbiased?
4. Is the evidence relevant?
5. Is the evidence specific?
6. Is the evidence sufficient?
7. Is the evidence timely?

oral footnote
Verbalized credit for ideas and supporting materials in your speech that are not your own.

Some speech topics, however, are timeless. If you speak about the gods of Mount Olympus, no one would question your use of Robert Graves's *Greek Gods and Heroes*, published in 1960. As a scholar of mythology, Graves earned a reputation that time is not likely to diminish. Similarly, if you deliver a speech on the ancient Olympic Games, your most authoritative sources may be history textbooks. If, however, your topic concerns current drug-testing procedures in Olympic competition, it would be vital for you to use the most recent sources of the best quality you can find. The date of your evidence must be appropriate to your specific argument.

Citing Your Sources

9.4 Cite sources while delivering your speech.

In this chapter, you have learned about different types of supporting materials and how to evaluate the quality of the support you choose. However, remember that there is a difference between *supporting materials* and the *sources* you began to research back in Chapter 7. They are, however, intimately related; sources refer to where you obtained your information whereas supporting materials refer to the type of information you extracted from a source. In fact, to boost the effectiveness of your supporting materials, you must cite your sources.

A bibliography of quality sources you consulted in researching your speech will build your credibility with your instructor. However, most of your listeners will not have an opportunity to see your bibliography. To acknowledge your sources and to take credit for the research you have done, you will need to provide **oral footnotes**, which are verbalized credits for ideas and supporting materials in your speech that are not your own. Doing so accomplishes two goals. First, clear source citations enhance the credibility of what you say by demonstrating that experts and data support your position. Second, clear source citations help interested listeners find published sources that they might wish to read or study.

How do you "orally footnote" sources as you deliver your speech? Your instructor may require more or less information in oral source citations than we do, so be sure to check with your instructor. Our rule of thumb is this: Give only the information necessary to build the credibility of the source but enough information to help listeners find your source if they wish.

Do you need to include *all* the information that was in your bibliographic entry for the source? No. Only the most active listener would remember the title and page numbers of a journal article or the publisher of a book that you cite, for example. Is there any information not in your bibliography that you *should* mention as you cite a source? Yes. To establish the credibility of any source you name, you need to explain at least briefly that individual's qualifications. You can usually find such information somewhere in the book, magazine, journal, or website you are using. If not, check a biographical database.

If the author is a newspaper or magazine staff writer, however, you do not need to name that individual. If the publication has a corporate author (a group, committee, or organization), just mentioning the name of the group or organization is probably sufficient. The date of publication may be extremely important to building credibility on a current topic. For periodicals published weekly or for online magazines that are frequently updated, specify the date, month, and year that the material was published or that you accessed the source.

Orally footnoting Internet sources poses special challenges. Though it is never acceptable just to say, "I found a webpage that said . . ." or "I found this on Yahoo!" most listeners will not remember a long URL. If the URL is simple and easily recognizable, mention it: "pbs.org," "cnn.com," or "espn.com," for example. Identifying the sponsor of a website is important. If you cannot identify the group or individual who published and maintains the site, you may need to look for a better source.

Compare the following source citations:

Instead of saying:	Say this:
"Viet Thanh Nguygen writes in his novel *The Sympathizer* . . ."	Viet Thanh Nguygen, 2016 Pulitzer Prize–winning fiction writer, says in his debut novel *The Sympathizer* . . ."
"In an article I found online . . ."	"Senior reporter Sandra Garcia's article titled 'Math Education' in the July 16, 2014, issue of the *Wilmington Star News* indicates that . . ."
"Leigh T. Hollins says in his article in the journal *Fire Engineering* . . ."	"Leigh T. Hollins, a certified EMT and battalion chief in the Manatee County, Florida, fire department, says in his article in the June 2005 issue of the journal *Fire Engineering* . . ."
"Based on the Bureau of Labor Statistics . . ."	"Based on the February 21, 2017, updates of U.S. Department of Labor's Bureau of Labor Statistics website . . ."
"I found an article at memory .loc.gov/ammem/jrhtml/ jr1940.html . . ."	"On March 12 of this year, I found an article titled 'Breaking the Color Line: 1940–1946.' It's a link from the Recreation and Sports collection of the Library of Congress's website American Memory . . ."

In each case, the oral footnote that takes a few more words identifies the source more clearly and more specifically, and would reinforce the speaker's credibility. Note that oral footnotes can be phrased in several different ways. To avoid redundancy, try to avoid citing all sources in a similar manner, such as "According to . . ." "Theory into Practice: Information for Oral Footnotes" summarizes our advice for citing books, articles, and other types of sources.

Journal: Varying Oral Footnotes

In the example below, notice how the speaker used the same style for both oral footnotes ("According to . . ."). Rewrite this excerpt to provide more variety in language when orally citing the sources below.

According to the website of the Mayo Clinic accessed March 1, 2017, chronic fatigue syndrome is "a complicated disorder characterized by extreme fatigue that can't be explained by any underlying medical condition." According to our campus nurse practitioner, Alice Wei, chronic fatigue symptoms do not necessarily improve with rest, like a good night's sleep or even a nap between classes.

Theory into Practice (TIP)

INFORMATION FOR ORAL FOOTNOTES

If you are citing:	Tell us:
A magazine/journal article	That it is an article, the title of the magazine or journal, the author's name and credentials (if other than a staff writer), and the date of publication
A newspaper article	That it is an article, the name of the newspaper, the author's name and credentials (if other than a staff writer), and the date of the issue you are citing
A website	The title of the webpage; the name of the individual, agency, association, group, or company sponsoring the site; and the date of publication, last update, and/or the date you accessed it
A book	That it is a book, the author's name(s) and credentials, the book's title, and the date of publication
An interview you conducted	That you interviewed the person, the person's name, and her or his position or title
A television or radio program	The title of the show, the channel or network airing it, and the date of broadcast
A movie	The title of the movie, producer/production company, and release date
A reference work	The title of the work and the date of publication
A government document	The title of the document, the name of the agency or government branch that published it, and the date of publication
A brochure or pamphlet	That it is a brochure; its title; the name of the agency, association, group, or company that published it; and the date of publication (if available)

CHAPTER 9

› SUMMARY

Supporting Your Speech

Purposes of Supporting Materials

9.1   Explain the four purposes of supporting materials.

- Supporting materials in a speech achieve four purposes: *clarity, vividness, relevance,* and *credibility.*
- *Clarity* helps the audience understand your ideas. *Vividness* assists them in remembering your ideas. *Relevance* enables the audience members to make a personal connection with the topic. *Credibility* makes you, your ideas, and supporting materials believable.

Types of Supporting Materials

9.2   Develop supporting materials that are appropriate to your topic, your audience, and yourself as the speaker.

- Types of material you can use to support the main ideas of your speech include example, definition, narration, comparison, contrast, statistics, and testimony.
- *Examples* are samples or illustrations of a category. Examples can be brief, extended, actual, or hypothetical.
- *Definitions* are explanations of an unfamiliar term or of a word having several possible meanings. We can define terms by synonym, etymology, example, or operation.
- *Narration* is storytelling. Narratives may be personal or third person.
- *Comparisons* associate two or more items to show the similarities between or among them. Comparisons can be either literal or figurative.

- *Contrasts* function like comparisons except that their purpose is to distinguish or show differences between or among two or more items. Contrasts can be either literal or figurative.
- *Statistics* are data collected in the form of numbers. Used properly, they can bolster a speaker's credibility and lend vivid support to the ideas of the speech.
- *Testimony* involves citing, quoting, or paraphrasing authoritative sources.

Tests of Evidence

9.3   Apply the seven guidelines for evaluating the validity and strength of your evidence.

To ensure that your supporting materials are credible, answer seven questions about each piece of evidence you consider using: (1) Is the evidence quoted in context? (2) Is the source of the evidence an expert? (3) Is the source of the evidence unbiased? (4) Is the evidence relevant to the point you are making? (5) Is the evidence specific? (6) Is the evidence sufficient to prove your point? (7) Is the evidence timely?

Citing Your Sources

9.4   Cite sources while delivering your speech.

If you use supporting materials that others have developed, you must cite them in your speech by providing oral footnotes. You should offer enough information to establish the credibility of the source without overwhelming the listener.

INTRODUCING AND CONCLUDING YOUR SPEECH

→ LEARNING OBJECTIVES

After studying this chapter, you should be able to

10.1 Construct an introduction that achieves the five objectives of effective speech introductions.

10.2 Construct a conclusion that achieves the four objectives of effective speech conclusions.

10.3 Apply the Outward Method of Speech Development to your speech.

I think the end is implicit in the beginning. It must be. If that isn't there in the beginning, you don't know what you're working toward. You should have a sense of a story's shape and form and its destination, all of which is like a flower inside a seed.

—Eudora Welty

Although famed southern writer Eudora Welty refers specifically to beginning and ending a short story or novel, her quotation also applies to public speaking. As a speaker, your first words can make a positive impression on your audience, capture their attention, prepare them to listen more effectively, and enlist their support. These first words are crucial, of course, because they can occur only once in a given speech.

In Chapter 8, you learned how to organize the most substantial part of your speech, the body. In this chapter, we examine how you frame the body of your speech by discussing the objectives of speech introductions and conclusions, as well as specific strategies you can use to enhance these crucial points in your presentation.

Introducing Your Speech

10.1 Construct an introduction that achieves the five objectives of effective speech introductions.

After you work on the body of your speech, you are ready to focus on the introduction and conclusion. An introduction should achieve five objectives: (1) get the attention of your audience, (2) state your topic or purpose, (3) establish the relevance of your topic, (4) establish your credibility to speak on your topic, and (5) preview the key ideas of your speech. Studying these objectives and the ways to achieve them will enable you to get your speech off to a clear, interesting start.

Get the Attention of Your Audience

Your first objective as a speaker is to secure the audience's attention. The way you get the audience involved in your speech will depend on your personality, your purpose, your topic, your audience, and the occasion. Your options include the following eight possible techniques.

Question Your Audience   A speaker can get an audience involved by asking a question. In our experience, this is the most frequently used attention-getting strategy in public speaking classes. However, before you decide to question your audience to get their attention, it is important to understand that you can ask two types of questions: rhetorical questions and direct questions. A **rhetorical question** stimulates thought but is not intended to elicit an overt response. For example, consider the following opening questions:

rhetorical question
A question designed to stimulate thought without demanding an overt response.

- How would your life change if you suddenly received $1 million?
- What would you do if you saw your best friend copying another student's answers during a test?
- Do you remember what first attracted you to this school?

A speaker who asks any of these questions does not expect an overt audience response. In fact, it would probably disrupt the rhythm of the presentation if someone answered orally. A question is rhetorical if it is designed to get the audience *thinking* about the topic.

A **direct question** seeks an overt response from the listeners. Audience members may be asked to respond vocally or physically. For example, in Austin's speech about "gum chewers," he got the audience members' attention by asking, "By a show of hands, how many of you in this room chew gum?" Other examples of questions that could be answered by a show of hands are:

direct question
A question that asks for an overt response from listeners.

- How many of you have worked as a volunteer for some charitable group within the last year? The last 6 months?
- Who in this room has experience adopting a pet from an animal rescue shelter?
- Who, here, is a registered organ donor?

Like the rhetorical question, a direct question gets the audience thinking about your topic. However, the direct question has the additional advantage of getting your listeners physically involved in your speech and, consequently, making them more alert. This strategy may be especially appropriate if you are the first or final speaker, or if you give your speech when your listeners are especially tired (think early morning or right after midterms).

When you ask a direct question and you want oral responses, you need to pause, look at your listeners, and give them sufficient time to respond. If you want a direct question answered by a show of hands, you might raise your hand as you end the question. In this way, you indicate nonverbally how you want the question answered. If you seek and get oral responses, however, make sure that you neither lose control nor turn your public speech into a group discussion. Practice these techniques as you rehearse in front of friends before making them part of your speech.

There are four final cautions about using a question to get the audience's attention. First, don't start your speech by saying, "I would like to begin by asking you a question" or "OK, let me ask you a question." Rather, jump right in and ask the question without a preface. Second, speak loudly, clearly, and maintain eye contact with your audience. Your audience members can't respond if they don't know what you said or didn't realize that you were seeking a response. Third, avoid asking embarrassing questions, such as, "How many of you are on scholastic probation?" or "Has anyone in here ever spent a night in jail?" Common sense should tell you that most people would be reluctant to answer direct questions such as these in a public setting. Finally, don't use a question without first considering its usefulness to your speech. Don't rely on a question just because you have not developed or found a more creative attention getter. Asking a relevant question that listeners answer either openly or to themselves gets them immediately involved and thinking about your speech topic.

Arouse Your Audience's Curiosity   A lively way to engage the minds of your listeners is through their natural curiosity. Get them wondering what is to come.

Angela chose to keep her audience in suspense in her attention-getting step as she described an arrest scene.

> On a dark and stormy night in May 2008 outside Chicago's O'Hare International Airport, Stefanie Giesselbach and Magnus von Buddenbrock thought they had gotten away with the perfect crime. Unfortunately for them, it wasn't their families waiting for them at the gate. After six years of investigations that began in Australia when imports from Singapore were intercepted, they were arrested for their involvement in an 80-million-dollar laundering scheme. Fifteen more people and six companies worldwide were stung with indictments in a scheme to avoid $80 million in anti-dumping duties.

Angela paused and then resolved the suspense by stating that the topic of her speech would be the crime of "honey laundering."[1]

When we attended college, one of our fellow public speaking students got our attention by arousing our curiosity when he brought a small cube-shaped cardboard box to class. He gently placed the box on a desk in the front of the classroom and began his speech by saying, "It slowly crawls up on its victim, wraps itself around its victim, and squeezes the life out of its victim." After a brief pause, he carefully opened the cardboard box, put his right hand inside the box, and quickly pulled out a Kudzu vine and smiled. In doing so, he aroused our curiosity about what might be hiding inside the box and therefore had our undivided attention.

Stimulate Your Audience's Imagination   A fun and creative way to engage the minds of your listeners is to stimulate their imagination. To do this, you must know what referents they share, and this requires some good audience analysis on your part. Notice in the following example how Shanika began her speech by relating her topic to an experience with which her audience would be familiar:

> Imagine yourself on a white sandy beach. The sun is shining and the clear blue water is only 25 to 30 feet away. You have a freshly squeezed orange drink in your hand and your best friend is next to you. As you enjoy this amazing moment you think about all the fun adventures and experiences you have ahead of you.

Notice Shanika's use of visualization and sensory appeal. In the rest of her speech, she provided four compelling reasons for why college students should consider Jamaica as a destination for spring break.

In Chapter 12, we discuss the use of language to create these and other sensory impressions in your audience.

Promise Your Audience Something Beneficial   We listen more carefully to messages that we expect to benefit us. If you can promise your audience members something that meets one or more of their needs, you secure their attention very quickly. In Chapter 5, Learning Objective 5.3, you learned about Maslow's hierarchy of needs. Remember that audience members who perceive the speaker's topic to be relevant are motivated to listen to the speaker. For example, beginning your speech with the statement, "Every person in this room can find a satisfying summer internship related to your major field of study," immediately secures the attention of your listeners—at least those not currently working in their dream jobs.

Other effective examples are ones in which a speaker promises that her information can save audience members hundreds of dollars in income tax next April, or in which a speaker says, "The information I will give you in the next 10 minutes will help you buy an excellent used car with complete confidence." Job satisfaction, savings, and consumer confidence—the promises of these three attention getters—are directly related to the interests of many audience members. As a college student, imagine how closely you would listen to a speaker who tells you that he can provide you with strategies that will improve your academic performance while studying less and therefore enabling you to spend more time with your friends. Wouldn't that be great?

Provide a Famous Quote   Quotes can be very powerful because we associate them with knowledgeable and influential people and movements. For example, most students in the United States are familiar with Martin Luther King Jr.'s repetition of the phrase, "I have a dream" from his famous speech delivered on August 28, 1963, at the Lincoln Memorial in Washington, D.C. It evokes a desire for justice, peace, and goodwill that will resonate with audience members. Javier channeled these powerful associations by quoting King's famous phrase in his speech to persuade his audience to support Syrian relief agencies in order to achieve a dream of a world in which children are not raised in refugee camps.

Similarly, Allison delivered a persuasive speech in which she encouraged her classmates to dedicate the year after graduation to working for AmeriCorps, an organization that provides intensive service at community and public organizations across the United States. Allison quoted former U.S. president John F. Kennedy to get her audience's attention by stating,

> Ask not what your country can do for you, ask what you can do for your country.

She then continued by saying,

> One way you can help your country, is to commit just one year of your life to serving with AmeriCorps in whatever way interests you the most, whether protecting the environment or helping to educate struggling elementary school students.

By providing famous quotes, you not only get the audience's attention, you also begin to establish your credibility to speak on your topic by demonstrating that you are well informed about your topic and citing your sources. We discuss this further in a subsequent section of this chapter.

Amuse Your Audience   The use of humor can be one of a speaker's most effective attention-getting strategies. Getting the audience to laugh with you makes them alert and relaxed. You can use humor to emphasize key ideas in your speech, to show a favorable self-image, or to defuse audience hostility. However, any humor you use should be tasteful and relevant to your topic or the speaking occasion. As a speaker, you must be able to make a smooth and logical transition between your humorous opening and your speech topic. Telling a joke or a funny story and then switching abruptly to a serious topic trivializes the topic and may confuse or offend your listeners.

Stacey encouraged her classmates to study a foreign language, introducing her classroom speech with the following attention-getting riddle:

> What do you call someone who is fluent in many languages? A polylingual. What do you call someone who is fluent in two languages? A bilingual. What do you call someone who is fluent in only one language? An American!
>
> Behind the apparent humor of this joke are some embarrassing truths about foreign language study in the United States.

Stacey combined humor and rhetorical questions to get her listeners' attention. She then discussed those "embarrassing truths" and the price we pay for speaking only one language.

Energize Your Audience   Sometimes speakers can command attention simply by their presence. Martin Luther King Jr. had that ability. Although few people can achieve such dynamism, most speakers can work to enliven their delivery. A positive attitude, appropriate dress, a confident walk to the platform, direct eye contact, a friendly smile, erect posture, a strong voice, and forceful gestures give an introduction as much impact as any of the preceding strategies. The absence of these elements can destroy the effect of even the best-worded opening statement.

For example, Siobhan was excited to share her love of Irish dancing in an informative speech on the topic. She determined that the best way to share her enthusiasm and engage her audience was to begin her speech with a brief dance to highlight the moves she had been studying since early childhood. She walked confidently to the front of

Tasteful and relevant humor can capture your audience's attention and prepare them to listen to the rest of your speech.

the room, smiled genuinely at her audience, and launched into her performance. When finished, she noted,

> I have been studying Irish dance since I was five years old, and over the past fifteen years have come to appreciate it as a vibrant, complex, and exciting form of art—and exercise, as you can see!

Not only can an "energized" presence get your audience's attention as you begin your speech, it can help keep their attention throughout your speech. In Chapter 13, Learning Objective 13.4, you will learn how your movements and gestures can energize your audience throughout your speech. Think about your favorite teachers. Do they move around and keep you energized in class? You likely enjoy your energetic and dynamic instructors more than those who remain behind the multimedia station. You'll want to have the same energetic effect on your audience.

Acknowledge and Compliment Your Audience   At some point in your life, you will probably be called on to deliver a formal, public speech to an assembled group. Perhaps you will be the keynote speaker for a convention, or maybe you will accept an award from a civic group. Such an occasion usually requires that you begin by acknowledging the audience and key dignitaries. On July 20, 2011, former U.S. secretary of state, Hillary Clinton, addressed the Working Women's Forum in Chennai, India. She began by acknowledging its founder and president, Dr. Jaya Arunachalam. Notice how Clinton praised the organization's mission of improving the "economic, social, and cultural status of poor working women" in India.

> I want to thank my friend and your friend, a wonderful woman who is viewed as a leader around the world, Jaya. [Applause] I want you to know that I have admired the work of the Working Women's Forum for many years. [Applause] In 1978, there were only 800 women members. Today, there are more than one million of you. I am honored to be here with you to celebrate your accomplishments in bringing micro-credit to women, in bringing healthcare and other services to women so that they could have a better life for themselves and their children. [Applause][2]

Secretary Clinton complimented her audience on their accomplishments and used words such as *I*, *my*, *you*, and *your* to demonstrate a shared commitment.

Similarly, when Dr. Melanie Booth-Butterfield was recognized for her lifelong contributions to the communication field at the 2015 annual meeting of the Eastern Communication Association, she began her speech by thanking the audience members for organizing her reception, for being great colleagues, and for being outstanding former students.

Key Points: Strategies for Getting Your Audience's Attention

1. Question your audience.
2. Arouse curiosity.
3. Stimulate imagination.
4. Promise something beneficial.
5. Provide a famous quote.
6. Amuse your audience.
7. Energize your audience.
8. Acknowledge and compliment your audience.

SPEAKING WITH CONFIDENCE

If you fail to attain your audience's attention in the introduction, you won't have it in the rest of your speech. My introduction's success in my speech on Virtual Cyber Charter Schools was important not only for the rest of my speech but also because it would become the audience's first impression of me. I asked the audience members to close their eyes and picture a classroom, not one of rows of desks, but one with a computer and headset that existed in virtual space. By starting off with this place I knew well and wanted to share, I felt confident in my ability to deliver an effective introduction.

When I asked my audience to open their eyes, I could see that their imaginations were stimulated. Their genuine interest allowed me to be confident throughout the entire speech, especially in the parts that were complicated, like explaining the nuances between curriculum choices available to cyber students. By asking my audience to close their eyes for the briefest of moments, my own were opened to a whole new facet of myself: self-assurance.

Amanda Gipson
Penn State Hazleton

A word of caution as this strategy does not tend to work well in classroom settings. Beginning your speech formally by acknowledging and complimenting your fellow students would seem stiff and insincere. You should not have to compliment fellow classmates; in fact, if you have prepared well, they should be thanking you for providing excellent information. For your classroom speeches, therefore, choose one of the other attention-getting strategies we have discussed.

State the Topic or Purpose of Your Speech

Once you have your audience's attention, state the topic or purpose of your speech directly and succinctly. For an informative speech, your statement of purpose typically takes the form of a simple declarative sentence: "Today, I will explain how you can save hundreds of dollars per year by doing your own car maintenance." In a persuasive speech, you will want to let the audience know how you hope your speech topic affects them. For example, "Over the next few minutes, I hope to encourage you to experience the many benefits of abstaining from meat eating one day per week." These statements leave little doubt about what the speaker will discuss.

This second goal of a speech introduction is vitally important, even though the actual statement of purpose will take only a few seconds for you to say. Consider the following beginning section of a speech introduction:

> How many of you have had a cholesterol count taken in the last year? Do you know what your numbers are and what they mean? It seems like we have all recently become much more aware of good cholesterol and bad; high-density lipoproteins and low-density ones; the dangers of high-fat diets and how difficult they can be to avoid in these fast-food, nuke-it-till-it's-hot times. People who never really considered exercising are spending a lot of money to join health clubs and work out. They know that a high cholesterol count can mean you are in danger of developing arteriosclerosis and finding yourself a candidate for surgery. Even if you don't have a heart attack, you may be hospitalized for one of several new procedures to clean out arteries clogged with plaque.

Now answer the following question: What was the speaker's purpose?

a. To discuss the interpretation of cholesterol tests.

b. To explain sources of cholesterol in popular food.

c. To encourage exercise as a key to reducing serum cholesterol.

d. To explain new nonsurgical procedures for opening clogged arteries.

e. I can't tell what the speaker's purpose was.

ETHICAL DECISIONS

REVEALING VERSUS CONCEALING YOUR PURPOSE

Yvonne has decided on a specific purpose for her persuasive speech: to convince her classmates that same-sex couples should have equal access to adopt children. As she analyzes her audience's attitudes, she concludes that some of her classmates disagree with her position, a few quite strongly. She is fearful that if she reveals her specific purpose in the introduction, some audience members will stop listening to her speech objectively and will either begin formulating counterarguments or simply tune her out. She decides that, instead, she will delay the announcement of her purpose and present some basic criteria for a good family.

After securing agreement on these criteria, she will then reveal her purpose for speaking—to an audience that is primed to listen.

Is Yvonne's strategy ethical? Is it acceptable for speakers to conceal their purposes in an introduction in order to keep their audiences' attention? If you think this strategy is legitimate, write an example of a situation in which it would be justifiable. If you don't think this strategy is legitimate, provide an explanation based on the ethical guidelines speakers should follow when making decisions about how to introduce their topics and speech content.

Unfortunately, in this case, the correct answer is e. What went wrong? The speaker started off well enough by using two legitimate questions—the first direct, the second rhetorical—as an attention getter. But then things got out of control; for almost a minute of speaking time, the speaker lapsed into a series of generalizations without ever stating the purpose of the speech. This excerpt represents a minute of wasted time. The speaker confused the audience with vague statements and lost their confidence. The real shame is that any of the four purposes just listed could be the goal of a good speech. Prepare properly and you will know your purpose. Then, state that purpose clearly as the second step of your introduction.

Establish the Relevance of Your Topic

The third goal in organizing the introduction to your speech should be to convince the listeners that the topic is relevant to them. This means that you relate your topic to the audience's interests, needs, and goals.[3] Recall what you learned about Maslow's hierarchy of needs in Chapter 5, Learning Objective 5.3.

In the introduction of his speech about heart disease in women, Jake provided statistics and examples to establish the relevance of his topic for the women and men in his audience:

> "[T]he truth," as stated in the *Pittsburgh Post Gazette* of December 12, 2000, "is that heart disease kills more women every year than all forms of cancer, chronic lung disease, pneumonia, diabetes, accidents, and AIDS combined." Whereas one in twenty-eight women will die of breast cancer, one in five will die of heart disease. And guys, before you take the next nine minutes to decide what you'll eat for lunch, ask yourself one question, "What would my life be like if the women who make it meaningful are not there?" Clearly, this is an issue that concerns us all.[4]

Note that Jake did not have to overtly state that the topic is relevant to the audience (e.g. "This is a relevant topic because. . . ." or "To establish the relevance of my topic. . . ."). Rather, the relevancy is immediately apparent because he chose his topic with care and used examples and language to establish relevancy.

Establish Your Credibility to Speak on Your Topic

The fourth goal of a speech introduction is to establish your credibility to speak on your topic. Getting a solid start on this front—and continuing to affirm your credibility throughout this speech—is particularly valuable as researchers have argued that speaker credibility is perhaps the most important factor influencing the relationship between speakers and their audience members.[5]

Introducing relevant supporting materials and citing sources are two ways to demonstrate that you have carefully researched and considered your topic. In Chapter 16, Learning Objective 16.4, you will learn how to maintain your perceived speaker credibility throughout your speech. For example, in his speech about gum chewers, Austin referenced two sources in his introduction, which indicated that he had conducted research on his speech topic. Not only did this help establish the topic's relevance for his listeners, it also established his credibility to speak on his topic. Austin stated, "In a survey consisting of American undergraduate students, 'nearly 87 percent confirmed that they chew gum at least occasionally.'" He added, "Chewing gum has grown into being one of the world's oldest candies [and] has even become a billion-dollar industry."

You can also enhance your credibility by drawing on your experience with your topic. When our friend Todd teaches skiing and snowboard lessons during the winter months, he always tells his students about his personal experiences as a skiing and snowboard professional. He also notes that he reads various skiing and snowboarding magazines, and that he continues to watch instructional videos to perfect his teaching skills. Therefore, Todd's students are likely to believe that Todd is a competent instructor, which bolsters his credibility.

As when you establish the relevance of your topic, do not state, "I am credible to speak on this topic because. . . ." Rather, by citing sources, referencing your research, and mentioning your personal experiences with your topic, it will become clear that you are credible.

Preview Your Key Ideas

A final objective in organizing your introduction is the **preview**, in which you "tell us what you're going to tell us." The preview, working like a map, shows a final destination and reveals how the speaker intends to get there. As a result, the audience can travel more easily through the body of the speech. A speaker addressing the issue of urban decay could preview her speech by saying, "To better understand the scope of this problem, we must look at four measurable conditions: the unemployment rate, housing starts, the poverty level, and the crime rate." That preview lists the four key ideas to be covered in the body of the speech and prepares the audience to listen more intently.

preview
A statement that orients the audience by revealing the speaker's key ideas.

Preview statements are usually only one sentence, but they can also be two or three sentences. Rarely do they need to be longer. Both of the following examples are appropriately brief and specific.

- Ashkan previewed his key ideas by stating, "The most important aspects of the Turkish culture that I will share with you today are its historical background, family structure, and foods."
- Austin previewed his key ideas by stating, "Today, I will inform you first on the positive effects of chewing gum, and second, I will inform you on the negative effects of gum-chewing."

Preview statements, however, are often bland and predictable. Use engaging language to accent the ideas that will follow. For example, in an informative speech about caring for a newly adopted cat, Amira could preview her key ideas by saying, "Today I will discuss food, toys, and companionship for your new cat." Although this statement adequately previews the three key ideas, it lacks energy. Instead, Amira chose to give a lively preview:

> Throughout my speech, I will inform you about cat food that is biologically appropriate for felines, toys that can stimulate and engage your new cat in order to avoid destructive boredom and ensure appropriate exercise, and the love and companionship that all cats need to be well-adjusted and healthy.

If you achieve the five objectives we have outlined for a speech introduction, your audience should be attentive, know the purpose of your speech, be motivated to listen, trust your qualifications to speak on the topic, and know the key ideas you will discuss. To see how one student achieved these goals, read "Theory into Practice: Annotated Sample Introduction."

Key Points: Functions of a Speech Introduction

1. Get the attention of your audience.
2. State the topic or purpose of your speech.
3. Establish the relevance of your topic.
4. Establish your credibility to speak on your topic.
5. Preview the key ideas of your speech.

Theory into Practice (TIP)

ANNOTATED SAMPLE INTRODUCTION

Tess Drager of South Central College in Minnesota was a semifinalist at the 2013 Interstate Oratorical Association contest. Notice how she developed a complete and effective introduction using the five steps we've discussed.[6]

Minnesota native and loving mother of five, Marilyn Joyce Moulds died at the age of 76. Marilyn dealt with severe uncontrollable diarrhea, dehydration, debilitating abdominal cramping, and an inability to keep foods or liquids down. Doctors removed parts of her colon to help stem the infection, but she only lived a few months after her routine abdominal surgery.

> Tess used description and visualization to arouse her listeners' curiosity.

Marilyn died due to a dangerous *Clostridium difficile* infection. *Clostridium difficile*, also known as C-Diff. It is a deadly bacterium that infects the human colon, causing a person to become extremely ill.

> Tess introduced her topic and defines C-Diff infection.

But death from this deadly disease is not uncommon. In fact, according to the *Federal Agency for Health Care Research and Quality* more than 9 percent of C-Diff-related hospitalizations end in death—nearly five times the rate for other hospital stays. This equates to 30,000 deaths a year. When you consider automobile accidents take 32,000 lives a year, one can see how serious this condition is. This deadly bacterium is running rampant and is not just costing human lives, but also costing us over $1 billion in extra in health care costs each year according to the Centers for Disease Control.

> Tess used statistics to establish the relevance of her topic and to establish her credibility to speak on her topic.

I work in a nursing home and I am exposed to C-Diff on a daily basis. This is a very serious bacterium, which very few of us know anything about. This bacterium causes serious problems and we cannot ignore it any longer.

> Tess continued to establish her credibility by mentioning her work experience.

Today we are going to look at this resilient bacterium by first exploring some of the harms associated with C-Diff. Second, I will elaborate on the causes of this spread before finally providing some simple suggestions on how to slow down C-Diff so people like Marilyn won't have to die anymore.

> Tess previewed the key ideas she developed in the body of her speech.

Concluding Your Speech

10.2 Construct a conclusion that achieves the four objectives of effective speech conclusions.

The final part of your speech is the conclusion. Although the conclusion is often shorter than the introduction, your conclusion is very important to achieving the purpose of your speech. The conclusion is the last section your listeners hear and see, meaning that audience members often remember it. Therefore, your conclusion must be well planned, carefully organized, and well delivered. It will be easier to develop and deliver your conclusion if you work to achieve four goals: (1) restate the topic or purpose of your speech, (2) restate your key ideas, (3) activate audience response, and (4) provide closure.

Restate the Topic or Purpose of Your Speech

Remember that the second objective of your introduction is to state the topic or purpose of your speech to give the audience members a general idea of what you will discuss. In the conclusion, you restate the topic or purpose of your speech by simply reminding the audience members about your overall speech topic or purpose. Consider the example of Keira, who began her conclusion by stating, "I hope you come away from this speech with a better sense of the many benefits of decluttering and owning fewer things" before she reminded her audience of the specific benefits (key ideas) she discussed.

Revolutionary and former South African president Nelson Mandela gave many speeches on the evils of apartheid. Arguably one of his most famous speeches is "I Am Prepared to Die," titled for his powerful concluding remarks about his willingness to give up his life to achieve a just and harmonious society.

Restate Your Key Ideas

When you restate your key ideas, you "tell us what you told us." Of all the steps in the process of organization, this should be the easiest to construct. You have already organized the body of the speech and, from it, constructed a preview statement. Restatement parallels your preview. If your speech develops three key ideas, you reiterate them. If your speech is on self-concept enhancement, for example, you may simply say, "A good self-concept, therefore, benefits us in three ways. It enhances our social interaction, our academic achievement, and our career success." A speech on the five stages of grief might reiterate them: "Denial. Anger. Bargaining. Depression. Acceptance. These are the five stages of grief described by Kübler-Ross."

Restating your key ideas is more than simply repeating key words. The objective is to show how those ideas support the goal of your speech. At the beginning of his speech, Ashkan said he was going to talk about three aspects of the Turkish culture when he previewed his key ideas. In his conclusion he restated those ideas and connected them to his topic by stating,

> Today I talked about Turkey's historical background, family structure, and foods. Hopefully what you have learned today has given you a better understanding of the basic components of the Turkish culture.

By adding one more sentence after reiterating his key ideas, he effectively connected the key points to the overall purpose of his speech, which was to provide a general understanding of the Turkish culture.

Activate Audience Response

What do you want your audience to do with the information you have provided or the arguments you have proved? The third function of a speech conclusion is to activate an audience response by letting your listeners know whether you want them to accept, remember, use, believe, or act on the content of your speech. Whether your speech is informative or persuasive, you want your audience to be involved with your information and ideas. The conclusion is your last opportunity to ensure this. If you have provided practical information that can make your listeners smarter, healthier, happier, or wealthier, challenge them to remember and use what they learned. If you have educated them about a problem and proposed a solution to it, remind them of the significance of not acting. If you have spoken on a topic that you find inherently interesting, hoping to generate audience interest by communicating your enthusiasm as well as your information, this is your last opportunity to invigorate or animate your listeners about the subject.

Rather than saying, "I hope you'll find what I've said about the film scores of Philip Glass useful," you might say something like this:

> The next time you find your attention drawn to a movie's sound track because you like the music or feel that it could stand on its own, think about the pains-taking process of matching sight and sound that an acclaimed composer like Philip Glass has to go through.

This function of the conclusion is generally easier to fulfill in a persuasive speech than in an informative speech. In persuasive speeches, your goal is to influence your listeners' attitudes, beliefs, values, or behaviors. So, when you activate audience response in a persuasive speech, you should emphasize how you want your audience to think, feel, or act. In her speech on motorists who run red lights, Kimberly used vivid examples, expert testimony, and compelling statistics to document the scope of the problem, and then called for individuals, communities, and the government to respond. After reiterating the key ideas in her speech's conclusion, Kimberly sought to activate personal responsibility in her listeners:

> On your way home tonight, when you approach that traffic light, think of the facts we have talked about today. These facts apply to you every time you approach a traffic signal. Don't run red lights! When we take an extra minute or two to stop for the light, we are helping to protect hundreds of innocent people. The life you save could be your neighbor's, your mother's, or your own.[7]

In an informative speech, however, you act like a teacher in that you provide information. It is then up to the audience to decide what to do with that information. Therefore, you should not tell your audience how to think, feel, or act when you activate audience response in your informative speeches. Instead, you have to approach this function objectively. Camilla gave an informative speech about festivals in Germany. Rather than encouraging her audience members to visit Germany during Oktoberfest, which would be persuasive, she said:

> The information I have shared with you today about three of Germany's exciting festivals may be useful to you in the future. *If* you are ever considering a trip to Germany, you *may* want to review this information, as it will help you save time and plan your vacation.

Provide Closure

When you restate your key ideas, you conclude your speech *logically*, but when you activate audience response and provide closure, you end the speech *psychologically*. An effective final statement ties the speech together and provides a strong note of closure. You should not have to tell your listeners that the speech is finished. Your wording, as well as your delivery, should make this clear by slowing your rate, maintaining direct eye contact with your listeners, and pausing briefly before and after your final sentence. Think of the closure statement of a speech like the end of a phone call. Can you tell when the conversation is about to end because of what your friend says and how it's said? Chances are you just *know* when the conversation is going to end. Your goal is to give your audience that same sense of closure.

circular conclusion

A closure statement that repeats or refers to material used in the attention-getting step of the introduction.

Sometimes a speaker employs what is called a **circular conclusion**, in which the final statement echoes or refers to the attention-getting step of the introduction. At the beginning of Ashkan's speech about Turkish culture, he aroused curiosity to get his audience members' attention by providing facts about Turkey without disclosing his topic. At the end of his speech, he brought his listeners back to the opening statements of his introduction by reminding them of the facts he provided:

> So if anybody ever asks you, "Hey, what country was known for being the Ottoman Empire?" or "Hey, what country is known for having rich influences?" you will know that it is, indeed, the country of Turkey.

Your final statement does not have to allude to your attention-getting step. Any of the specific techniques we discussed for gaining audience attention can help bring your speech to a psychologically satisfying conclusion. You can ask a question, even the same one you began with or a variation of it. Or you can answer the question you initially asked. Once you arouse your audience's curiosity in your speech, you must satisfy it in order to provide closure. You could stimulate their imaginations through vivid imagery or promise them that the information you have provided can benefit them. You might conclude with a joke or humorous story relevant to your topic. Through lively delivery, you could energize the audience to act on the information you have provided. In a speech presented on more formal occasions than a classroom assignment, you may end by complimenting and thanking the audience.

All four functions of the conclusion are important. Restating your topic or speech purpose as well as your key ideas reinforces the *point* and *ideas* of your speech. Activating an audience response and providing closure reinforce the *impact* of your speech. To see how one student achieved these goals, read "Theory into Practice: A Sample Speech Conclusion."

Journal: Writing the Closure Statement

Rewrite the closure statement of Jennell Chu's speech on flash mobs in Appendix E using a strategy other than the one Chu uses. Which closure strategy—hers or yours—do you prefer? Why?

Key Points: Functions of a Speech Conclusion

1. Restate the topic or purpose of your speech.
2. Restate your key ideas.
3. Activate audience response.
4. Provide closure.

Theory into Practice (TIP)

A SAMPLE SPEECH CONCLUSION

In the introduction of his speech on breaking the silence about ovarian cancer, Viqar presented a startling statistic: "According to the National Cancer Coalition, every 9 minutes in the United States a woman is diagnosed with ovarian cancer."[8] Notice how Viqar used this statistic to frame his four-step conclusion.

> In the last 9 minutes we've explored ovarian cancer and the deadly problems associated with the disease, and analyzed a solution to break the silence.
> In the last 9 minutes, a woman has been diagnosed with ovarian cancer. Women like the mother of Rene Rossi, who in the last 9 months of her life told her daughter, "You must do something about this disease." In the last 9 minutes, you have been given the power to do just that. Do it for the women in our lives—our mothers, our daughters, our loved ones.
> Shout out this silent killer.[9]

Viqar restated his speech topic and key ideas.

Using a statistic and an example, Viqar activated audience response.

Viqar provided closure with a direct, five-word sentence.

The Outward Method of Speech Development

10.3 Apply the Outward Method of Speech Development to your speech.

In earlier chapters you learned how to organize and develop the body of a speech. In this chapter you have learned the five functions of a speech introduction and the four functions of a speech conclusion. Take a moment to review the individual steps in a well-organized speech.

1. Attention-getting step
2. Statement of speech topic or purpose
3. Emphasis on topic's relevance
4. Emphasis on speaker's credibility
5. Preview of key ideas
6. Body of speech (discussed in Chapter 8)
7. Restatement of speech topic or purpose

8. Restatement of key ideas

9. Activation of audience's response

10. Provide closure

This is the correct sequence to follow as you *deliver* a speech. It is not, however, how you should *develop* your speech. There are several approaches to developing a speech; your instructor may offer her or his own.

One approach is to prepare the body of the speech first, the introduction second, and the conclusion last. Some instructors suggest developing the body first, the conclusion second, and the introduction third.

We suggest a sequence we have named the Outward Method of Speech Development (Figure 10.1). In Stage 1 you construct the body of your speech, determining your key ideas and developing them using the 4 S's approach that you learned in Chapter 8, Learning Objective 8.3. After completing this stage, you then work outward.

In the remaining stages, work on the introduction and conclusion simultaneously, focusing on elements that have similar purposes. In Stage 2 you work on stating your speech topic or purpose and restating your speech topic or purpose. In this step, you also word your preview and your restatement of key ideas. These steps are similar because they highlight the speech's topic or purpose as well as the key ideas. As you complete Stage 2, you have fulfilled the overall strategy of a well-organized speech: You are ready to "tell us what you're going to tell us," "tell us," and "tell us what you told us."

In Stage 3 you work on the remaining elements of the introduction and conclusion. You decide how you will establish the relevance of your topic, how to establish your credibility, and how to activate audience response. If you prefer circular conclusions as discussed earlier in this chapter, you may develop the attention getter and closure statement at the same time to enhance the unity of your speech.

Journal: Developing Your Speech

What is your preferred method of developing your speech? In which order do you prefer to proceed? Why?

Figure 10.1   The Outward Method of Speech Development

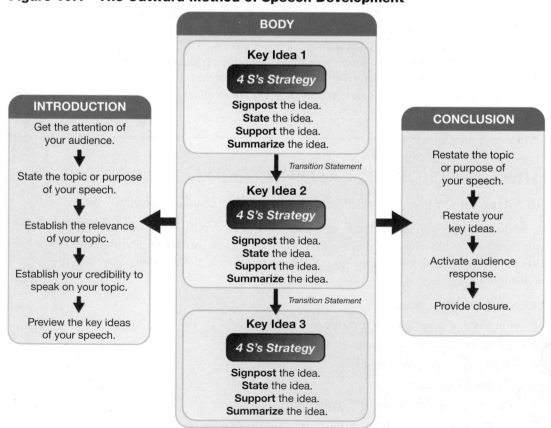

› SUMMARY

Introducing and Concluding Your Speech

Introducing Your Speech

10.1 Construct an introduction that achieves the five objectives of effective speech introductions.

- The introduction should achieve five goals: (1) get the attention of your audience; (2) state your topic or purpose; (3) establish the relevance of your topic; (4) establish your credibility to speak on your topic; and (5) preview the key ideas you will develop in the body of the speech.

- To get your audience's attention, you can question your listeners, arouse their curiosity, stimulate their imaginations, promise them something beneficial, provide a famous quote, amuse them, energize them, or acknowledge and compliment them (though this final strategy is not typically necessary in college courses).

Concluding Your Speech

10.2 Construct a conclusion that achieves the four objectives of effective speech conclusions.

In an effective conclusion, you as the speaker do the following: (1) restate the topic or purpose of your speech; (2) restate your key ideas; (3) activate audience response; and (4) provide closure.

The Outward Method of Speech Development

10.3 Apply the Outward Method of Speech Development to your speech.

- The sequence of events in delivering a speech often differs from the sequence of developing a speech.

- The Outward Method of Speech Development encourages speakers to begin by developing the body of the speech and then working outward.

OUTLINING YOUR SPEECH

→ **LEARNING OBJECTIVES**

After studying this chapter, you should be able to

11.1 Apply the five functions of outlining a speech.

11.2 Apply the five principles of outlining a speech.

11.3 Construct working, formal, and speaking outlines.

When a friend of ours attended high school in North Carolina, he was required to learn all of the 100 counties in the state. This was a challenging task because he had not even heard of most of the counties before. First, he tried to memorize the counties in alphabetical order, but that proved very challenging.

Second, he attempted to learn all 100 counties based on their geographical location, but again he was unsuccessful. Finally, after studying for several days, our friend realized that if he constructed a sentence with 100 letters in which each letter was the first letter in a county name, it was much easier to remember all 100 counties. In other words, he merely reorganized the counties until they formed a pattern that was easy for him to remember and repeat. When you outline your speech, you perform essentially the same task. You organize and reorganize the material into a pattern that is easy for you to recognize and remember.

Previously, we discussed the importance of organization to the delivered speech and suggested some ways of achieving a well-organized presentation. Outlining your speech is the preliminary written work necessary to foster clear organization of your oral message. In this chapter, you will learn why outlines are important to your speech, examine some different types of outlines, and learn how to write an excellent outline.

Functions of Outlining

11.1 Apply the five functions of outlining a speech.

A well-prepared outline serves five important functions for a speaker, which is why outlining is time well spent:

1. It tests the scope of the speaker's content.
2. It tests the logical relations among the parts of the speech.
3. It tests the relevance of supporting ideas.
4. It checks the balance or proportion of the speech.
5. It serves as speaking notes during the delivery of the speech.

Let's examine each of these functions in turn.

Tests the Scope of the Content

The first purpose of outlining is to test the **scope** of the speaker's content. Have you narrowed the topic sufficiently to cover your key ideas in some depth? Or are you trying to cover too much material and consequently skimming the surface of the subject, repeating things your audience already knows? Outlining allows you to organize your key ideas and then add, delete, regroup, shuffle, condense, or expand these ideas so you approach your topic in a manageable way. Thus, outlining is a process of setting goals for the speech.

scope
The breadth of an area or subject matter.

Tests the Logical Relations among the Parts

Second, outlining allows speakers to test the logical relations among the various parts of the speech. Does one idea in the outline lead to the next in a meaningful way? Do the arguments or subtopics under each of your key ideas really develop that point? To answer these questions, you must understand the concepts of coordination and subordination. **Coordinate ideas** are those of equal value or importance in the overall pattern of the speech. **Subordinate ideas** are those that support more general or more important points in a speech. The following example illustrates the relationship between coordinate and subordinate ideas.

coordinate ideas
Ideas that have equal value in a speech.

subordinate ideas
Ideas that support more general or more important points in a speech.

Imagine that you are tutoring a fellow student and are trying to explain the components of a "good speech." You will likely organize your thoughts topically and focus on these three aspects of a "good speech."

I. Content
II. Organization
III. Delivery

These three key ideas are coordinate because they seem to be of equal value. You might have more information on one of them than the other two, and thus spend more time in the speech discussing that key idea. However, neither is a subtopic of any of the other two key ideas. Under the first key idea, you would then list subordinate ideas, or subpoints, that support that particular key idea. You would then repeat the same process for your second and third key ideas.

I. Content
    A. Sources
    B. Supporting materials
    C. Oral footnotes

Notice that subpoints A, B, and C are not only subordinate to the key idea—content—but also coordinate with one another because they seem to be equally important. Subordinate points for the second key idea could include the following:

II. Organization
    A. Organizing the introduction
    B. Organizing the body
    C. Organizing the conclusion

Again, note that points A, B, and C are subordinate to the key idea—organization—and they coordinate with each other because they appear to be equally important aspects of organization. For your last key idea, you may select the following subordinate points:

III. Delivery
    A. Delivery methods
    B. Vocal delivery
    C. Physical delivery

As with the previous two key ideas, points A, B, and C are subordinate to your last key idea—delivery—and they also coordinate with each other because they seem to be equally important.

Your outline is not yet complete, but you can begin to ask yourself the following questions: Are my key ideas different enough to qualify as separate key ideas? Do my subordinate points really support the key ideas? At this stage, the answers to both of these questions seem to be yes. The visual form of the outline helps you test the logical connections among the parts of your speech. You continue this process to further refine and add to the outline.

Tests the Relevance of Supporting Ideas

Third, an outline helps the speaker test the relevance of supporting ideas. To understand how this works, assume that you have written the following portion of an outline for a speech on roller coasters:

I. Famous roller coasters
    A. Coney Island's "Cyclone"
    B. Montreal's "Le Monstre"
    C. Busch Gardens's "Kumba"
    D. New design technology

Notice that the fourth subpoint, "new design technology," is out of place because it is irrelevant to the key idea. "New design technology" is not an example of a famous roller coaster.

Checks the Balance of the Speech

A fourth function of outlining is to check the balance or proportion of the speech. Consider the previous outline about roller coasters. Once you remove "new design technology" from the key idea "famous roller coasters" (because it doesn't fit logically), you have two options. One option is to make "new design technology" a separate key idea.

Like any good structure, a speech's points must be balanced to hold it all together.

I. Famous roller coasters
   A. Coney Island's "Cyclone"
   B. Montreal's "Le Monstre"
   C. Busch Gardens's "Kumba"
II. New design technology

Notice, however, that the first key idea has three supporting subpoints, but the second key idea does not have any. This suggests that the outline is not balanced.

How can you fix such an imbalance? First, you could do additional research to determine if there are two or three supporting subpoints you could use to support "new design technology." However, if there aren't, you'd likely want to eliminate this topic from your speech. You might then focus the entire speech on famous roller coasters and bump up your subpoints on the individual roller coasters to key ideas, like this:

I. Coney Island's "Cyclone"
II. Montreal's "Le Monstre"
III. Busch Gardens's "Kumba"

As you can see, by testing the balance of your speech, an outline can lead you to alter the scope and specific purpose of your speech.

Serves as the Delivery Notes

Fifth and finally, a special type of abbreviated outline can serve as notes for the speaker during the speech's delivery. The *speaking outline*, discussed later in this chapter, has only one rule: It must be brief. If you have prepared adequately for your speech, you should need only key words and phrases to remind you of each point you want to discuss. Moreover, having your notes in outline form rather than arranged randomly on notecards or sheets of paper will remind you of the importance of clear organization as you deliver your speech.

Principles of Outlining

11.2 Apply the five principles of outlining a speech.

Correct outlines take two possible forms: the **complete sentence outline** and the **key word or phrase outline**. In a complete sentence outline, each item is a sentence; each item in a key word or phrase outline is a word or group of words. These two forms of outlines should be kept consistent and distinct. Combine them only in the speaking outline from which you deliver your speech. So far in this chapter, we have used only phrase outlines. More word or phrase outlines and an example of a complete sentence outline follow.

As you construct your outline, you will work more efficiently and produce a clearer outline if you follow a few rules, or principles.

Singularity

First, each number or letter in the outline should represent only one key idea or subpoint. A chief goal of outlining is to achieve a clear visual representation of the connections among parts of the speech. This is possible only if you separate the key ideas from other key ideas and separate the subpoints from other subpoints. For example, suppose a speaker preparing a speech on color blindness has worded a key idea as "causes of and tests for color blindness." The phrase contains two distinct ideas, each requiring separate discussion and development. Instead, the speaker should divide the statement into two coordinate key ideas: "causes of color blindness" and "tests for color blindness."

Key Points: The Functions of Outlining

1. Tests the scope of the content
2. Tests the logical relations among the parts
3. Tests the relevance of supporting ideas
4. Checks the balance of the speech
5. Serves as the delivery notes

Journal: Key Ideas and Subordinate Points

Consider a topic that you would like to hear one of your classmates talk about. (It can be a simple topic, like "How to Grocery Shop.") Next, identify two or three potential key ideas. Lastly, offer some potential subpoints for each of your key ideas. Does your outline appear balanced? Do the subpoints support the key ideas? Are the subpoints coordinated ideas? If not, how would you revise your outline?

---

complete sentence outline
An outline in which all numbers and letters introduce complete sentences.

key word or phrase outline
An outline in which all numbers and letters introduce words or groups of words.

Consistency

Second, coordinate and subordinate points in the outline should be represented by a consistent system of numbers and letters. Key ideas are typically represented by Roman numerals: I, II, III, and so forth. Label subpoints under the key ideas with indented capital letters: A, B, C, and so forth. Beneath those, identify your supporting points with indented Arabic numerals: 1, 2, 3, and so on. Identify ideas subordinate to those with indented lowercase letters: a, b, c, and so on. Using this notation system, the labeling and indentation of a typical outline of the body of the speech would appear as follows:

I. Key idea
  A. Subpoint
    1. Sub-subpoint
    2. Sub-subpoint
    3. Sub-subpoint
  B. Subpoint
    1. Sub-subpoint
    2. Sub-subpoint
      a. Sub-sub-subpoint
      b. Sub-sub-subpoint

II. Key idea
  A. Subpoint
  B. Subpoint
    1. Sub-subpoint
    2. Sub-subpoint
  C. Subpoint

Adequacy

A third principle is that if any key idea has subpoints under it, there must be at least two. A basic law of physics is that you cannot divide something into only one part. If you have an A, you must also have a B. (You may, of course, also have subpoints C, D, and E.) If you have a 1, you must also have at least a 2. In other words, the following outline is unacceptable because the first key idea has only one subpoint.

I. Key idea
  A. Subpoint

II. Key idea
  A. Subpoint
  B. Subpoint

Uniformity

Fourth, each symbol (I, A, 1, etc.) in a sentence outline should introduce a complete sentence. Each symbol in a word or phrase outline should introduce a word or phrase. Keep the form of the outline consistent. Sentences and phrases should be mixed only in your speaking outline.

Parallelism

Finally, coordinate points throughout the outline should have parallel grammatical construction. For example, a key phrase outline of a speech on how to write a résumé begins with a first key idea labeled "Things to include." The second point should be "Things to omit," rather than "Leaving out unnecessary information." The first point

ETHICAL DECISIONS

FAIR AND BALANCED?

Chloe serves as president for her campus's student government association (SGA). She and the other SGA members have drafted a proposal titled, "The Clean Air Act," in which they recommend that smoking should be banned on the main campus walkway and within 15 feet of any building entrance. As the SGA president, Chloe is responsible for giving an informative presentation about "The Clean Air Act" to her campus community and to the faculty senate.

As she outlines her speech using a pro–con pattern, Chloe identifies three benefits of "The Clean Air Act": less secondhand smoke inhalation, less doorway congestion, and less smoke inside the buildings. However, the only con (drawback) of "The Clean Air Act" that she can think of is some limited costs of printing "No Smoking" signs. Chloe really wants her peers and the faculty members to make an educated decision regarding "The Clean Air Act." She also has asthma, so she feels a little biased as she outlines her speech.

Which outlining principles can help Chloe develop her organization and supporting materials? List and explain ethical guidelines that speakers should follow to ensure a fair and balanced discussion of issues.

is worded as a noun phrase; therefore, you should follow it with another noun phrase ("Things to omit") rather than a predicate phrase ("Leaving out unnecessary information"). This does not mean that you must choose noun phrases over verb phrases, but that all points must match grammatically. In this next example, all coordinate points have parallel grammatical construction.

> **Key Points: Principles of Outlining**
>
> 1. Singularity
> 2. Consistency
> 3. Adequacy
> 4. Uniformity
> 5. Parallelism

I. Including essential information
   A. Address
   B. Career objective
   C. Educational background
   D. Employment history
   E. References

II. Omitting unnecessary information
   A. Marital status
   B. Religious denomination
   C. Political affiliation
   D. Ethnicity
   E. Nationality

As you can see, coordinate key ideas I and II are verb phrases, while the coordinate subpoints are all nouns or noun phrases.

Stages of Outlining

11.3 Construct working, formal, and speaking outlines.

If you have difficulty generating or discovering the key ideas for a speech topic you have chosen, don't worry; you are not alone. Many people are intimidated by the prospect of selecting and organizing ideas, particularly for a first speech. Keep the following in mind when organizing and outlining your speech.

First, there is no one right way of organizing all speeches on a particular topic. True, some topics logically lend themselves to certain patterns of organization (see Chapter 8, Learning Objective 8.2). Speeches about processes often organize themselves chronologically. Speeches about people may be arranged chronologically or topically. Persuasive speeches on social issues are perhaps most logically organized according to a problem–solution format. Yet different speakers may use different structures. You must determine what works best for you, your topic, and your audience.

Second, the early stages of organizing and outlining a speech are filled with uncertainty. You may find yourself asking these questions:

- Do I have enough key ideas, too many, or too few?
- Can I find adequate information to support my key ideas?
- Am I overlooking other key ideas the audience would be interested in hearing me discuss?

Rather than feeling pressured by such questions, look on the early stages of outlining as a period of flexibility. The early, informal versions of your working outline are all provisional—temporary and open to change. Don't be afraid to experiment a little, particularly as you begin your working outline. You can then use what you develop and learn to progress through the creation of the formal outline and, finally, the speaking outline you'll use when you deliver your speech.

Working Outline

working outline

An informal, initial outline recording a speaker's process of narrowing, focusing, and balancing a topic.

The first step in preparing an outline is to construct a **working outline**, an informal, initial outline recording your process of narrowing, focusing, and balancing your speech topic.

The beginning stages of this outline may result from research you have already done or some productive brainstorming. Once you have spent significant time researching the subject, you will notice topics that are repeated in different sources on the subject. If, for example, you are a psychology major you may select "depression" as your topic for an informative speech. After researching your topic, you may decide to talk about causes, symptoms, and treatments of depression. Notice that these same topics could be applied to any medical condition.

Brainstorming can also help you generate topics and explore areas of your final topic.[1] Your creative brainstorming might even reveal interesting areas of your topic that have not been adequately treated in the existing research. (See Chapter 6, Learning Objective 6.1 for a discussion about brainstorming.) This discovery provides you an opportunity to conduct original research or experimentation.

As you can see, at this stage, the term *outline* is very loose; the list of key ideas you are developing does not have any numbers or letters attached to it. That's fine, because these notes are for your benefit alone. This working outline is merely a record of the process you go through in thinking about a speech topic.

To illustrate these first steps in preparing an outline, consider one student's experience as he developed his speech about chewing gum. Our student Austin never enjoyed chewing gum, but noticed that many fellow students and friends did enjoy it. Therefore, he became interested in why people chew gum and how it affects them. He spoke with his fellow students and friends to get a general idea of why and how frequently they chew gum. Next, he conducted some preliminary research on gum chewing and reflected on the few times he had chewed gum himself.

At this point, Austin knew that he wanted to give an informative speech about chewing gum. He also knew from his preliminary research that he would have no trouble finding enough information about his topic. Just by brainstorming topics that might apply to any person chewing gum, Austin developed the following working outline:

I. Reasons people chew gum
II. Effects of chewing gum
III. Culture of gum chewers

As Austin researched his topic further, he found some interesting information about the history of chewing gum. He also learned about potential benefits and drawbacks of chewing gum. He found several articles comparing sugar-free gum and regular gum with sugar, and added these topics to his working outline. Then, he added subtopics as he thought of them or encountered them in his research.

After completing his research, Austin realized that his information was too broad and several topics seemed to overlap. He also had a great deal of interesting information about the history of chewing gum. However, he could not include all this information within the time limit for his speech. As a result, he decided to develop three key ideas: history of chewing gum, pros of chewing gum, and cons of chewing gum. But when reviewing his key ideas, he concluded that the first key idea (history of chewing gum) did not seem to match well with the second (pros of chewing gum) and third (cons of chewing gum) key ideas. Therefore, he narrowed down his organizing question to: What does research tell us about the pros and cons of chewing gum? Austin's working outline of the body of his speech was revised as follows:

I. Pros of chewing gum
II. Cons of chewing gum

So was all the time spent learning the history of chewing gum, the reasons people chew gum, the effects of chewing gum, and the culture of gum chewers wasted? Not at all. Austin learned a great deal about his topic—something that lends credibility and confidence when speaking—and had the option to use this information to add details, vividness, and interest to his topic with relevant examples. Next, he developed the pros and cons of chewing gum that he would include in his formal outline and speaking notes.

Formal Outline

Your **formal outline** is a complete sentence outline reflecting the full content and organization of your speech. In its final form, it is the finished product of your research and planning for your speech. A stranger picking up your formal outline should be able to understand how you have organized and supported all your key ideas. If you keep that goal in mind, you should have no trouble deciding what to include and what to exclude.

If you are required to turn in an outline when you speak, find out if it should be a formal outline or if it can use key words or phrases. The actual outline should follow the accepted pattern of symbols and indentations that we showed you earlier in this chapter. Some instructors also ask students to label the superstructure of the speech—introduction, body, and conclusion—by inserting those words at the appropriate places in the outline but without any symbols attached to them.

Austin Willis developed and delivered his informative speech on the pros and cons of chewing gum. Although Austin was not required to complete a formal outline, below is an example of what the complete sentence outline of the body of his speech might look like. A full transcript of Austin's speech can be found in Appendix E.

Speech title: Gum Chewers
Specific purpose: To inform my classmates about the pros and cons of chewing gum
Central idea: Chewing gum is believed to have both positive and negative effects on people's ability to focus, their stress, and their memory.

Body of the Speech

I. First, let's uncover the positive effects of chewing gum. Specifically, we will focus on the ideas that chewing gum can help enhance persons' ability to focus, maintain their stress, and even enhance their memory.
   A. First, we'll consider the notion that chewing gum helps us focus.
      1. Chewing gum "had a significant and positive effect on concentration performance" according to Tanzer and colleagues (2009).
      2. Chewing gum has a positive effect on healthy adults' abilities in maintaining focus during extended periods of time, according to Tucha and Simpson (2011).
   B. Second, let's review how chewing gum may help us manage our stress.
      1. "Fifty-six percent of frequent gum chewers and 42 percent of infrequent [gum] chewers stated that managing their stress is a reason why they chew gum" according to Zibell and Madansky.
      2. Studies revealed that abstaining from chewing gum resulted in higher levels of anxiety and stress among all participants.

Journal: Constructing a Working Outline

Suppose you are working on a speech on the topic of "Latin music" and you have come up with the following list of all the things you wish to cover. Which *four* of these entries would be the best choices for you to use as your key ideas, for you to be able to use all of the entries in your speech outline?

Mariachi	Romeo Santos
Small folk band	Countries
Cuba	*Merengue*
Styles	Shakira
Marc Anthony	*Salsa*
Artists	*Mariachi* band
Puerto Rico	Mexico
Rumba	Prince Royce
Latin big band	Elvis Crespo
Instrumentation	Brazil
Spain	*Mambo*

formal outline

A complete sentence outline written in sufficient detail so that a person other than the speaker could understand it.

Note Austin's use of Roman numerals to denote his two key ideas; capital letters A, B, and C to denote his subpoints; followed by numbers 1 and 2 to denote his sub-subpoints. If you simply glance at Austin's formal outline (complete sentence outline), you will not only know what his speech is about, but you will also see that his speech is balanced and crafted using parallel language and sentence structure.

Austin also did a great job using internal signposts (first, second, and third) within his first key idea to help his audience members follow his discussion about the three different subpoints (pros of chewing gum). Under each subpoint, there are two statements describing the content of that specific subpoint. Therefore, his speech was also nicely balanced.

C. Third, chewing gum may enhance our memory.
1. "An increase of learning performance of at least 30 percent was claimed following chewing gum" as stated in an August 2012 article, "Gum Chewing and Cognition: An Overview" by Tucha and Koerts.
2. Researchers Wilkinson and colleagues published a study revealing significant improvements in both immediate and delayed memory.

II. Second, let's discuss the negative implications of chewing gum.
A. First, let's go over the questionable belief that chewing gum has the ability to enhance our ability to focus.
1. According to a *Journal of Behavioral and Neuroscience Research* article titled "A Review of the Evidence that Chewing Gum Affects Stress, Alertness and Cognition," two experiments found "alertness reaction time was significantly slower for a spearmint gum control group compared to not chewing [gum]" at all, indicating that chewing gum slows down and inhibits a person's full potential to focus.
2. Researcher Smith in 2010 challenged this claim by concluding that chewing gum led to a prolonged attention rate by using a choice reaction time task, but studies did not confirm this point.
B. Second, I will discuss the inconsistent relationships found between chewing gum and stress.
1. Torney, Johnson, and Miles (2009) were unable to find a benefit of chewing gum related to self-reported stress.
2. An experimental study showed that chewing gum has no effect on the different levels of acute stress.
C. Third, does chewing gum really enhance our memory?
1. Researchers Johnson and Miles (2008) concluded: "Although flavorless gum and mint-flavored strips reported change in current mouth activity . . . [t]hey didn't [show signs] that induce context-dependent memory."
2. Further research showed that chewing gum during a learning period actually may cause *poorer* recall.

In his second key idea, Austin followed the same internal organizational structure by including three subpoints, which all had two supporting sub-subpoints, leading to a balanced outline and speech.

Speaking Outline

speaking outline

A brief outline for the speaker's use alone, containing source citations and delivery prompts.

The **speaking outline**, the one you actually use to deliver your speech, is a pared-down version of your full formal outline. You construct the formal outline for an interested reader having no necessary prior knowledge of your topic. However, you write the

An effective outline can serve as notes when delivering your speech.

speaking outline for yourself, meaning that it does not need to follow the rules of outlining that are essential to a working or formal outline. The only rule for the speaking outline is that it be brief.

Why is the speaking outline briefer than the formal outline? This outline, made up of essential words and phrases, serves as your speaking notes. If you spoke from a complete sentence outline, you might be tempted to read the speech, sacrificing eye contact and other vital interaction with your audience. Alternatively, you might try to memorize the formal outline, another dangerous tactic because you then risk forgetting part of the speech. If, instead, you speak using the outline having just key words and phrases to jog your memory, your delivery will seem more natural and conversational, and you will find yourself freer to interact with your audience.

Though the speaking outline leaves out a lot of what the formal outline includes, it also contains some important items not found in the formal outline. For example, you can include directions to yourself about the speech's delivery. A speaker with a tendency to speak too softly could write reminders in the margins, such as "Volume" or "Speak up!" You could also note places where you want to pause, slow down, move around, or use presentational aids. Some speakers find it particularly helpful to make these delivery notes in a color different from the rest of the outline.

Second, most speaking outlines include supporting materials you plan to use. Quotations and definitions should be written in complete sentences, even though the rest of the outline is in words and phrases. Why? Because when you quote others, you must be exact. For that reason, also insert notes about the exact sources you want to cite. Examples, illustrations, and statistics could be noted in only a few words or numbers. Any symbols or abbreviations you are comfortable with are likely appropriate in your speaking outline.

We believe that keeping your speaking notes in outline form will remind you of the importance of clear organization in the speech you deliver. Ultimately, though, they are *your* notes. As long as they help you without drawing attention to themselves, they are doing their job. If you tend to forget things under pressure, you may need a few more words in notes than some other people do. Resist the temptation to write out too much of the speech,. If you write it, you'll want to read it. Instead, try the suggestions offered in "Theory into Practice: Developing the Speaking Outline".

Austin Willis agreed to share his speaking outline, which consisted of four note-cards depicted in this section.[2]

Austin used "I" for the introduction, "II" for the body, and "III" for the conclusion of his speech. In his speaking notes, he recorded "II. First" and "II. Second" for pro and con divisions in the body of his speech. Although not correct for a formal outline, it's okay here. Again, speaking notes need only to make sense for the speaker. Also,

Theory into Practice (TIP)

DEVELOPING THE SPEAKING OUTLINE

A few simple tips can have you well on your way to developing a useful speaking outline to keep you organized and calm as you present your material.

- Use key words or phrases to remind you of each step in your introduction and conclusion. Then try to deliver those crucial parts of the speech without referring to your notes.

- In the body of the speech, your key ideas must be worded precisely and powerfully. Use a key word or phrase to remind you of the wording you practiced.

- Use key words to remind yourself of supporting material and transitions; use numbers to remind you of statistics.

- Include just enough information to be able to cite each of your sources clearly.

- Write out (word for word) any material you want to quote, using complete sentences.

- Insert delivery prompts using words, colors, or any other symbols that will jog your memory.

- If you are using notecards, consider selecting a different colored notecard for each key idea in the body of the speech (a tip we picked up from a former student). This reinforces the organization of the speech, which is the point of outlining and preparing speaking notes.

someone who had not seen Austin's formal outline might be confused by the abbreviations FSM, PR, and JBNR on his notecards. See what these abbreviations mean as you read his notes.

Notecard #1

I. Introduction

  A. Question audience [PAUSE]

  B. Britt, Collins, and Cohen—"nearly 87% reported chewing gum at least occasionally."

  C. Wrigley (statisticbrain.com) "chewing gum is one of the oldest candies in the world [and] has grown to be a billion dollar industry in the U.S."

  D. Preview—positive effects and negative effects

[MOVE]

Delivery prompts are in capital letters so that Austin can see them at a glance and not confuse them with content prompts.

Notecard #2

II. First—Pros (FSM)

  A. Focus: Tänzer and colleagues (PR, 2009—8- to 9-year-old students remained focused).

    • Chewing gum "had a significant and positive effect on concentration performance."

    • Tucha and Simpson (2011) same for adults

  B. Stress: Zibell and Madansky—"56% of frequent gum chewers and 42% of infrequent gum chewers said that dealing with stress was a reason that they chewed gum."

  C. Memory: Tucha and Koerts (2012)—"an increase of learning performance of at least 30% was claimed following gum chewing."

    • Wilkinson & colleagues: *Immediate* vs. *delayed* memory [EMPHASIZE]

[MOVE]

The FSM abbreviation reminds Austin to preview his key points: *focus*, *stress*, *memory*.

PR is Austin's prompt to state the journal title, *Psychological Reports*.

Notecard #3

II. Second—Cons (FSM)

  A. Focus: JBNR—"Alertness reaction time was significantly slower for a spearmint gum condition compared to not chewing [gum]"

    • Smith (2010)—mood and attention

  B. Stress: Torney, Johnson, and Miles (2009)—anagram, no change in stress; infrequent [gum] chewers said that dealing with stress was a reason that they chewed gum.

  C. Memory: Johnson & Miles (2008)—"Although flavorless gum and mint-flavored strips reported change in current mouth activity . . . they did not induce context-dependent memory."

    • *Poorer* recall [EMPHASIZE]

[MOVE]

JBNR is Austin's prompt to state his source, the *Journal of Behavioral and Neuroscience Research*.

Austin wrote out researchers' conclusions that he wanted to quote directly.

Notecard #4

III. Conclusion—Pros and cons (FSM)

  A. Unique perspective

  B. Keep on chewing [SMILE]

References

Allen, A. P., & Smith, A. S. (2011). A review of the evidence that chewing gum affects stress, alertness, and cognition. *Journal of Behavioral and Neuroscience Research*, 9, 7–23.

Britt, D. M., Collins, F. L., & Cohen, L. M. (1999). Cigarette smoking and chewing-gum use among college students. *Journal of Applied Biobehavioral Research, 4*, 85–90.

Firestone, A. (n.d.). *Chew on this: Is gum addiction real?* Retrieved from www.divinecaroline.com/self/chew-gum-addiction-real

Statisticbrain.com (2013). *Chewing gum statistics*. Retrieved from www.statisticbrain.com/chewing-gum-statistics/

Tucha, L., & Koerts, J. (2012). Gum chewing and cognition: An overview. *Neuroscience & Medicine, 3,* 243–250.

Tucha, L., & Simpson, W. (2011). The role of time on task performance in modifying the effects of gum chewing on attention. *Appetite, 56*, 299–301.

Note that Austin has documented his sources using APA style.

SPEAKING WITH CONFIDENCE

In order for a speech to be as effective as possible, it needs to be well organized. Outlining is an important first step in the speech-making process. Without an outline, it's easy to trail off from your key ideas, or worse, forget them altogether, which increases speaker nervousness. When I outlined my speeches, I was not only able to remember and present my ideas in a well-organized manner, but my audience was also more engaged, which boosted my confidence. Instead of randomly writing down different points I wanted to make and bouncing back from one topic to another, I always began by creating a working outline to help me think through my topic and refine my key ideas. Then, I was able to create my formal outline and my speaking notes. Realizing how important outlining is for both me as the speaker and for my audience, I will always make sure I develop outlines for all my speeches. It actually makes the process easier, it keeps my thoughts more organized and concise, and it enables me to deliver my speeches with confidence.

Kyndall Dysard
UNC Wilmington

› SUMMARY

Outlining Your Speech

Functions of Outlining

11.1 Apply the five functions of outlining a speech.

- Outlining allows the speaker to check the scope of the topic. Is the topic too broad? Is there too much or too little information?

- Outlining tests the logical relationship between key ideas and subpoints. Are the points related and yet distinctive enough to qualify as separate ideas?

- Outlining checks the relevance of subpoints. Are all subpoints related to the key idea under which they are listed?

- Outlining gauges the balance of the speech. Does it look as though the speaker will be spending too much time on one point and too little on others? Should the speaker eliminate the points that have little support and reorganize those with a great deal of support?

- Outlining provides speaking notes, jogging the speaker's memory with key words in correct order.

Principles of Outlining

11.2 Apply the five principles of outlining a speech.

- *Singularity:* Each symbol—number or letter—should represent only one idea.

- *Consistency:* Coordination and subordination should be represented by a consistent system of letters and numbers properly indented.

- *Adequacy:* Any point divided into subpoints must have at least two subpoints.

- *Uniformity:* Complete sentences and key words should be mixed only in the speaking outline.

- *Parallelism:* Coordinate points throughout the outline should have simple, parallel grammatical construction.

Stages of Outlining

11.3 Construct working, formal, and speaking outlines.

- The first phase of outlining is a *working outline,* an informal list of different aspects of the selected speech topic.

- Next, the speaker should develop a complete sentence outline, or *formal outline,* that is clear and thorough enough to communicate the essence of the speech to any reader.

- Having checked the scope of the topic and the logical connections, relevance, and balance of the subpoints, the speaker can then select key words and phrases for a *speaking outline.* That outline may also include transitions, quotations, and source citations, as well as personal directions or prompts for the speaker's delivery.

- While effective outlining does not guarantee clear organization in the delivered speech, chances are good that any well-organized speech has been carefully outlined at some stage in its development.

WORDING YOUR SPEECH

→ LEARNING OBJECTIVES

After studying this chapter, you should be able to

12.1 Word your speech carefully to share the intended meaning.

12.2 Word your speech using clear language.

12.3 Word your speech using vivid language.

12.4 Word your speech using inclusive language.

12.5 Word your speech using appropriate oral style.

Socrates was a famous Greek teacher who went around giving people advice. They killed him. Socrates died from an overdose of wedlock. After his death, his career suffered a dramatic decline.

— From a student paper[1]

Sisters Reunited after 18 Years in Checkout Line at Supermarket

— Newspaper headline[2]

ocrates died of an overdose of hemlock, not wedlock. Also, we doubt that those sisters had to wait in the supermarket checkout line for 18 years, even if there were lots of double-coupon days. Examples of language error ar abuse, both spoken and written, are all around us and their effects can be comic (as the quotes we shared) or serious. A speaker's words communicate ideas to an audience, information about the speaker, and information about how the speaker perceives listeners. The words you choose help determine your success in informing, persuading, and entertaining your audience.

We dedicate this chapter to helping you learn how to use language as a tool to achieve greater success as a speaker. You will learn to choose words carefully in order to share your intended meaning, as well as use language that is clear, vivid, and inclusive. Finally, we'll consider how to best utilize oral style to reach your listeners.

Convey the Message You Intend

12.1 Word your speech carefully to share the intended meaning.

When you give a speech, you have an intended goal in mind. You may want to inform your listeners about productivity apps, or persuade them to get 8 hours of sleep per night, or entertain them by roasting your tennis coach. But if you are not careful and thoughtful about the words you choose—or you choose the wrong words all together—your point may never get across; it could be confusing, embarrassing, insensitive, offensive, or simply unconvincing. For this reason, you must keep in mind the meaning of your words and the correctness of your language to ensure the intended meaning gets across.

Use Denotative and Connotative Language

At times, we focus on getting our meaning across to our listeners quickly and clearl If you were reporting a fire or some other emergency to a group of people and advising them to vacate the building, you would try to communicate that information directly and simply, without causing panic. You would not waste time mentally editing and practicing the message to make it more clever or memorable. Because your goal in these circumstances is getting your message across to a listener, you would use language with clear denotations. **Denotation** is the dictionary definition of a word.

On other occasions, you speak to get a message across and to convey it in an especially vivid way. At such times, you pay particular attention to the way you encode the message, choosing your words carefully. When your purpose is to signal your feelings about a subject, to strengthen the social bonds between you and your listeners, or to engage them in verbal play, you will likely use language that draws attention to itself and has strong connotations.[3] **Connotation** is the emotional association that a particular word has for an individual listener. (Recall that in Chapter 1, Learning Objective 1.2, you learned about the triangle of meaning; we construct our own definitions based on our experiences.) The word *fire* may have pleasant connotations for you if you spent some time around a campfire recently. The same word will have negative connotations for someone whose house burned down.

Your choice of language depends on the purpose of your speech. Usually, you will use a combination of denotative and connotative language. Whether the wording of your speech is straightforward or evocative, direct or highly embroidered, however, you must use language carefully to convey your intended meaning.

Use Correct Language

When you use language incorrectly in your speech, you risk sending unintended messages and undermining your credibility. For example, on February 18, 2017, President Donald Trump delivered a speech to his constituents in Florida. At one point in his

denotation

The dictionary definition of a word or phrase.

connotation

The emotional association(s) that a word or phrase may evoke in individual listeners.

Journal: Denotative and Connotative Language

What is the denotative meaning of the word "feminism"? What are some connotative associations that listeners may have with this word?

speech when discussing national security and immigration, Trump said: "You look at what's happening last night in Sweden."[4] This sentence singlehandedly caused a media panic in both the United States and Sweden. Why? Because nothing related to national security or immigration happened in Sweden the day before his speech. What Trump was referring to was a Fox News report about immigration in Sweden that aired the night before his speech. Therefore, he should have said: "Look at last night's Fox News report about what's happening in Sweden." That sentence would have been correct and he would have shared his intended meaning. So, using incorrect language in your speeches can have far-reaching effects.

Your language, like your physical and vocal delivery, should be free of all distractions. Errors in subject-verb agreement, misplaced modifiers, and incorrect word choice attract the attention of everyone who recognizes these errors. They may stop listening carefully to *what* you say—and miss the message you desire to share—because they are paying attention to *how* you say it. The following examples illustrate some common language errors we have heard in student speeches:

- "The first criteria for selecting a good wine is to experience its bouquet." (The speaker should use the singular noun *criterion*.)
- "So, you may be thinking, 'I could care less about student government elections. They don't affect me.'" (The speaker should say, "I *couldn't* care less. . . .")
- "Because they conduct most of their missions at night, a drug trafficker often alludes our understaffed border patrol." (*They* is plural, so the speaker should use *drug traffickers*. Also, the correct word is *elude*, not *allude*.)
- "Less than twenty students attended the lecture given by Dr. Hinojosa last Wednesday." (Use *fewer* for people or items that can be counted. Yes, those "10 Items or Less" supermarket checkout signs are wrong!)
- "The researchers conducted a study in which they infected 100 people with the human immunodeficiency virus (HIV)." (The student meant to say that the researchers studied 100 people who had been infected by the HIV, not that the researchers infected them. Who would agree to participate in such a study?)

You can speak correctly if you follow a few simple guidelines. First, make a note of grammatical mistakes you hear yourself and other people make in casual conversations. Attentive listening is the first step to improving your use of language. Second, when you are unsure of a word's denotative meaning, consult a dictionary. Third, if you have a question about proper grammar, refer to a handbook for writers. Fourth, when practicing your speech, record it and play it back, listening for mistakes you may not have noticed as you were practicing. Fifth, practice your speech in front of friends and ask them to point out mistakes. Using these strategies, your speaking will improve, and you will have a better chance of reaching your audience with your intended message (in addition to saving yourself some embarrassment).

Errors in grammar can be amusing, but they can also cause confusion and most certainly inhibit the intended message.

Use Language Clearly

12.2 Word your speech using clear language.

Have you ever had an instructor who used vague, ambiguous, and unfamiliar language to explain important concepts, which limited your understanding of the course material? Most likely. As a speaker, you should strive to use clear language to enhance your listeners' understanding.

Several research studies focusing on speaker clarity that were summarized by Joseph Chesebro and Melissa Wanzer indicate that

audience members report high levels of learning, motivation, and speaker liking when the speakers use language clearly.[5] Similarly, we have noticed that students provide positive feedback on their classmates' speeches when the speakers use clear language. So, spend some extra time evaluating the clarity of your intended language, ensuring that it is specific, familiar, and powerful.

Use Specific Language

Many communication problems spring from the fact that there are always two messages involved when two people are communicating: the message that the speaker intends and the message that the listener infers or interprets. If you tell your instructor that you missed a deadline because you were "having some problems," you leave yourself open to a wide range of interpretations. Are they health problems, family troubles, or study and work schedule conflicts? These and other interpretations are possible because *problem* is an abstract term.

To clarify your ideas, use the lowest level of abstraction possible. Words are not either abstract or concrete but take on these qualities in relation to other words. Look at the following list of terms:

cooking

cooking a turkey

cooking a Thanksgiving turkey dinner

cooking a Thanksgiving turkey dinner using a smoker

cooking a Thanksgiving turkey dinner using a smoker while camping

The term at the top of this list is more abstract than the phrase at the bottom. As we add those limiting, descriptive words, or *qualifiers*, the **referent** becomes increasingly specific. The lower the level of abstraction used, the more clearly the listener will understand the speaker.

Suppose you were giving a speech on how citizens can protect their homes from burglaries and you made the following statement:

> Crime is rampant in our city. Burglary alone has gone way up in the past year or so. So you can see that having the right kind of lock on your door is essential to your safety.

What's wrong with this statement? The language is vague. What does "rampant" mean? How much of an increase is "way up"—15 percent, 50 percent, 400 percent? Is "the past year or so" 1 year, 18 months, or more? What is "the right kind of lock"? As a speaker, you should help your audience by making these ideas more concrete. After some research, you might rephrase your argument like this:

> Last week I spoke with Captain James Winton, head of our City Police Department's Records Division. He told me that crime in our city has increased by 54 percent in the last year, and the number of burglaries has doubled. We can help deter crime by making our homes burglarproof, and one way of doing this is to make sure that all doors have solid locks. I brought one such lock with me: it's a double-keyed deadbolt lock.

Notice the improvement in the second paragraph. The message is clear, and with that clarity you would gain credibility as a speaker.

Use Familiar Language

Your language may be specific but still not be clear. If listeners are not familiar with your words, communication is impaired.

Speakers sometimes try to impress listeners with their vocabularies. Phrases such as "the anathema of censorship" and "this obviates the need for" detract from rather than enhance the speaker's message. "We must ever be mindful to eschew verbosity

referent

The object or idea each interpreter attaches to a symbol.

ETHICAL DECISIONS

USING SPECIFIC LANGUAGE

We often hear politicians talking about their plans to improve our society. It is not uncommon to hear a politician say, "We are going to suspend [insert policy or law] and replace it with something better. It will be better than anything you've ever seen before. It will probably be the best [insert policy or law] our country has ever seen."

Similarly, during crisis situations, politicians often use statements such as, "We take this matter very seriously and we are developing a strategic, comprehensive plan to resolve this issue." Again, at first glance, this statement may instill confidence in the listeners, but when analyzing the message, they

will likely inquire about what this "strategic, comprehensive plan to resolve this issue" is all about.

Although the speakers may be truthful when delivering their messages, the audience members will not develop a clear understanding of their intentions.

As a member of our society, what ethical responsibility do you think our politicians have to use specific language to make sure all citizens understand their message and what actions will be taken? Is it the speaker's or the audience members' responsibility to ensure the message is clear and understood as intended?

and deprecate tautology" is good advice and fun to say. But if you are trying to communicate with another person, it's probably better to say simply, "Avoid wordiness."

The use of jargon can also undermine clarity. **Jargon** is the special language of a particular activity, business, or group of people. For example, a doctor performing a knee surgery may say, "We will scope your knee." Unless you are in the medical profession, you may not understand the jargon term "scope." This would probably make you and most other patients quite uneasy about the upcoming procedure. Wouldn't it be nice if the doctor said, "We will perform a simple surgery on your knee, which only requires three small incisions that heal in less than a week"?

If you are certain that the people you are addressing know such terms, jargon presents no problem. In fact, it is usually quite specific and can save a lot of time. Jargon can even increase your credibility by indicating that you are familiar with the subject matter. If you have any doubts about whether your listeners know the jargon, however, either avoid such terms or define each one the first time you use it.

jargon
The special language used by people in a particular activity, business, or group.

Avoid Powerless Language

To enhance the clarity of your speech and to increase your perceived credibility, it is important that you avoid *powerless* language in your speeches. Powerless language refers to words and phrases that reduce the clarity and exactness of your message; it also decreases your perceived speaker credibility and ability to influence your audience members. Four common types of powerless language are disclaimers, hedges, hesitations, and tag questions. Suggestions for avoiding them can be found in "Theory into Practice: Avoiding Powerless Language."

- *Disclaimers* are words or phrases that preface your statements. Some examples of disclaimers are "Don't get me wrong, but . . ."; "I could be wrong, but . . ."; and "I'm not sure how this is pronounced, but. . . ." If you use disclaimers in your speech, the audience members may think that you don't fully support your opinions or claims.

- *Hedges* are noncommittal words and phrases that reduce the exactness of your message. Some examples of hedges are "I guess," "I think," "kind of," "pretty much like," and "somewhat." If you use hedges in your speech, the audience members may get the impression that you lack confidence or that you question the accuracy of your message.

- *Hesitations* are filler words or filler sounds that are unintentionally added in a speech. Some examples of hesitations are "ah," "like," "umm," "well," and "you know." The use of hedges is often distracting to the audience members. To avoid hesitations, practice your use of pauses and take a moment to breathe before continuing to the next point in your speech.

Theory into Practice (TIP)

AVOIDING POWERLESS LANGUAGE

	Powerless language: Instead of saying . . .	Powerful language: Say
Disclaimers	"I could be wrong about this, but if you . . ."	"If you . . ."
Hedges	"Drake is pretty much the best . . ."	"Drake is the best . . ."
Hesitations	"People should, you know, try to like, avoid . . ."	"People should avoid . . ."
Tag questions	"Earning good grades is important, isn't it?"	"Earning good grades is important."

Key Points: Use Language Clearly

1. Use specific language.
2. Use familiar language.
3. Avoid powerless language.

- *Tag questions* are words and phrases at the end of a point, which suggest that the speaker needs to have her or his point confirmed or validated by the audience members. Some examples of tag questions are "don't you think?" "isn't it?" "right?" and "wouldn't it?" Speakers who use tag questions appear tentative and unsure about their message.

Use Language Vividly

12.3 Word your speech using vivid language.

In addition to selecting language that is correct and clear, speakers should choose language that is colorful and picturesque. Vivid language engages the audience and makes the task of listening easier. Consider the following critiques of the speeches of the 29th U.S. president, Warren Harding:

1. Warren Harding was not an effective public speaker. His speeches often were confusing and uninspired. He did not make his points well.

2. "[Warren Harding's] speeches left the impression of an army of pompous phrases moving over the landscape in search of an idea; sometimes these meandering words would actually capture a straggling thought and bear it triumphantly a prisoner in their midst, until it died of servitude and overwork." — William G. McAdoo, Democratic Party leader[6]

SPEAKING WITH CONFIDENCE

When speaking on a controversial topic, the wording of a speech is particularly important. This was certainly my experience when I was giving a persuasive speech on gun policies in the United States. First, I made sure that my language was clear and easy to follow. Since there is a lot of gun law jargon, I used familiar language to help my audience members, even if they were completely unfamiliar with the second amendment. I also focused on using denotative language in order to define concepts, such as "microstamping" and "ballistic identification." Though I referenced both, I defined both terms to tie them into my message about gun policies.

I know from having listened to other speeches that long lists of statistics can be incredibly boring and cause the audience to tune out. I needed to use a lot of statistical information in my speech, so I tried to make this easier on my audience by using repetition to drive home my points and also by relating the numbers to relevant stories.

Finally, when speaking on a controversial topic, it's important to have credibility—particularly with audience members who disagree with the message. So, I used short sentences filled with powerful language. I also made sure to pronounce things correctly and avoided words that might have a negative connotation with my listeners. Doing this made me seem like a more credible speaker to those who agreed and disagreed with me.

Lauren Rojas
UNC Wilmington

Which of these two statements did you enjoy reading more? Which characterization of Harding's speaking did you find more colorful? Which paragraph contains the more vivid images? We're fairly certain that you selected the second statement. Why? The language of the first critique communicates an idea as simply and economically as possible. Its language is transparent, but also drab and colorless. On the other hand, the language of the second statement calls attention to its sounds, textures, and rhythms.

Vivid language does not always require lengthy, descriptive statements as in the previous example. Instead, you can replace one or two words to enhance your vividness in a speech. For example, you could describe a meadow as having "a lot of wildflowers in bloom" or describe it as "teeming with colorful, fragrant wildflowers." The second example gives listeners a more vibrant illustration.

One of the fiercest enemies of vivid language is the **cliché**, a once-colorful expression that has lost most of its impact through overuse. Many clichés involve comparisons. For example, complete the following phrases:

Like mother, like _____.

Truth is stranger than _____.

Between a rock and a _____.

Did you have any trouble completing these expressions? Probably not. In fact, *daughter*, *fiction*, and *hard place* most likely popped into your mind without much thought. Each of these sayings is a cliché that doesn't require (or stimulate) much thinking. Clichés are bland and hackneyed. Avoid them!

So, how can you make your language more vivid? The answer may be limited only by your imagination. Certainly using active language and specific literary devices will give you a good start on making your speeches more colorful and memorable.

Poet, novelist, and educator, Maya Angelou made the written word come alive through vivid and picturesque language. Successful speakers use these same techniques to make the spoken word evoke vivid images.

cliché
A once-colorful figure of speech that has lost impact through overuse.

Use Active Language

Which of the following statements is more forceful?

> It was decided by the Student Government Association that the election would be delayed for a week.

> The Student Government Association decided to delay the election for a week.

The second one, right? The first sentence uses passive voice, the second active. Active voice is more direct because it identifies the agent producing the action and places it first in the sentence. In addition, active voice is more economical than passive voice; the second sentence is shorter than the first by five words.

Active language, however, involves more than active voice. Active language has energy, vitality, and drive. It is not bogged down by filler phrases such as "you know," "like," "actually," and "stuff like that." Rather than being cliché-ridden, it may convert the commonplace into the unexpected. Language that is lively and active has impact.

Use Literary Devices

Important ideas are easier to remember if they are memorably worded. Although there are hundreds of figures and structures of speech, we focus on a more manageable number to help you enliven the language of your speech. Seven of the most common devices are simile, metaphor, personification, alliteration, parallelism, repetition, and antithesis.

Simile and **metaphor** are comparisons of two seemingly dissimilar things. In simile, the comparison is explicitly stated using the words *as* or *like*—for example, "Trying to pin the senator down on the issue is like trying to nail a poached egg to a tree."

simile
A comparison of two things using the words *as* or *like*.

metaphor
An implied comparison of two things without the use of *as* or *like*.

In metaphors, the comparison is not explicitly stated but is implied, without using *as* or *like*. Metaphors help us accommodate the new in terms of the familiar. For example, a friend who had a rough day student teaching might tell you, "My classroom is a zoo." To produce metaphors is to extend meanings, to improvise, to let your imagination go.[7] Fresh metaphors have the power to surprise us into new ways of seeing things. Theodore Roosevelt created a memorable metaphor when he made the following comparison: "A good political speech is a poster, not an etching."[8]

personification

A figure of speech that attributes human qualities to a concept or inanimate object.

Personification gives human qualities to objects, ideas, or organizations. "Blind justice," the "angry sea," and "jealousy rearing its ugly head" are all examples of personification.

Amanda used personification in her speech on drummers. Notice how the drumbeat takes on human qualities as she introduces her topic:

> It's the catalyst to any gut wrenching rock song, the groove behind any rapper's flow, and the driving force behind any marching band. It's a drumbeat. No matter where or when you hear it, a drumbeat grabs you by the lapels, screams in your face, and then slams you back into your seat for the ride of your life.

Another student, Phillip, began his speech, "Nearly 8 years ago, a new neighbor moved to East Liverpool, Ohio. But residents of this low-income, minority town didn't greet the newcomer with welcoming signs." This "Unwanted Neighbor," the title of Phillip's speech, was just "400 yards from an elementary school site." The neighbor? A toxic waste incinerator. Using personification, Phillip made the incinerator an enemy, someone who needed to be turned away.[9]

alliteration

The repetition of beginning sounds in words that are adjacent, or near one another.

Alliteration is the repetition of beginning sounds in adjacent or nearby words. The sounds of words give your speech impact. A speaker who asks us "to dream, to dare, and to do" uses alliteration. A student speaking on the topic of child abuse described the victims as "badly bruised and beaten." These words themselves convey a severe problem, and the repetition of the stern, forceful "b" sound vocally accentuates the violence of the act. Holocaust survivor Elie Wiesel used alliteration in a speech titled, "The Shame of Hunger," when he spoke of "faith in the future," "complacency if not complicity," and "hunger and humiliation."[10]

parallelism

The expression of ideas using similar grammatical structures.

repetition

Restating words, phrases, or sentences for emphasis.

Speakers use **parallelism** when they express two or more ideas in similar language structure. When they restate words, phrases, or sentences, they use **repetition**. Parallelism and repetition work in concert to emphasize an idea or a call for action. For example, Travis used an alarm clock image to summarize his persuasive speech on the dangers of sleep deprivation. He then used parallelism and repetition in his call to action and closure steps:

> Today, we've sounded the alarm about the harms of sleep deprivation, opened our eyes to the reasons this situation has developed, and finally awakened to the steps we must take to end this nightmare. Before we are all, literally, dead on our feet, let's take the easiest solution step of all. Tonight, turn off your alarm, turn down your covers, and turn in for a good night's sleep.[11]

Parallelism and repetition can also simplify the outlining process. If your first key idea is "The effects of exercise on our physical well-being," you can, and probably should, word your second key idea, "The effects of exercise on our psychological well-being," and your third key idea, "The effects of exercise on our social well-being." By using parallel and repeated language, you simplify your task of wording and remembering your speech, and also reinforce the message that exercising has positive effects on our well-being.

antithesis

The use of parallel construction to contrast ideas.

Antithesis uses parallel construction to contrast ideas. You can probably quote from memory John F. Kennedy's challenge: "Ask not what your country can do for you, ask what you can do for your country." Dedicating a memorial for soldiers who died in the Civil War battle at Gettysburg, Abraham Lincoln proclaimed, "The world will little note nor long remember what we say here, but it can never forget what they did here." The fact that we do remember both of these statements attests to the power of antithesis. Notice also that each speaker places what he wants the audience to do or remember at the end of the comparison. Antitheses are usually more powerful if they end positively.

Sarah Meinen of Bradley University gave an award-winning speech, "The Forgotten Four-Letter Word." She carefully researched and organized her speech on the problem of compassion fatigue, "the inability to care anymore about social issues." She crafted her language carefully, using the figures and structures of speech we have just discussed. Sarah's work paid off. She captured the attention and tapped the concern of her listeners, encouraging them to rekindle a passion for AIDS awareness and activism.

With statistics and expert opinions, Sarah reminded her listeners of the "savage spread" of this "vicious virus" [alliteration]. "AIDS has been too grim, too overwhelming, and it's been around too long" [parallelism and repetition]. She lamented that "despite our exposure to death and destruction, facts and figures, names and Quilt squares, AIDS has slowly faded from our national consciousness . . ." [alliteration and antithesis]. Sarah concluded, "Our well of compassion has run dry . . ." [metaphor].

Sarah urged her listeners to become advocates for change on a national and personal level. "Closing our eyes won't make a monster of this magnitude go away" [personification]. "We may be over AIDS, but AIDS is not over . . ." [antithesis]. "We may be immune to the stories and statistics, but none of us is safe from the reality of AIDS" [alliteration and antithesis]. Sarah exhorted her audience to do "whatever you have to do to be shocked, to be scared, to be involved, to be compassionate, and to keep this pandemic from being ignored, dismissed, and forgotten" [parallelism].[12]

Simile, metaphor, personification, alliteration, parallelism, repetition, and antithesis enable speakers to create vivid language and images. Remember, though, that your objective as a speaker is not to impress your listeners with your ability to create vivid language. Vivid language is not an end in itself, but a means of achieving the larger objectives of the speech. As language expert William Safire notes, "A good speech is not a collection of crisp one-liners, workable metaphors, and effective rhetorical devices; a good speech truly reflects the thoughts and emotions of the speaker. . . ."[13]

Use Language Inclusively

12.4 Word your speech using inclusive language.

We have argued that ethics is a working philosophy that we apply to daily life and bring to all speaking situations. Nowhere is this more evident than in the words we select to address and describe others. Ethical communicators neither exclude nor demean others on the basis of their race, ethnicity, sex, gender identity, sexual orientation, disability, age, religion, or other characteristics. Rather, they use **inclusive language** that is unbiased and respectful.

At least three principles should guide you as you become a more inclusive communicator: using appropriate group labels, using people-first language, and using nonsexist language.[14]

Journal: Literary Devices

Look at the photo of Glacier National Park in Montana on this page. Write a brief description of the photo using at least two of the following literary devices: alliteration, antithesis, metaphor, parallelism, personification, repetition, simile.

Key Points: Literary Devices

1. Simile
2. Metaphor
3. Personification
4. Alliteration
5. Parallelism
6. Repetition
7. Antithesis

inclusive language
Language free from certain expressions or words that might be considered to exclude particular groups of people.

Use Appropriate Group Labels

In referring to individuals and groups of people, be audience-centered and use the names they wish to be called. Acceptable terms when referring to race or ethnicity include African American or black; Asian or Asian American; Native American or American Indian; white or Caucasian; and Hispanic, Latino, or Chicano. Refer to individuals' sexual orientations, not their sexual preferences. *Lesbians, gay men, bisexual women and men*, and *transgendered persons* are acceptable terms. Address females and males who are over age 18 as *women* and *men*, not *girls* and *boys*. Not everyone with these characteristics favors the terms listed, and you should consider those preferences as you address a specific audience. Your goal, though, should be to respect individuals' rights to choose how they would like to be identified.

Use People-First Language

Use the people-first rule when referring to individuals who have disabilities. As the name implies, we should place people before their disabilities. Avoid calling someone a disabled person, an epileptic, or a diabetic. Instead, refer to a person *with* disabilities, a person *with* epilepsy, or a person who *has* diabetes.

Use Nonsexist Language

A colleague recently bought a house. Prior to finalizing the purchase, he had a home inspection completed in order to identify potential structural or electrical problems. We were discussing the inspection over lunch, and another friend asked, "So what did *he* say?" Our friend was referring to the inspector and assumed that it was a man performing the job, when in fact it was a very competent woman.

Avoid using language that is sex-biased. Language is sexist if it "promotes and maintains attitudes that stereotype people according to gender. **Sexist language** assumes that the male is the norm—the significant gender. **Nonsexist language** treats all people equally and either does not refer to a person's sex when it is irrelevant or refers to men and women in symmetrical ways when their gender is relevant."[15]

Sex bias occurs when language creates special categories for one sex, with no corresponding parallel category for the other sex. *Man* and *wife*, for example, are not parallel terms. *Man* and *woman* or *husband* and *wife* are parallel. Other examples of nonparallel language are nurse and male nurse, chairman and chairperson, and athletic team names such as *The Tigers* (the men's team) and *The Lady Tigers* (the women's team).

Perhaps the most common display of sexist language comes from the inappropriate use of a simple two-letter word: *he*. Sometimes called the "generic he," this word is used to refer to men and women alike, usually with the fallacious justification that there aren't acceptable alternatives without cluttering speech with intrusive phrases such as "he and she" and "him and her." This assumption is false. Consider the following sentence: "A coach must be concerned with his players' motivation." This statement is sexist because both women and men are coaches. Now, consider a simple revision that removes bias without changing the meaning of the sentence. First, use the plural form: "Coaches must be concerned with their players' motivation." Second, eliminate the pronoun: "A coach must be concerned with player motivation." A third way to avoid sex bias is to include both pronouns: "A coach must be concerned with her or his players' motivation." Although the use of "he and she" may seem wordy and intrusive, speakers sometimes use this double-pronoun construction strategically to remind listeners that both men and women perform the role being discussed.

sexist language

Language that excludes one sex, creates special categories for one sex, or assigns roles based solely on sex.

nonsexist language

Language that treats both sexes fairly and avoids stereotyping either one.

Speaking inclusively is an ethical obligation for those who value civil discourse. Rosalie Maggio highlights both the limitations and possibilities of the role language can play in achieving tolerance, acceptance, and change:

> There can certainly be no solution to the problem of discrimination in society on the level of language alone. Replacing *handicap* with *disability* does not mean a person with disabilities will find a job more easily. Using *secretary* inclusively does not change the fact that fewer than 2 percent of U.S. secretaries are men. Replacing *black-and-white* in our vocabularies will not dislodge racism. However, research indicates that language powerfully influences attitudes, behavior, and perceptions. To ignore this factor in social change would be to hobble all other efforts.[16]

Use Appropriate Oral Style

12.5 Word your speech using appropriate oral style.

To speak appropriately, you must recognize that your oral style differs from your written style. Unless your instructor asks you to deliver some speeches from a manuscript, we believe it's better to think of "developing" speeches rather than "writing" them for two reasons. First, you will likely try to memorize what you have written, and the fear of forgetting part of the speech will add to your nervousness and could make your delivery mechanical. Second, and more important, the act of writing itself often affects the tone of the communication. **Tone** is the relationship established by language and grammar between a writer or speaker and that person's readers or listeners. Many of us think of writing as something formal. For that reason, we tend not to write the way that we speak.

If you compose parts of a speech on paper, make certain that you read what's on the page aloud to see if it sounds oral rather than written. How can you tell the difference?

Our oral style differs from our written style in at least four important ways.

- First, *in speaking, we tend to use shorter sentences than we write*. Speakers who write their speeches often find themselves gasping for air when they try to deliver a long sentence in one breath.

- Second, *when we communicate orally, we tend to use more contractions, colloquial expressions, and slang*. Our speaking vocabulary is smaller than our writing vocabulary, so we tend to speak a simpler language than we write. Speakers who write out their speeches often draw from their larger written vocabularies. As a result, their presentation style seems formal and often creates a barrier between them and their listeners.

- Third, *oral style makes greater use of personal pronouns and references than written style does*. Speakers must acknowledge their listeners' presence. One way of doing this is by including them in the speech. Using the pronouns *I*, *we*, and *you* makes your speech more immediate and enhances your rapport with your listeners. You may even want to mention specific audience members by name: "Last week, John told us how to construct a power résumé. I'm going to tell you what to do once your résumé gets you a job interview." Notice how the name of the student, coupled with several personal pronouns, brings the speaker and audience together and sets up the possibility for lively interaction.

- A fourth difference is that *oral style uses more repetition*. Readers can slow down and reread the material in front of them. They control the pace. Listeners don't have that luxury. Speakers must take special care to reinforce their messages, and one way of accomplishing this is by using repetition.

Journal: Using Nonsexist Language

Determine nonsexist words that could be substituted for each of the following examples:

a. Manpower
b. Salesmanship
c. Mother country
d. Man's best friend

Key Points: Use Inclusive Language

1. Use appropriate group labels.
2. Use people-first language.
3. Use nonsexist language.

tone
The relationship established by language and grammar between speakers and their listeners.

No matter which of the world's nearly 7,000 languages you speak, the words you choose telegraph messages about your background, your involvement with your topic, and your relationship with your listeners.[17] Like the unique voice and body you use to deliver your speeches, your language is an extremely important part of your delivery. If you are conscientious, you must know when to speak simply and directly and when to embellish your language with specific language techniques. In short, you don't have to be a poet to agree with poet Robert Frost: "All the fun's in how you say a thing."[18] (For more tips on oral style, see "Theory into Practice: Keys to Effective Oral Style.")

Theory into Practice (TIP)

KEYS TO EFFECTIVE ORAL STYLE

Oral style checklist	Instead of this:	Say this:
Use familiar language	Such an action would not be prudent at this juncture.	I don't think we should do that.
Use personal pronouns	People need to stand up and say, "Enough is enough."	We must stand up and say, "Enough is enough."
Use contractions	He is hesitant to share his experience out of fear that we will judge him.	He's hesitant to share his experience out of fear that we'll judge him.
Use short sentences	According to Nigel Hawkes in his book *Structures: The Way Things Are Built*, an accidental discovery by well diggers in 1974 has led archaeologists in central China to unearth an army of possibly 8,000 terracotta figures of warriors and horses in the tomb of China's first emperor.	According to Nigel Hawkes in his book *Structures: The Way Things Are Built,* well diggers in central China discovered pieces of broken terracotta in 1974. Since then, archaeologists have unearthed what may be a total of 8,000 figures. They are terracotta figures of warriors and horses guarding the tomb of China's first emperor.
Use repetition	Several studies have estimated that approximately 80 percent of college students have talked on a cell phone or texted while driving.	Several studies have estimated that approximately 80 percent of college students have talked on a cell phone or texted while driving. That's eight out of ten students. And if our class is typical, approximately twenty of us are guilty.

CHAPTER 12

› SUMMARY

Wording Your Speech

Convey the Message You Intend

12.1 Word your speech carefully to share the intended meaning.

- Your choice of language depends on the purpose of your speech. Speakers often use a combination of denotative and connotative language.
- To use language correctly, you should (1) note grammatical mistakes you hear yourself and other people make; (2) consult a dictionary when you're unsure of the meaning of a word; (3) refer to a handbook for writers for grammar questions; (4) record your speech and play it back to identify mistakes; and (5) practice your speech in front of friends and ask them to point out mistakes.

Use Language Clearly

12.2 Word your speech using clear language.

- The more concrete and specific your language, the more closely your referents will match those of your listeners.
- Language must also be familiar. Listeners must know the meanings of the words you use.
- Avoid powerless language to enhance the clarity of your message and your speaker credibility.

Use Language Vividly

12.3 Word your speech using vivid language.

- Active language avoids clichés and filler phrases, using instead active voice, coined words, and well-turned phrases.

- Useful literary devices include simile, metaphor, personification, alliteration, parallelism, repetition, and antithesis.

Use Language Inclusively

12.4 Word your speech using inclusive language.

- To use language *inclusively*, consider audience diversity and avoid stereotypes about people based on characteristics such as race, ethnicity, age, and sex.
- Always use preferred terms for groups and put people first in your language choices. In addition, use nonsexist language that treats both females and males symmetrically and fairly.

Use Appropriate Oral Style

12.5 Word your speech using appropriate oral style.

To achieve appropriate *oral style*, use shorter sentences than you ordinarily write; use contractions, colloquial expressions, and slang when appropriate; use personal pronouns (*I*, *we*, *us*, *they*); and use more repetition than you normally would in writing.

DELIVERING YOUR SPEECH

→ LEARNING OBJECTIVES

After studying this chapter, you should be able to

13.1 Distinguish among the four methods of delivering speeches.

13.2 Apply the three qualities of effective delivery in your speech.

13.3 Incorporate the seven elements of effective vocal delivery into your speech.

13.4 Incorporate the six elements of physical delivery into your speech.

13.5 Identify the four challenges of delivering speeches online.

Communication scholar Karlyn Kohrs Campbell said, "Ideas do not walk by themselves; they must be carried—expressed and voiced—by someone."[1] Each of us has a unique voice, body, and way of wording ideas. Your manner of presenting a speech—through your voice, body, and language—forms your style of delivery. In other words, *what* you say is your speech content and *how* you say it is your **delivery**. If you and a classmate presented a speech with the same words arranged in the same order (something we don't recommend!), your listeners would still receive two different messages. This is because your delivery shapes your image as a speaker and changes your message in subtle ways.

This chapter is about the process of presenting your speech vocally and physically. Before we survey the individual elements that make up delivery (and consider how those elements play out in an online speaking situation), let's first consider four basic methods of delivering a speech.

delivery
The way a speaker presents a speech, through voice qualities, bodily actions, and language.

Methods of Delivery

13.1 Distinguish among the four methods of delivering speeches.

The four basic ways you can deliver your public speeches are (1) from a manuscript, (2) from memory, (3) impromptu, or with little or no advance preparation, and (4) extemporaneously, or from notes.

Speaking from Manuscript

Speaking from manuscript, or delivering a speech word for word from a complete text prepared in advance, ensures that the speaker will not be at a loss for words and is essential in some situations (though rarely in a public speaking course). An address that will be quoted or later published in its entirety is typically delivered from a manuscript. For example, major foreign policy speeches and State of the Union addresses by U.S. presidents are always delivered from manuscript because it is important that the speaker be clearly understood. Speeches of tribute and commencement addresses are often scripted as well.

Having every word of your speech scripted may boost your confidence, but it does *not* ensure effective delivery. If you must deliver a speech from manuscript, you should write it in a conversational style. In other words, the manuscript must sound like something you would say in conversation rather than submit as an essay in a course. In addition, if you do not also take time to practice delivering your speech in a fluent, conversational manner and with appropriate emphasis, well-placed pauses, and adequate eye contact, you are unlikely to have a successful delivery.

speaking from manuscript
Delivering a speech from a text written word for word and practiced in advance.

Speaking from Memory

Speaking from memory is only appropriate on rare occasions. We speak from memory when we prepare a written text and then memorize it word for word. At best, a memorized speech allows a smooth, almost effortless-looking delivery because the speaker has neither notes nor a manuscript and can concentrate on interacting with the audience. For most of us, however, memorizing takes a long time and our fear of forgetting part of the speech can make us sound mechanical or programmed. For these reasons, speaking from memory is usually appropriate only for brief speeches, such as those introducing another speaker or presenting or accepting an award.

speaking from memory
Delivering a speech that is recalled word for word from a written text.

Speaking Impromptu

We engage in **impromptu speaking** whenever someone calls on us to express an opinion or unexpectedly asks us to "say a few words" to a group. In these informal situations, other people may not expect us to be forceful or well organized, and we

impromptu speaking
Speaking with little or no advance preparation.

are probably somewhat comfortable speaking without preparation. The more important the speech, however, the less appropriate the impromptu method of delivery. Although impromptu speaking is excellent practice, no conscientious person should risk a grade, an important proposal, or professional advancement on an unprepared speech. Therefore, you should keep the following points in mind when speaking impromptu:

- If you have a choice, *speak on a topic you know well.* The more you know about your topic, the better you will be able to select relevant ideas, organize them, and explain them as you speak.

- *Make the most of the time you have.* Don't waste "walking time" from your seat to the front of the room worrying. Instead, ask yourself, "What do I want the audience to remember when I sit down?"

- *Focus on a single or a few key points.* If you have been asked to explain why you support building a new library instead of renovating the existing facility, think of two or three important reasons underlying your position. And remember to use the 4 S's as you present those reasons to your audience.

- *Be brief.* One public speaking axiom is, "Stand up! Speak up! Shut up! Sit down!" Although this can be carried to an extreme, it's probably good advice for the impromptu speaker. An impromptu speech is not the occasion for a long, rambling discourse. Say what you need to say, and then be seated.

Speaking Extemporaneously

speaking extemporaneously

Delivering a speech from a combination of your notes and knowledge of the topic.

The final method of delivery, and by far the most popular, is **speaking extemporaneously**, or from notes. Speaking from notes offers several advantages over other delivery methods. You do not need to worry about one particular way of wording your ideas because you have not scripted the speech. Neither do you have to worry that you will forget something you have memorized. With your notes in front of you, you are free to interact with the audience in a natural, conversational manner. If something you say confuses the audience, you can repeat it, explain it using other words, or use a better example to clarify it. Your language may not be as forceful or colorful as with a carefully prepared manuscript or a memorized speech, but speaking from notes helps ensure that you will be natural and spontaneous.

When speaking from notes, keep the following five suggestions in mind:

- *Practice with the notes you will actually use in delivering the speech.* If you use sheets of paper, use a weight slightly heavier than bond so that it's easier to handle. Double- or even triple-space speech notes on paper and format text in a font size that's easy for you to see. On note cards, be sure to write legibly. These strategies will make your words easier to read and help you keep your place.

- *Number your notecards or sheets of paper.* Check their order before you speak.

- *Determine when you should and should not look at your notes.* Looking at your notes when you quote an authority or present statistics is acceptable. In fact, doing so may even convey to your audience your concern for presenting supporting materials accurately. However, do not look down while previewing, stating, or summarizing your key ideas. If you cannot remember your key ideas, what hope is there for your audience? Also, avoid looking down when you use personal pronouns such as *I, you,* or *we* or when you address audience members by name. A break in your eye contact at these points suddenly distances you from the audience and creates the impression that the speech is coming from a script rather than from a combination of your notes and knowledge of the topic.

- *Slide your notes rather than turning them.* To avoid picking them up and turning them over, do not write on the back of your notes. As a rule, if you use a lectern, do not

Key Points: Methods of Delivery

1. Speaking from manuscript
2. Speaking from memory
3. Speaking impromptu
4. Speaking extemporaneously

let the audience see your notes after you place them in front of you. The less aware the audience is of your notes, the more direct and personal your communication with them will be.

- *Devote extra practice time to your conclusion.* Your final words can make a deep impression, but not if you rush through it or deliver it while gathering your notes and walking back to your seat. Your goal at this critical point in the speech is the same as your goal for all your delivery: to eliminate distractions and to reinforce your message through your body, voice, and language.

In 2014, Oscar winner Lupita Nyong'o gave a powerful keynote speech on fear, at the Massachusetts Conference for Women. She delivered her speech extemporaneously, focusing on her audience, but referring to notes when appropriate.

The most satisfactory way of delivering your classroom speeches may combine all four of the methods we have discussed. To demonstrate that you are well prepared and to ensure eye contact with your audience, you may want to memorize your introduction and conclusion. If you deliver the body of your speech extemporaneously, look at your notes occasionally. Just don't look at your notes while you are stating or summarizing each main point. If you quote sources in your speech, you are, in effect, briefly using a manuscript. Finally, as an audience-centered speaker, you should be flexible enough to improvise a bit. You speak impromptu whenever you repeat an idea or think of a clearer or more persuasive example. If you are well prepared, this combination of delivery methods should look natural to your audience and feel comfortable to you.

Qualities of Effective Delivery

13.2 Apply the three qualities of effective delivery in your speech.

As you begin to think about the specifics of delivering your speech, keep in mind three characteristics of effective delivery. First, *effective delivery helps both listeners and speakers.* Your audience has only one chance to receive your message. Just as clear organization makes your ideas easier to remember, effective delivery can underscore your key points, sell your ideas, or communicate your concern for the topic. Concentrate on your ideas and how the audience is receiving them. Pay attention to their interest in and understanding of your speech. If you notice listeners text messaging, whispering to friends, or snoozing, they may be bored. At this point, enliven your delivery with movement and changes in your volume. To ensure listeners understand the point you are making, slow your rate of delivery and use more pauses and descriptive gestures to reinforce your ideas.

Second, *the best delivery looks and feels natural, comfortable, and spontaneous.* Some occasions and audiences require you to be more formal than others. Speaking to a large audience through a stationary microphone, for example, will naturally restrict your movement. In other situations, you may find yourself moving, gesturing, and using presentational aids extensively. You want to orchestrate all these elements so that your presentation looks and feels relaxed and natural, not strained or awkward. You achieve spontaneous delivery such as this only through practice.

Third and finally, *delivery is best when nonverbal messages complement and reinforce the verbal messages.* We are reminded of the importance of nonverbal communication when someone breaks a nonverbal rule. Suppose Darnay walks reluctantly to the front of the classroom, clutches the lectern, stands motionless, frowns, and says, "I'm absolutely delighted to be speaking to you today." Do you believe him? No. Why not? Darnay's speech did not begin with his first words, but with the many nonverbal messages that

Journal: Delivery Methods

Public speaking shares many similarities with delivering a lecture or lesson plan, including the methods we have shared. Think about your current and previous instructors. Have you had instructors who seemed to "wing it" or, alternatively, rely heavily on notes? Have you had an instructor teach extemporaneously or seem to have his or her entire lesson memorized? Share at least two such instances and analyze which method was most effective for learning and why.

Journal: Qualities of Delivery

As an audience member, which of the three qualities of effective delivery is most important to you? Why is this quality more important to you than the other ones?

signaled his reluctance to speak. Nonverbal messages should complement and reinforce verbal ones. When they do not match, we tend to trust the nonverbal message.

Any prescription for effective delivery will include three basic elements: the *voice* or vocal delivery; the *body*, or physical delivery; and *language*. Earlier we discussed how your language affects your delivery style. In the next two sections, we focus on vocal and physical delivery.

Elements of Vocal Delivery

13.3 Incorporate the seven elements of effective vocal delivery into your speech.

Have you ever gotten into an argument with someone not because of what you said, but the way you said it? If so, you've had firsthand experience with the power of **vocal delivery** (also known as paralanguage) or how speakers orally present the content of their speech. Vocal delivery includes rate, pause, volume, pitch, inflection, articulation, and pronunciation.

Rate and Pause

You've probably heard the warning, "Watch out for him; he's a fast talker." Such a statement implies that someone who talks fast may be trying to trick us. At the other end of the spectrum, we often grow impatient with people who talk much slower than we do, even labeling them uncertain, dull, or dense. Though these stereotypes may be inaccurate, the impressions people form based on our nonverbal communication can become more important than anything we intend to communicate.

Your **rate**, or speed, of speaking can communicate something, intentionally or unintentionally, about your motives in speaking, your disposition, or your involvement with the topic. Your goal in a speech, therefore, should be to avoid delivery that is uniformly too fast or too slow. Instead, use a variety of rates to reinforce your purpose in speaking and make you seem conversational.

Although we can process information at rates faster than people speak, our comprehension depends on the type of material we are hearing. You should slow down, for example, when presenting detailed, highly complex information, particularly to a group that knows little about your subject. However, in some situations, speaking slightly faster than the rate of normal conversation may actually increase your persuasiveness by conveying the message that you know exactly what you want to say.

vocal delivery

The way in which speakers orally present the content of their speech; also known as paralanguage.

rate

The speed at which a speech is delivered.

ETHICAL DECISIONS

DELIVERY VERSUS CONTENT

A minister once wrote a delivery prompt in the margin of his speaking notes: "Shout here—argument weak!" Most of us would agree that using delivery to mask weak content is unethical. However, delivery can also demonstrate genuine confidence and enthusiasm for the topic.

As a future employee in your desired area of work, you have been asked by your supervisor to hire a new colleague who will be responsible for explaining and demonstrating the products your company manufactures and sells. After reviewing more than 50 applications, you decide to interview your two favored applicants—Ms. Arlovski and Ms. Greenberg.

As a part of the interview process, each applicant delivers a presentation intended to (a) inform audience members about the product, and (b) encourage audience members to buy the product. Ms. Arlovski's delivery is excellent, but she seems to have limited knowledge of the product. Conversely, Ms. Greenberg knows the product very well, but her delivery is lacking.

All other factors being equal, which applicant would you select? What ethical obligations do you have to your boss, your company, and your future customers?

Pauses, or silences, can be an important element in your rate of delivery. You pause intentionally to allow the audience time to reflect on something you have just said or to heighten suspense about something you are going to say. Achim Nowak, author of *Power Speaking: The Art of the Exceptional Public Speaker*, contends:

> [A] pause allows the listener to make a personal connection to the words she just heard. A pause invites the listener to relax into a presentation. A pause makes it possible for the speaker to sense the response of an audience to a presentation. Pauses are those beautiful moments when meaning happens and common ground emerges.[2]

Pauses also mark important transitions in your speech, helping you and your audience shift gears. However, an unintentional pause at the wrong time may disrupt the flow of your speech and prevent your listeners from following the logic of your argument.

To test the importance of pauses, let's look at a sentence from a speech that former President Barack Obama delivered at the memorial service for the victims of the 2011 shooting at a political gathering outside a Tucson, Arizona, supermarket. Consider the President's placement of pauses, with double slashes indicating longer pauses:

> We may not be able to stop all evil in the world // but I know that how we treat one another/ is entirely up to us. // I believe that for all our imperfections, we are full of decency and goodness,/ and that the forces that divide us /are not as strong /as those that unite us.//[3]

Notice how reading this excerpt with pauses gives the words more meaning and power than would have been possible if the President had said the same thing without pauses. Remember, though, that to be effective in a speech, pauses must be used intentionally and selectively. If your speech is filled with too many awkwardly placed pauses—or too many **vocalized pauses**, such as "um" and "uh"—you will seem hesitant or unprepared, and your credibility will erode quickly.

Volume

Your audience must be able to hear you in order to listen to your ideas. **Volume** is simply how loudly or softly you speak. A person who speaks too loudly may be considered boisterous or obnoxious. In contrast, an inaudible speaker may be considered unsure or timid. Adapt your volume to the space in which you are speaking. In your classroom, you can probably use a volume just slightly louder than your usual conversational level, unless you are dealing with specific environmental noise like the "whoosh" of an air conditioner, a boisterous group of people in the hallway, or the sound of traffic outside the window.

When you speak before a large group, a microphone may be helpful or even essential. If possible, practice beforehand so that the sound of your amplified voice does not startle you. You may even be called on to speak before a large audience without a microphone. This is not as difficult as it sounds. In fact, your voice will carry well if you support your breathing from your diaphragm. To test your breathing, place your hand on your abdomen while repeating the sentence "Those old boats don't float" louder and louder. If you are breathing from the diaphragm, you should feel your abdominal muscles tightening. Without that support, you are probably trying to increase your volume from your throat, a mistake that could strain your voice.

Pitch and Inflection

Pitch refers to the highness or lowness of vocal tones, similar to the notes on a musical staff. Every speaker has an optimal pitch range, or key. This is the range in which you are most comfortable speaking, and your voice is probably pleasant to hear in this range. For advice on achieving a natural and appropriate pitch, see "Theory into Practice: Achieving Natural Pitch."

---

pause
An intentional or unintentional period of silence in a speaker's vocal delivery.

vocalized pause
A sound or word such as *ah*, *like*, *okay*, *um*, *so*, and *you know* inserted to fill the silence between a speaker's words or thoughts.

volume
The relative loudness or softness of a speaker's voice.

pitch
The highness or lowness of a speaker's voice.

Theory into Practice (TIP)

ACHIEVING NATURAL PITCH

Speakers who are unusually nervous sometimes raise their pitch. Other speakers think that if they lower their pitch, they will seem more authoritative. In truth, speakers who do not use their normal pitch usually sound artificial.

The following practice technique may help you retain or recapture a natural, conversational pitch in your delivery.

- Begin some of your practice sessions seated. Imagine a good friend sitting across from you.

- Imagine your friend asks you what your speech is about. Answer her question by summarizing and paraphrasing your speech. For example, "Lin, I'm going to talk about the advantages of consuming grass-fed rather than grain-fed beef. I've divided my speech into two key ideas. Grass-fed beef has half the saturated fat of grain-fed beef, and grass-fed cattle are treated more humanely than factory-farmed, grain-fed beef."

- Listen closely to the tone of your voice as you speak. You are having a conversation with a friend. You're not tense; you feel comfortable.

- Now, keeping this natural, conversational tone in mind, stand up, walk to the front of the room, and begin your speech.

- As you speak extemporaneously, your words will change, but your pitch should be comfortable and conversational, as it was before. In a sense, you are merely having a conversation with a larger audience.

We have found this technique helpful for students whose vocal delivery sounds artificial or mechanical. They find their natural pitch ranges and incorporate more meaningful pauses.

---

inflection

Patterns of change in a person's pitch while speaking.

articulation

The mechanical process of forming the sounds necessary to communicate in a particular language.

Ben Stein may have achieved fame with his monotone, but it will not help you achieve speaking success.

A problem more typical than an unusually high- or low-pitched voice is vocal delivery that lacks adequate **inflection**, or changes in pitch. Someone who speaks without changing pitch delivers sentences in a flat, uniform pitch that becomes monotonous. Indeed, the word *monotone* means "one tone," and you may have had instructors whose monotonous droning invited you to doze. Inflection is an essential tool for conveying meaning accurately. You can give a simple four-word sentence four distinct meanings by raising the pitch and volume of one word at a time:

"**She** is my friend." (Not the young woman standing with her.)

"She **is** my friend." (Don't try to tell me she isn't!)

"She is **my** friend." (Not yours.)

"She is my **friend**." (There's nothing more to our relationship than that.)

In public speaking, women can generally make wider use of their pitch ranges than men can without sounding affected or unnatural. For this reason, men often find that they need to vary other vocal and physical elements of delivery—volume, rate, and gestures, for example—to compensate for a limited pitch range.

Articulation and Pronunciation

The final elements of vocal delivery we will discuss are articulation and pronunciation. **Articulation** is the mechanical process of forming the sounds necessary to communicate in a particular language. Most articulation errors are made from habit and take four principal forms: deletion, addition, substitution, and transposition.

Deletion is leaving out sounds—for example, saying "libary" for "library" or "goverment" for "government." If you have heard someone say "Warshington" for "Washington," you've heard an example of an articulation error caused by the *addition* of a sound. An example of errors caused by the *substitution* of one sound for another is "kin" for "can." The final type of articulation error is one of *transposition*, or the reversal of two sounds that are close together. This error is the vocal equivalent of transposing two letters in a typed word. Saying "lectren" for "lectern" or "hunderd" for "hundred" are examples of transposition errors.

Articulation errors made as a result of habit may be so ingrained that you can no longer identify your mistakes. Your speech instructor, friends, and classmates can help you by pointing out articulation problems. You may need to listen to recordings of your speeches to locate problems and then practice the problematic words or sounds o correct your articulation.

Pronunciation, in contrast to articulation, is simply a matter of knowing how the letters of a word sound and where the stress falls when that word is spoken. Pronunciation errors can be a minor distraction or a major disaster, depending on how far off your mispronunciation is and how many times you make the error. If you have any doubt about the pronunciation of a word you plan to use in a speech, listen to its pronunciation in a current online dictionary and then practice the correct pronunciation aloud.

Pronunciation of proper nouns—the names of specific people, places, and things—can be particularly tricky. Proper nouns should be pronounced the way that the people who have the name (or who live in the place or who named the thing) pronounce them. For instance, the city Newark, in Delaware, is pronounced "new-ARK," but Newark, in New Jersey, is pronounced "new-URK."

Once you have mastered these elements of vocal delivery, your speech will be free of articulation errors and mispronounced words. Your voice will be well modulated, with enough inflection to communicate your ideas clearly. You will speak loudly enough that all your listeners can hear you easily. You will adapt your rate to the content of your message, and you will pause to punctuate key ideas and major transitions. In short, your sound will be coming through loud and clear. Now let's consider the picture your listeners will see by examining the aspects of physical delivery.

pronunciation
How the sounds of a word are to be said and which parts are to be stressed.

Key Points: Elements of Vocal Delivery

1. Rate
2. Pause
3. Volume
4. Pitch
5. Inflection
6. Articulation
7. Pronunciation

Elements of Physical Delivery

13.4 Incorporate the six elements of physical delivery into your speech.

Like vocal delivery, **physical delivery** is a form of nonverbal communication that sends a visual message to the audience. Important aspects of our physical delivery include appearance, posture, facial expressions, eye contact, movement, and gestures.

physical delivery
Nonauditory delivery; all aspects of delivery excluding the speaker's words and voice.

Appearance

We all form quick impressions of people we meet based on subtle nonverbal signals. **Appearance**, in particular our grooming and the way we dress, is an important nonverbal signal that helps people judge us. Why is appearance so important?

Studies demonstrate that people we consider attractive can persuade us more easily than those we find unattractive.[4] In addition, high-status clothing carries more authority than does low-status clothing. For example, we are more likely to jaywalk behind a person dressed in a dark blue suit, a crisp white shirt, and a dark tie who is carrying an expensive black-leather briefcase than we would behind a person dressed in rags or even in jeans. We will also take orders more easily from that well-dressed person than we would from someone poorly dressed. These studies reinforce the adage that "clothes make the person," a saying any public speaker would do well to remember.

The safest advice on appearance that we can offer the public speaker is to be neat, to be clean, and to avoid extremes in dress and grooming. Use clothes to reinforce your purpose in speaking, not to draw attention. Every moment that the audience spends admiring your suit or wondering why you wore a torn T-shirt is a moment they are distracted from your message.

In selecting your attire, consider the occasion, audience, topic, and your image as a speaker.

appearance
An aspect of physical delivery, in particular our grooming and the way we dress.

1. *Consider the Occasion.* The speaking occasion dictates, in part, how formally or informally you can dress. A speech in your classroom probably permits you to be more informal than you would be delivering a business presentation to a board of directors or an acceptance speech at an awards ceremony.

We may often think of public speaking as requiring formal attire, but the reality is that appropriate attire differs by speaking situation.

2. *Consider Your Audience.* Some of your listeners dress more casually than others. In any audience, there is a range of attire. As a rule, dress at or near the top of that range. You should appear as nicely dressed as the best-dressed people in your audience.

3. *Consider Your Topic.* Your clothing can underscore or undermine the impact you want your speech to have. A hot-pink dress or a lime-green shirt might be entirely appropriate for a speech on Mardi Gras, but not for one on the high cost of funerals. On the other hand, you would look and feel silly wearing a business suit to demonstrate basic poses of Bikram yoga.

4. *Consider Your Image.* The clothing you select can shape—or even change—the image you want to create of yourself as a speaker. Darker colors convey authority and seriousness; lighter colors establish a friendlier image. A student perceived as the class clown may want to dress more formally to help dispel this image.

Clothing also shapes self-perception. You probably have certain clothes that give you a sense of confidence or make you feel especially assertive or powerful when you wear them. Dressing "up" conveys your seriousness of purpose to your listeners. It also establishes this same positive attitude in your own mind. This is why people often dress up even for phone interviews.

Decide what you will wear before the day of your speech and practice at least once in those clothes. One of our students discovered that she was distracted during her presentation because when she moved her arms to gesture, her coat made a rustling sound. She could have eliminated this distraction if she had practiced in that suit coat before the day of her speech. Whatever the problems, it's best to encounter and fix them before the speech.

Posture

posture

The position or bearing of a speaker's body while delivering a speech.

A public speaker should look comfortable, confident, and prepared to speak. You have the appropriate attire. Your next concern is your **posture**, the position or bearing of your body. The two extremes to avoid are rigidity and sloppiness. Don't hang onto or drape yourself across the lectern, if you are using one. Keep your weight balanced on both legs, and avoid shifting your weight back and forth. Equally distracting is standing on one leg and shuffling or tapping the other foot. You may not realize that you do those things. One student told us that she tied bells to her shoes when she practiced her speeches so that she would "hear what her feet were doing." If you practice in front of friends, ask them to point out delivery distractions. Remember that for your delivery to reinforce your message, it must be free of distracting mannerisms.

Facial Expression

facial expression

The tension and movement of various parts of a speaker's face.

Estimates of the number of possible human facial expressions range from 5,000 to 250,000.[5] Even if the actual number is closer to 5,000, that's still a significant amount of communication potential. Yet many people giving a speech for the first time put on a blank mask, limiting their **facial expression** to one neutral look.

Rather, your facial expression must match the thoughts and feelings that motivate your words. The speaker who smiles and blushes self-consciously through a speech on date rape will simply not be taken seriously and may offend many listeners. If you detail the plight of earthquake victims, make sure your face reflects your concern. If you tell a joke and your listeners can't stop chuckling, break into a smile.

The way to use facial expression appropriately to bolster your message is simple: Concentrate as much as possible on the ideas you present and the way your audience receives and responds to them. Try not to be overly conscious of how you look and sound. This takes practice, but your classroom speeches provide a good forum for such rehearsal.

Eye Contact

We've all heard the saying, "The eyes are the window to the soul." **Eye contact** can convey truthfulness, as well as confidence, concern, sincerity, interest, and enthusiasm. A lack of eye contact, on the other hand, may signal deceit, disinterest, or insecurity.

eye contact
Gaze behavior in which a speaker looks at listeners' eyes.

Your face is the most important source of nonverbal cues as you deliver your speech, and your eyes carry more information than any other facial feature. As you speak, you will occasionally look at your notes. You may even glance away from the audience briefly as you try to put your thoughts into words. Yet you must keep coming back to the eyes of your listeners to check their understanding, interest, and evaluation of your message.

As a public speaker, your goal is to make eye contact with as much of the audience as often as possible. To do this, make sure that you take in your entire audience, from front to back and from left to right. Include all those boundaries in the scope of your eye contact, and look especially at those individuals who seem to be listening carefully and responding positively. Whether you actually make eye contact with each member of the audience is immaterial. You must create that impression. Again, this takes practice.

Movement

Effective **movement** benefits you, your audience, and your speech. First, place-to-place movement can actually help you relax. Moving to a presentational aid, for example, can help you energize and loosen up physically. From the audience's perspective, movement adds visual variety to your speech, and appropriate movement can arouse or rekindle listeners' interest. Most important, though, physical movement serves your speech by guiding the audience's attention. Through movement, you can underscore key ideas, mark major transitions, or intensify an appeal for belief or action.

movement
A speaker's motion from place to place during speech delivery.

Remember that your speech starts the moment you enter your audience's presence. Your behavior, including your movements, sends signals about your attitudes toward the audience and your speech topic. When your time to speak arrives, approach your speaking position confidently, knowing that you have something important to say. If you use a lectern, don't automatically box yourself into one position behind it. Moving to the side or the front of it reduces both the physical and the psychological distance between you and your listeners and may be especially helpful when you conclude your speech with a persuasive appeal.

Make certain that your movements are selective and serve a purpose. Avoid random pacing. Instead, we recommend small movements within each key idea or major part of the speech, but large movements when you transition from one key idea to the next. Movement to mark a transition should occur at the beginning or the end of a sentence, not in the middle. Finally, bring the speech to a satisfying psychological conclusion, and pause for a second or two before gathering your materials and moving toward your seat.

SPEAKING WITH CONFIDENCE

Delivery is an important part of the speech that is associated with speaker nervousness. For me, speaking extemporaneously helped me feel more confident because I didn't have to memorize my speeches. However, I still get nervous when delivering my speeches, which made me feel like I had extra energy flowing through my body. In this chapter, I learned that all that energy can be used to my advantage and actually make me speak more confidently. For example, I channeled my nervous energy to my voice by speaking loudly and clearly. Additionally, I managed my nervousness by walking when transitioning and using hand gestures, which reduced the nervous energy in my body. To ensure my delivery was effective and that it would help me feel more confident when delivering my speeches, I always practiced my delivery in front of my friends. My friends gave me suggestions about how to gesture and what words to emphasize and that made me less nervous when delivering my speeches in class.

Lilibeth Fuentes
Penn State Hazleton

Gestures

gestures
Movements of a speaker's hands, arms, and head while delivering a speech.

Gestures—movements of a speaker's hands, arms, and head—are as natural a part of human communication as spoken language. Gestures punctuate and emphasize verbal messages for the benefit of listeners and ease the process of encoding those messages for speakers. Studies show that people asked to communicate without gestures produce labored speech marked by increased hesitations and pauses. Such speakers also demonstrate decreased fluency and inflection, and they use fewer high-imagery words.[6] Hand gestures, then, seem to help speakers retrieve elusive words from their memories.[7]

Gestures are important supplements to our verbal messages; at times, they even replace words altogether. As a public speaker, you can use gestures to indicate the size of objects, to recreate some bodily motion, to emphasize or underscore key ideas, to point to things such as presentational aids, or to trace the flow of your ideas.

To be effective, gestures must be coordinated with your words and must appear natural and spontaneous. Any gesture should be large enough for the audience to see it clearly. The speaker whose gestures are barely visible over the top of a lectern may appear timid, unsure, or nervous. Speakers who gesture too much—who talk with their hands—may be perceived as nervous, flighty, or excitable.

The following two generalizations from research on gestures are particularly helpful for the public speaker. First, people who are confident, relaxed, and have high status tend to expand into the space around them and use gestures that are wider than those of other people. Speakers who wish to emphasize their authority can do so by increasing the width of their gestures. Second, a wide, palms-up gesture creates an openness that is entirely appropriate when a speaker is appealing for a certain belief or urging the audience to some action. A palm-down gesture carries more force and authority and can be used to command an audience into action or to exhort them to a certain belief.

As a speaker, adapt the size of your gestures to the size of your audience. Before a crowd of several thousand, your gestures should be more expansive than when you stand at the front of a small classroom. In a cavernous auditorium, you must adjust your gestures, facial expressions, and eye contact so they will be clear to those in the back rows.

Journal: Improving Physical Delivery

Think of a person (a classmate, an instructor, a celebrity, a politician) you believe is an ineffective speaker. What aspects of her or his physical delivery do you find problematic? Jot down two pieces of advice to improve his or her delivery, using suggestions from this module.

Key Points: Elements of Physical Delivery

1. Appearance
2. Posture
3. Facial expression
4. Eye contact
5. Movement
6. Gestures

Delivering Speeches Online

13.5 Identify the four challenges of delivering speeches online.

The number of college students taking courses online is growing exponentially. As such, it is no surprise that students have favorable attitudes toward online education and often take online courses because it is convenient. Students enrolled in online courses indicate that they learned just as much, or even more, than they would have in a traditional face-to-face class.[8] Research also indicates that students who take public speaking classes online do not differ in terms of their communication apprehension or perceived public speaking skills. In fact, students who complete online public speaking courses are just as competent speakers as their peers who complete a traditional face-to-face public speaking class.[9]

So far in this chapter, you have learned about the four methods of delivery and the importance of proper vocal and physical delivery. Although these principals were developed for speeches delivered in face-to-face contexts, they certainly apply to speeches delivered online as well. However, there are some differences as well as unique challenges to delivering online speeches (whether prerecorded or live streaming) that speakers should keep in mind. In the following sections, we discuss four such challenges that are adapted from iTalk LLC's manual for creating and delivering effective online presentations.[10]

Radio broadcasts, such as those delivered in the first half of the 20th century by politicians such as former British Prime Minister Winston Churchill and former U.S. president Franklin Delano Roosevelt, are technically examples of mass communication. However, they share many of the same challenges that you will face when delivering speeches online.

Using Technology

When recording your speech, it's essential that you are familiar with how the technology and equipment work. (Can you imagine how disappointing it would be to deliver a fabulous speech only to find out it didn't record or transmit appropriately?) Practice using technology as part of your overall rehearsal, asking friends for feedback not only on your content and organization, but also on your use of and interaction with the equipment. Consider the following: Are you standing an appropriate distance from the camera? Are you close enough to the microphone to be audible? If this is a live speech, are you familiar with any feedback options from the audience, such as a live chat?

In addition to the technology you use to record or transmit your speech, you may also use technology as a presentational aid. Showing interesting graphics and videos (via PowerPoint, Prezi, etc.) prevents your online speech from being 5 to 7 minutes of "talking head"—a phenomena much more pronounced when delivering speeches online than in person. You will study specific tips on developing outstanding presentational aids in Chapter 14, but for now remember that such aids bring needed variety when recording your speech.

Engaging a Virtual Audience

As in face-to-face presentations, your vocal and physical delivery are important tools to energize and engage an online audience. The same advice on pauses, eye contact, pronunciation, and appearance apply, with a few additional considerations. Keep the following points in mind:

- Your *appearance* may be even more important when delivering online speeches compared to face-to-face speeches because your audience may not have prior knowledge of who you are (e.g., your skills, your experiences). So, they will "judge" you immediately based on your attire and grooming.
- Your *facial expressions*, *movements*, and *gestures* need to be expanded when delivering speeches online. To engage in movements between parts of your speech and key

ideas, you will have to zoom out on your camera to ensure you remain within the recording frame. Therefore, subtle facial expressions and hand gestures will need to be exaggerated so your audience members can see your facial expressions and gestures clearly via their screens.

- Similarly, you will likely need to increase the *volume* of your voice slightly when delivering speeches online. There may be times when you move farther away from the recording equipment, which will reduce the recording volume. In short, speak up, especially when you move away from the camera.

- *Eye contact* remains important in an online speech. Although you can't scan your audience for a friendly face, you do need to interact with the camera as the gateway to your audience. If that strikes you as unnerving or unnatural, you might have a friend present to serve as someone with whom you can make eye contact (if that is permissible with your instructor), or even have a photo of a loved one next to the camera. In some cases, students delivering online speeches are required to assemble an audience, which will make your eye contact appear more natural.

Keeping these tips in mind, as well as the other advice on vocal and physical delivery you learned in this chapter, will help to ensure confidence and success.

Dealing with a Lack of Immediate Feedback

In Chapter 5 Learning Objective 5.6, you learned about the importance of analyzing your audience while you speak. This is a luxury you are not always afforded when delivering speeches online. Although the chat function may be enabled in a live-streaming speech, you may not be able to see your audience members to tell if they are confused or bored versus engaged and intrigued. To ensure that this constraint is a nonissue, go back to the basics. Remember the "Golden Rule of Public Speaking"—tell them what you are going to tell them, tell them, then tell them what you told them. Spend some extra time studying the functions of an effective introduction, the strategy of 4 S's along with transitions, and the functions of an effective conclusion. A well-organized speech is easy to follow, particularly when your audience lacks the means to deliver that feedback at all or in a subtle manner.

Personalizing Your Presentation

In your traditional face-to-face classes, you have the benefit of chatting with your classmates before or after class, overhearing their conversations with other students, or even running into them on campus. But in online classes, you may not know who your fellow students are; they may live next door, five states away, or halfway around the world. While technology and social media may allow you to get to know them, the format of an online class does not always encourage close relationships. Therefore, when you give an online speech, we recommend that you personalize your speech to help your audience members get to know you. Consider two suggestions.

First, emphasize your personal experience with your topic. When possible, support your key ideas with a narration of your personal experiences combined with solid research and testimony from experts. Second, let your personality show in your delivery. You might incorporate some appropriate and tasteful humor if that feels comfortable to you. After all, humor is an effective attention-getting strategy and we often evaluate people we find humorous quite favorably. Humor is not limited to your words! Think of Mr. Bean's facial expressions, gestures, and movements as an example of nonverbal means to amuse the audience.

Online speeches are nothing to fear. With the knowledge you accumulate throughout this book, you will be prepared and confident to engage audiences both near and far with your ideas and stellar delivery.

› SUMMARY

Delivering Your Speech

Methods of Delivery

13.1 Distinguish among the four methods of delivering speeches.

As a speaker, you can select one, or a combination, of four methods of delivery: *impromptu speaking*, or speaking without advance preparation; *speaking from memory*; *speaking from manuscript*; and *speaking extemporaneously*, or from notes.

Qualities of Effective Delivery

13.2 Apply the three qualities of effective delivery in your speech.

As you begin to think about the way you deliver a speech, keep in mind three qualities. First, effective delivery helps both listeners and speakers. Second, your best delivery looks and feels natural, comfortable, and spontaneous. Third, delivery is best when nonverbal and verbal messages complement and reinforce each other.

Elements of Vocal Delivery

13.3 Incorporate the seven elements of effective vocal delivery into your speech.

Vocal delivery includes your rate, use of pauses, volume, pitch, inflection, articulation, and pronunciation.

Elements of Physical Delivery

13.4 Incorporate the six elements of physical delivery into your speech.

Your appearance, posture, facial expressions, eye contact, movements, and gestures make up the elements of your *physical delivery*.

Delivering Speeches Online

13.5 Identify the four challenges of delivering speeches online.

Speakers should consider four challenges of delivering speeches online: using technology, engaging a virtual audience, dealing with lack of feedback, and personalizing the speech.

USING PRESENTATIONAL AIDS

→ LEARNING OBJECTIVES

After studying this chapter, you should be able to

14.1 Articulate the five benefits of using presentational aids in speeches.

14.2 Describe, with examples, the nine classifications of presentational aids.

14.3 Use the four types of projected presentational aids.

14.4 Apply the strategies for using presentational aids effectively before and during a speech.

An officer carries the lifeless body of a three-year-old Syrian refugee ashore.

Air Force One touches down in Havanna.

Women voters cover suffrage leader Susan B. Anthony's grave with "I Voted" stickers in November 2016.

Doctors in full protective gear treat a young boy suffering with Ebola in Liberia.

I f you form a vivid mental image of any of these events, you prove the haunting power of pictures. We have all grown up in a visually oriented society. Even our language reflects the power of the visual message: "A picture is worth a thousand words." "I wouldn't have believed it if I hadn't seen it with my own eyes."

Today, our newspapers, magazines, and device screens are filled with pictures. When the news is bad, we expect to see pictures or videos of the airplane wreckage, the flooding, or the aftermath of the earthquake. When the news is good, we expect to see pictures of the winning team or the heroic rescue. We are, indeed, people for whom "seeing is believing." As a speaker, you need not rely only on words to communicate your ideas precisely and powerfully; you can also add force and impact to many messages by incorporating a visual dimension.

In this chapter, we discuss **presentational aids**, which may be an important component of your speech. In the next few sections, we consider the benefits of using presentational aids, the different types available to speakers, and strategies for using presentational aids effectively. Although presentational aids often enhance the quality of a presentation, it is important that you understand why and when using a presentational aid serves you well.

presentational aids
Visual and/or auditory aids used to enhance the clarity and impact of your message.

The Value of Presentational Aids

14.1 Articulate the five benefits of using presentational aids in speeches.

Students often ask us if it's worthwhile to use presentational aids in their speeches. Our answer is consistently, "It depends; you need a good reason for developing and using presentational aids." We have seen far too many speakers assume that if they pull together a cool Prezi presentation, show an elaborate poster, or play a segment of music that their speech will captivate their audience. Nothing could be further from the truth. The best presentational aid in the world will not save you from a speech that is inappropriate, disorganized, poorly worded, or sloppily delivered. However, a well-designed, appropriate presentational aid can add significantly to the effectiveness of the speech that is *already* carefully constructed, worded, and delivered in five ways: increased message clarity, reinforced message impact, enhanced speaker dynamism, enhanced speaker confidence, and increased speaker credibility.

Increased Message Clarity

First, presentational aids give your speech greater clarity. They can show the ornate beauty of the Grand Palace in Thailand, illustrate the demographic breakdown of voters in the past election, or explain the process of monitoring and controlling air traffic. You can convey detailed statistical information more clearly in a simplified line graph than by merely reciting the data. Speeches using a spatial organizational pattern often benefit particularly from visual reinforcement.

Presentational aids are not unlike the figures in this book. Recall that Figure 1.2 reveals the communication elements in the model of public speaking. We explain these elements within our narrative; the model clarifies that content and allows you to visualize it.

Reinforced Message Impact

Second, presentational aids give your speech greater impact. Because listeners both hear and see your message, they are more involved with your speech. This added sensory participation appeals to audience members with various learning styles, lessens the opportunity for distractions, and increases message retention for longer periods of time.

One student, Leeba, used three photographs to enhance the impact of her speech in which she encouraged her classmates to try snowboarding. The first picture was of Leeba and her friends—all smiling and looking happy. The second picture was of a gorgeous sunset behind the snow-covered mountains. The third picture was an action shot of Leeba doing a 360-degree spin midair as she soared over the half-pipe edge. She ended her speech by stating, "You will love snowboarding. You will make some great friends. And you will be all smiles on the mountain," as she displayed her first picture one last time to enhance the impact of her message.

Increased Speaker Dynamism

Third, presentational aids increase your speaker dynamism. Gestures and movements are important parts of your delivery, but many speakers have difficulty incorporating them in a natural and meaningful way. Using presentational aids forces you to move, to point, and to become physically involved with your speech. Your gestures and movements become motivated and meaningful, and, consequently, you appear more dynamic and forceful.

Enhanced Speaker Confidence

Fourth, using presentational aids in your speech can increase your confidence as a public speaker. Clear, stylish presentational aids that you have practiced using can help you relax in two ways. First, knowing that your presentational aids will enhance the clarity and impact of your message will help you feel secure that your audience will retain your message. Second, revealing your presentational aids gives purpose to your movement and gestures, and this will help burn off some of your nervous energy.

Enhanced Speaker Credibility

Fifth, using presentational aids can enhance your perceived speaker credibility. Research summarized in Timothy Mottet and his colleagues' *Handbook of Instructional Communication: Rhetorical and Relational Perspectives* indicates that speakers who are clear, impactful, dynamic, and confident are perceived to be credible by their audience members.[1] Other studies suggest that speakers' credibility is affected by how well they use technology and presentational aids.[2] Unfortunately, many speakers not only use the wrong type of presentational aids, but they also use them incorrectly. Therefore, we encourage you to carefully consider what type of presentational aids to use (the topic of our next section) and that you practice using your presentational aids well in advance of your speaking date. Just as properly used presentational aids can enhance your speaker credibility, poorly used presentational aids will decrease your speaker credibility. You don't want to make that mistake.

> **Journal: Beneficial Aid?**
>
> Suppose you are giving a speech to persuade your audience to purchase ethically made clothing, and you used photographs of the working conditions in third-world sweatshops as a presentational aid. Would this impact your audience members' understanding of your message and their perception of you as the speaker? If so, how?

SPEAKING WITH CONFIDENCE

Visual aids emphasize and stir interest in a speaker's topic. They can add dimension to the spoken word. My persuasive speech was on stem cell research. I knew that this topic was very controversial, and I didn't want my audience to get caught up in their own preconceived opinions. Using a visual aid that included a computer image of Christopher Reeve attached to a respirator in his wheelchair immediately captured the attention of my audience. I proceeded to explain all the possible medical advances and the thousands of individuals who could possibly be cured of their ailments by stem cell research. The visual image accompanied by my words left a lasting impression. Seeing the expressions on the audience's faces when they saw my visual aid helped me to feel more confident in my speaking ability.

Lauren Fishman
Suffolk County Community College, Selden

Types of Presentational Aids

14.2 Describe, with examples, the nine classifications of presentational aids.

Presentational aids come in many forms, but they can generally be divided into these classifications: objects, pictures, diagrams, graphs, charts, maps, film and video, handouts, and audio aids. You need to determine the type most appropriate to your presentation.

Objects

Objects may be either actual size, such as a digital camera, or scaled, such as an architect's model. Other three-dimensional presentational aids are, for instance, a fishing rod, a replica of the White House, or an iPad®.

Also included in the category of objects are people or animals you employ in delivering a speech. You might enlist a volunteer to help you demonstrate tests for color blindness or, with your instructor's permission, bring in a therapy dog for a speech on that topic. Objects used effectively can vivify your speech and carry a great deal of impact.

object
An actual item or three-dimensional model of an item used during the delivery of a speech.

Pictures

You have most likely heard the saying, "A picture is worth 1,000 words." A **picture** can make a speaker's presentation more concrete and vivid. It is difficult to imagine the differences among split-level houses, ranch-style houses, and shotgun-style houses without pictures of these different types of homes. A speaker trying to persuade the audience members to visit Raja Ampat Misool near West Papua (a province of Indonesia) without showing pictures of the colorful reefs, the volcanic islands, or the flocks of birds hovering over the crystal clear blue waters would be less effective compared to a speaker who showed powerful images of this beautiful area.

picture
A photograph, painting, drawing, or print used to make a point more vivid or convincing.

Speakers can also use pictures to vivify a point. Mateo delivered a persuasive speech about wearing a bicycle helmet. A few years earlier, he had a serious bicycle accident and spent several days in the hospital. During that time, Mateo's family took several pictures of his injuries. When delivering his speech, Mateo displayed several of these pictures as a part of his PowerPoint presentation. The pictures were quite graphic and therefore enhanced the impact of his speech.

When you use pictures, make sure you select them with size and clarity in mind. Holding up a photo of the Palace of Versailles on your phone detracts from, rather than reinforces, your purpose because it is too small to be seen by audience members in the back of the room or online audience members. Pictures used as presentational aids often must be enlarged. If the room in which you'll speak has a visual document camera, such as an Elmo, you can project small pictures (as well as transparencies, videos, slide shows, etc.) on a screen for easy audience viewing. In an online speech, you may be able to share your desktop with the picture loaded.

Diagrams

Diagrams are graphics showing the parts of an object or organization or the steps in a process. A diagram could show the features of a commercial spacecraft design, the organizational structure of the U.S. judicial system, or the steps in the lost-wax method of casting jewelry. The best diagrams achieve their impact by simplifying and exaggerating key points. For example, no diagram of manageable size could illustrate all the parts of a hybrid, gas–electric car engine. However, a carefully constructed diagram, whether drawn on poster board or projected, could isolate and label key parts of that engine design.

diagram
A graphic, usually designed on a computer or drawn on poster board, showing the parts of an object or organization or the steps in a process.

Graphs

Graphs can be easily created using commonly available spreadsheet software such as Microsoft Excel and are effective presentational aids taking several forms.

line graph

A diagram used to depict changes among variables over time.

Line Graph   A **line graph** is useful in depicting trends and developments over time. A speaker might convincingly use a line graph to illustrate the rising cost of a college education during the previous 20 years. Some line graphs trace two or more variables. For example, one of our students, Ashkira, used a two-line graph in which she displayed the changes in gasoline prices and the average annual income during the past 10 years. Her line graph was easy to interpret because she used two different colors (blue and red) and she provided a legend on her graph where she noted: blue = gasoline prices, red = annual income. This chapter's "Ethical Decisions" feature also includes examples of line graphs.

pie, or circle, graph

A circular diagram used to show the relative proportions of a whole.

Pie, or Circle, Graph   A second type of graph, the **pie, or circle, graph**, is helpful when you want to show relative portions of the various parts of a whole. If you are analyzing the federal budget, for example, a pie graph could illustrate the percentage allocated for defense. Pie graphs can show proportions that people spend in particular activities in a typical 24-hour day, the causes of cancer deaths, and the composition of your university according to declared majors. When using a pie graph, emphasize the pertinent "slice" of the graph.

Edith used a pie graph to highlight key statistics in her informative speech about energy consumption in the United States. She had read conflicting assertions about the amount of renewable energy as a source and thought that her audience would benefit from learning how this particular source compared to other sources to make up U.S. energy consumption. A pie graph allowed her to do this effectively, as shown in Figure 14.1.

bar graph

A diagram used to show quantitative comparisons among variables.

Bar Graph   A **bar graph** is useful when comparing quantities or amounts. We can measure the economic health of an institution, a company, or a nation, for example, by learning whether it is "in the red" or "in the black." A bar graph contrasting deficits and profits, showing their relative size, provides a clear, visual indication of economic health, particularly when income is represented in black and deficits in red.

Edith also used a bar graph in her speech about U.S. energy consumption. After revealing the sources of energy consumption in her pie graph, she wanted to break down the specifics of renewable energy further. Edith found that there are seven noted sources of renewable energy, so she initially placed these into a pie graph as well. However, she found that seven "slices" were too many in a pie graph, so she transferred her data into a much clearer bar graph. See Figure 14.2.

Figure 14.1   Edith's Pie Graph

Pie graphs compare the percentages of a variable, here the sources of energy consumption.

SOURCE: U.S. Energy Information Administration, Monthly Energy Review, Table 1.3 and 10.1 (April 2016), preliminary data.

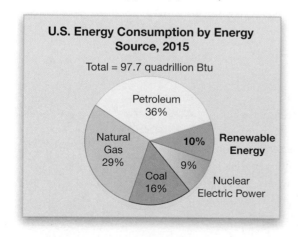

Figure 14.2   Edith's Bar Graph

Bar graphs compare quantities or amounts, here the sources of renewable energy.

SOURCE: U.S. Energy Information Administration, Monthly Energy Review, Table 1.3 and 10.1 (April 2016), preliminary data.

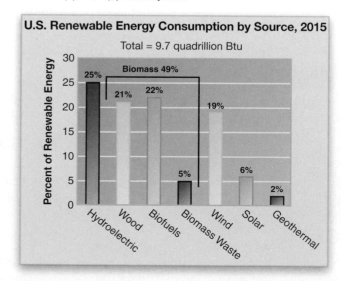

ETHICAL DECISIONS

IS SEEING BELIEVING?

Jayden chose involvement in student government as the topic for his persuasive speech. In his research, he discovered a decrease in the percentage of students voting in Student Government Association elections. He chose to focus on the past 6 years. He compiled the voting percentages and prepared his line graph, as shown in Figure 14.3A.

When Jayden evaluated the graph, he didn't think it sufficiently dramatized the decline in voting. He decided to include only the past 4 years when the percentage of students voting had decreased significantly. He increased the spacing in the vertical axis of his graph to emphasize the decline, as seen in Figure 14.3B.

Do you think Jayden's second graph is an unethical manipulation of data? Why or why not? What ethical guidelines should speakers follow as they design presentational aids to be vivid and memorable? Provide some examples of presentational aids speakers might use that would be unethical.

Figure 14.3A

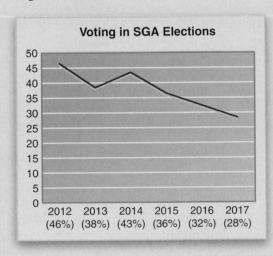

Figure 14.3B

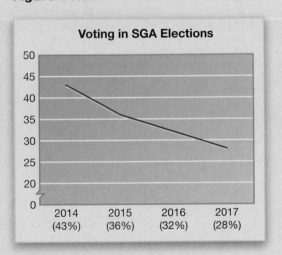

Charts

Like diagrams and graphs, **charts** condense a large amount of information into a small space. Speakers introducing new terms will sometimes list those words on a chart. This strategy is particularly effective if the words can be uncovered one at a time in the order they are discussed. Using charts, you could list the top 10 states in per capita lottery ticket sales or rank professional sports according to players' average salaries. A speaker detailing the solution phase of a problem–solution speech could list steps advocated on a chart and introduce them in the order they are discussed.

Joyce chose to inform her audience about how the Internet had facilitated greater global connectedness. Early in her speech she presented a chart (Figure 14.4) that showed the top five locations of the World's 3,424,971,237 Internet users. Using PowerPoint, she "flew in" her numbered list from bottom to top, creating suspense as to which country ranked first on the list.

chart
A graphic used to condense a large amount of information, to list the steps in a process, or to introduce new terms.

Maps

Maps lend themselves especially well to speeches discussing or referring to unfamiliar geographic areas. Speakers informing their listeners about the Temple City of Angkor Wat in Cambodia, the city of Fukuoka located on the northern coast of the Japanese island Kyushu, or the Bay of Pigs Invasion in Cuba would do well to include maps to illustrate their ideas. Although commercial maps are professionally prepared and look good, they may be either too small or too detailed for a speaker's purpose, particularly when delivering a speech online. If you cannot isolate and project a section of the map for a larger audience, prepare a simplified, large-scale map of the territory in question.

map
A graphic representation of a real or imaginary geographic area.

Figure 14.4 Joyce's Sample Chart

Charts gather information into a convenient format, here the top five countries for Internet use worldwide.

SOURCE: Internet World Stats, 2016 http://www.internetlivestats.com/internet-users-by-country/

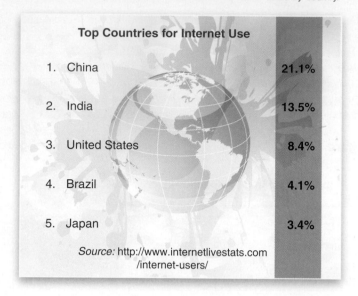

Film and Video

Films and videos are appropriate whenever action will enhance a visual presentation. For example, many speeches on social problems are significantly more compelling if the audience hears and sees graphic evidence of the problem (e.g., footage of a protest or rally; a segment of an interview with a Holocaust survivor). However, it is important that you, not your presentational aid, organize and present the ideas of your speech. Use only short video clips to illustrate your key ideas. (A grad school colleague once showed a 15-minute interview with the founder of a communication theory in order to explain that theory to the class in her 20-minute speech. Needless to say, she failed.)

Your imagination and your ability to limit yourself to brief clips are your primary obstacles when incorporating film and video into your speech. For example, using YouTube, Google Video, Netflix, or other online video sources, you might show listeners gymnast Alexander Artemev's amazing moves on the pommel horse; vintage concert clips of singer/performer Nina Hagen; world-renowned mime Marcel Marceau's character Bip; or newsreel of the 1940 collapse of the Tacoma Narrows Bridge, known as Galloping Gertie. Video and film can also introduce viewers to aspects of various cultures. One of our students, Henry, delivered an informative speech on the topic of Sufism, an Islamic tradition that is both mystical and multicultural. He informed his listeners how this tradition combines dance and music to express spiritual ecstasy. He played a videotape of the "whirling dervishes" dances of the Mevlevi Order, pointing out the religious significance of the dancers' gestures and movements.

Just remember that reliability is important when using film and video. Are you sure the clip you want won't disappear from YouTube? Does your classroom have reliable wifi? What will you do if Netflix encounters technical problems? Prepare for these situations in advance in order to avoid surprises the day of your speech.

Handouts

Another method of visually presenting material is the **handout**. Copies of any presentational aid—pictures, diagrams, graphs, charts, or maps—may be handed out to individual audience members. (The equivalent for an online speech would be posting the relevant document with your video, or emailing the audience members, if applicable.)

Handouts are appropriately used when the information cannot be effectively displayed or projected or when the audience needs to study or refer to the information after the speech.

Gwen, a student presenting her speech "The Power Résumé," used a handout to great benefit. She distributed a sample power résumé and referred to it at key intervals in her speech: "If you look at line 15, you will see . . . ." She had numbered the lines of the résumé in the margin so that the audience could find the references without fumbling. Not only could the audience refer to the résumé as Gwen discussed its key features, but many also probably saved it to use later as they prepared their own résumés. In a similar way, if you try to persuade your audience to contribute time and money to local charities, you will more likely achieve your goal if you distribute a handout with the name, address, telephone number, and a brief description of each charity.

If you are distributing handouts to listeners who are likely to receive handouts from other speakers on the same day you speak, use colored paper to distinguish your materials from your peers' materials. If you are the only speaker and are distributing several handouts, consider putting each one on a different color paper. It's easier to identify which handout you want your listeners to look at if you can say, "On the blue sheet . . . ," for example.

Audio and Other Aids

Audio aids are audio files (including music you play from iTunes or Amazon Music), Certain speech topics lend themselves to audio reinforcement of the message. A speech on Janis Joplin or Yo-Yo Ma, for example, would be more vivid and informative if the audience could hear a clip of a performance. Lindahl began her speech on the savant syndrome by playing 30 seconds of a recorded piano performance of Chopin's Polonaise no. 6 in A-Flat Major. Her first words were, "The person who was playing that music is considered disabled, but he heard this piece of music for the first time only minutes before sitting down to play it." A speech comparing Rod Stewart's and Sheryl Crow's versions of "The First Cut Is the Deepest" could hardly be effective without letting listeners hear examples from each of those artists.

audio aid
An audio file (e.g., mp3 file) used to clarify or prove a point by letting listeners hear an example.

Audio aids need not be confined to music topics, however. An audience listening to a speech on former British Prime Minister Winston Churchill could benefit from hearing his quiet eloquence as he addressed Great Britain's House of Commons and declared, "I have nothing to offer but blood, toil, tears, and sweat." And a speaker analyzing the persuasive appeals of radio and television advertisements could play pertinent examples.

You may want to appeal to senses other than sight and hearing. For example, a student of ours gave each audience member an envelope before her speech on aromatherapy. When she discussed the effects of certain scents on behavior, she had students open the envelopes and remove strips of lavender- and vanilla-scented paper, two of the scents she discussed. Think creatively and critically as you consider ways of supporting what you say.

Projection of Presentational Aids

14.3 Use the four types of projected presentational aids.

Once you have decided what type of presentational aids will best serve your audience, you must decide how to display them most effectively. **Projection** is especially appropriate when your audience is too large to see the presentational aids easily and clearly. In such a case, you may want to use projections such as PowerPoint slides, Breeze presentations, Prezi, or document cameras. (If you are using a projected presentational aid when delivering a speech online, you may want to send your audience members a

projection
A manner of displaying presentational aids by casting their images onto a screen or other background.

Presentational aids help listeners see as well as hear your message. Well-designed PowerPoint slides, for example, can enhance the impact of your ideas.

PowerPoint

Software that enables speakers to supplement their presentations with text, graphics, images, audio, and video.

copy of your slide show prior to your speech. You can then make references to the various slides throughout your speech to enable your audience members to follow along.)

PowerPoint

PowerPoint is software that enables speakers to supplement their presentations with text, graphics, images, audio, and video. The software's attractions are undeniable. PowerPoint can reassure an inexperienced speaker because in developing your slides you are predetermining your content and organization. Used well, PowerPoint can present a seamless blend of image, text, and spoken words.

Unfortunately, PowerPoint is not always used well. Two communication scholars surveyed research and concluded that "students are becoming less and less engaged by professors presenting with PowerPoint."[3] Some corporations have even restricted reliance on the use of PowerPoint in company presentations. Remember that *you* are the presenter, not PowerPoint. Avoid the temptation to blend into the background and narrate a slide show.

Many excellent online tutorials can help you learn how to use PowerPoint or adapt to specific versions of the software. Your college may offer workshops or courses that teach PowerPoint. Additionally, most libraries have ebooks with tutorials that can walk you through common features of the software.

Among the many display options PowerPoint provides, these are some things to keep in mind:

- *Clear the screen when you want listeners to focus just on you.* To replace any screen with solid black, just press B on the keyboard. Press the same key again to restore the PowerPoint image. Doing the same with the keyboard letter W replaces the image with a white screen.

- *Be familiar with your slides so you can skip ahead or go back if you need to.* Print the Outline View of your slides and keep it handy as a reference. To skip to a slide, just type the number of the slide you want to go to.

- *Limit or eliminate moving text.* Transitions that have text flying or spiraling in make the audience wait until movement has stopped in order to read. Eliminate animations or sound effects that distract listeners' attention from you and your message.[4]

- *Follow Guy Kawasaki's 10-20-30 rule.* Kawasaki, former Apple chief evangelist, is well known for touting his 10-20-30 PowerPoint use guidelines: (1) Never use more than 10 slides. (2) Never speak for more than 20 minutes. (3) Never use a font smaller than 30 points. While all three rules may not apply to every speaking class, rule 3 helps to guard against the problem of too much text on slides. At 30-point font, you are helping ensure that those in the back row will actually see your slides, and you prevent the corresponding problem of reading your speech from a bulleted list crammed into your slides.[5]

There are some occasions when using PowerPoint is counterproductive. For example, when you are trying to engage your audience's emotions or imaginations, when you are primarily interested in connecting with your listeners, when you want your listeners to be actively involved in creating the presentation with you, when your preparation time is limited, and when your audience suffers from PowerPoint fatigue.[6] Nick Morgan may have said it best: "You should use PowerPoint . . . sparingly. Don't think of it as wallpaper that's always there behind you, but a discrete moment in your talk when you turn to an illustration because it's too difficult to put the idea into mere words."[7]

Breeze Presentations

For many years, PowerPoint was the leading slideshow software used to aid speakers. Lately, however, Breeze Presenter has become increasingly popular. Breeze presentations, which are flash-based online presentations, can be created by converting existing PowerPoint presentations. You can also add narrations, audio files, video clips, pictures, and much more. Thus, because the general format of Breeze presentations is similar to that of PowerPoint presentations, we encourage you to follow the PowerPoint guidelines previously discussed when developing and using Breeze presentations.

Prezi Presentations

A 2016 survey that focused on the use of projected visual aids indicates that presenters are looking for new ways of visualizing their ideas and to make their presentations more conversational. Therefore, many professionals and academics are turning to Prezi presentations. A **Prezi** is a presentation that includes both text and visuals such as graphs, photos, and diagrams. Unlike PowerPoint that uses multiple slides, Prezi presentations only contain one slide. During your presentation, you can zoom in and out of different parts of your Prezi. You also have display options for different speaking situations. For example, in a face-to-face class, you can simply display your Prezi through your classroom projector. In an online public speaking class, you can show a Prezi to your audience on a computer through your Prezi account, or better yet, you can provide a link to your Prezi presentation so your remote audience members can view it on their own computers as they listen to your speech. As of the time of this writing, you can visit the Prezi website to learn more about how to use this newer method of projected presentational aids and download a free manual titled "How to Give a Killer Presentation to Impress Your Boss" as a PDF file.[8]

Prezi
A one-slide presentation that includes both text and visuals such as graphs, photos, and diagrams.

Document Cameras

Today's high-tech visual presenters such as Elmo offer the advantage of enlarging and projecting visual aids without the work of preparing transparencies. These document cameras can project transparencies, computer slide shows, and computer animation as well as images of three-dimensional objects. Many models feature autofocus and power zoom magnification controlled by wireless remotes.

Journal: Best Use of Projected Presentational Aids
Based on your experiences as an audience member in your public speaking class and as a student in other classes, what would you say are the most important characteristics of a successfully projected presentational aid? Please explain your answer.

Strategies for Using Presentational Aids

14.4 Apply the strategies for using presentational aids effectively before and during a speech.

Remember that even the most brilliant presentational aid cannot salvage a poorly planned, poorly delivered speech. Visuals can aid, but they cannot resuscitate, a weak speech. On the other hand, even the most carefully designed and professionally executed presentational aid can be spoiled by clumsy handling during a presentation. The effect of public speaking is cumulative, with each element contributing toward one final effect. This section offers some practical guidelines on how to use presentational aids in your public speaking class and in your future professional career.

Before the Speech

Effective use of presentational aids begins well before the day of your speech. Consider the following tips.

Journal: Visual Information

If you were asked to deliver a speech in which your goal is to persuade your classmates to refrain from texting while driving, what types of information would be appropriate to display visually? Provide two examples, including the type of visual aid you would select. Support your selections.

Determine the Information to Be Presented Visually Sections of a presentation that are complex or detailed may be particularly appropriate for visualization. Be careful, however, not to use too many presentational aids. The focus in a speech is on the spoken word. Multimedia presentations can be exciting; they may also be extremely difficult to coordinate. Handling too many objects or charts quickly becomes cumbersome and distracting.

Select the Type of Presentational Aid Best Suited to Your Resources and Speech The information you need to present, the amount of preparation time you have, your technical expertise at producing the aid, the equipment available to you, and the cost involved will all influence the presentational aid you select. If preparing quality presentational aids to illustrate your speech will take more time or expertise than you have, you are probably better off without them. A presentational aid that calls attention to its poor production is a detriment, no matter how important the information it contains.

Ensure the Correct Sizing A speaker addressing an audience of 5,000 would not want to use a video clip displayed on a single, small screen. In a face-to-face class, a bar graph on poster board should be visible to more than just the first few rows of students. In an online speech, your audience's view of an object may be limited by the distance you stand from the camera.

If possible, practice with your presentational aids in the environment in which you will speak to ensure that they are an appropriate size. For example, position or project the aid and then sit in the farthest seat possible. If you can read your aid from that distance, it is sufficient in size. If you cannot, either enlarge or eliminate the aid.

Ensure the Presentational Aid Communicates the Information Clearly Simplicity should be your guiding principle in constructing your presentational aid. Michael Talman, a graphic design consultant, compares a graphic in a presentation to "going by a highway billboard at 55 miles per hour. Its effectiveness can be judged by how quickly the viewer sees and understands its message."[9]

Speakers sometimes construct PowerPoint presentations using all the special effects or posters and slides in Technicolor to make them lively and interesting. However, too many effects or too much color, like too much information, clutters and confuses. Limiting special effects and the range of colors, as well as muting secondary visual elements such as frames, grids, arrows, rules, and boxes, can clarify the primary information you want to convey.[10] For specific advice, see "Theory into Practice: Designing Clear Presentational Aids."

Construct a Presentational Aid That Is Professional in Appearance In the business and professional world, a hand-lettered poster, no matter how neatly done, is inappropriate. Professionals understand the importance of a good impression and are willing to pay graphic designers to help them create polished presentational aids. Graphics programs can allow you to create a neat and polished presentational aids, but if you aren't comfortable doing this, you might hire an art student to draw and letter a presentational aid you have designed.

If you throw together a chart or graph the night before your speech, that is exactly what it will look like. Your hastily prepared work will undermine an image of careful and thorough preparation.

Practice Using Your Presentational Aid A conscientious speaker will spend hours preparing a speech; presentational aids are a part of that presentation. Just as you rehearse the words of your speech, you should rehearse referring to your presentational aid; uncovering and covering charts; advancing slides; zooming in and out in your Prezi presentation; and writing on a whiteboard, a flip chart, or a sheet of paper projected by a document camera. In short, if you plan to use presentational aids, learn how to use them

Theory into Practice (TIP)

DESIGNING CLEAR PRESENTATIONAL AIDS

Whether your presentational aids will be projected slides or transparencies, or charts displayed on poster board, these aids will have a positive impact only if they are clear and readable. Consider the following guidelines before preparing any visuals.[11]

Focus

- *Focus on a few key points.* Resist the temptation to present all your information visually. Select ideas that are the most important or that can best be made through the use of presentational aids.

- *Present ideas one at a time.* Don't let the audience get ahead of you. For example, if you are discussing the first of five solutions for road rage, keep steps 2 through 5 out of audience view. If you are using PowerPoint, build your list through a series of slides. If you display a list of steps using a document camera, cover the steps you have not yet discussed, revealing each when you get to it.

Layout

- *Use a landscape (horizontal) page format rather than a portrait (vertical) format.* Text displayed horizontally is easier to read and gives you a better chance of expressing an idea in a single line.

- *Use left-margin alignment.* It is easier to read than full- or right-margin justification.

- *Use bullets or numbers to highlight your key points.* If you have several key ideas, number them. Listeners can more readily focus on the appropriate part of the visual aid if they see a number when they hear you say, "My third suggestion. . ."

- *Use no more than six words per line.* Longer sentences are more difficult to read and remember. Learning how to condense and simplify your message also hones your speaking skills.

- *Compose your text in the top half or two-thirds of your slide or document, with no more than six lines per page.* This ensures better viewing for those in the back of the room.

Fonts

- *Use strong, straight fonts.* Arial, Helvetica, and Times New Roman are good choices. Ornate fonts are more difficult to read.

- *Use no more than two fonts per page or screen.* Too many fonts can make your presentational aid more difficult to read.

- *Select a font size large enough to be read easily from the back row.* Minimum font size will vary according to room size and the distance between the projector and the screen. Check font size before your presentation.

Color and Art

- *Use color to enhance your presentational aids.* Research suggests that color can increase the audience's understanding and retention of information. Select colors that highlight the ideas you present. For example, a red line may reinforce a line graph showing a decline in student contributions to charitable organizations. Color can also complement the mood of a speech. A presentational aid for an informative speech on the celebration of Mardi Gras might use bright colors.

- *Limit the number of colors in your presentational aid.* Too many colors make reading a visual aid more difficult. Use no more than six colors per presentational aid and even fewer if the aid contains only text.

- *Avoid "chartjunk."*[12] Irrelevant graphics and art clutter and detract from your aid. An effective presentational aid draws the reader's attention to key points you are making in your speech.

Animations and Video Clips

- *Use the "insert" option in PowerPoint and Breeze Presentations to add animations and video clips to your presentational aids.* If you have downloaded or recorded your own video clips, you can insert the video clips directly into your presentation. If you're using a video clip found online, you can insert the URL to the video clip. If so, we suggest you queue up the video clip before you begin your presentation to avoid delays while it is buffering.

- *Use brief animations and video clips that illustrate your point.* Remember that you, as the speaker, should be the focus of your presentation, not your presentational aid.

effectively *before* your speech. As previously discussed, speakers who use technology well are perceived as credible. On the other hand, speakers who mismanage their use of technology are perceived as incompetent and untrustworthy.

Arrange for Safe Transportation of Your Presentational Aids   Presentational aids worth using are worth transporting safely. Your laptop or device needs obvious care. Poster boards should be protected from moisture and bending. Cover your presentational aid with plastic to protect it from that freak rainstorm you encounter just before speech class.

If you roll up paper or poster board charts, carry them to different classes, or leave them in a car trunk throughout the day, you cannot expect them to stay flat when you speak.

Carry Backup Supplies with You An exciting and informative presentation can be ruined when technology fails as you are preparing to speak. Make an inventory of equipment you may need—such as extension cords, bulbs, and batteries—and then take them with you. Also, email your presentational aids or post them to the cloud. Sometimes students' flash drives aren't recognized by the classroom computer, so having a backup file elsewhere is a safe and secure way of accessing your work.

Position the Presentational Aid Properly Get to the place where you will speak *before* the audience arrives. Check the height of the easel if you are using a flip chart or poster board. If you are projecting text and images, make sure that the equipment works. Ensure that wifi is working and that you can load your files. Position or project your presentational aid in the most desirable location. Make sure that the maximum number of people will see it and that nothing obstructs the audience's view. If you are not to be the first speaker, have your presentational aid and any necessary equipment out of the way but readily located so that you can set up quickly and with little disruption.

Test Your Presentational Aid Finally, if you are using PowerPoint slides or projected documents, make sure that they are in focus and in the correct order, and that any remote control you plan to use works. If possible, have any online videos ready to display to keep the audience from suffering lag time during your speech while you wait for a video to buffer. If there are people already in the room, you may not want to "give away" your topic by displaying one of your presentational aids. Some speakers prepare a test aid with the word Test on it. Although this keeps the audience from seeing part of the speech before you deliver it, it reveals little thought or creativity. A test aid with a creative title for your speech can create interest in your topic without revealing key information. In fact, it could motivate your audience to listen even before you utter your first word as it arouses curiosity.

During the Speech

Not even the most careful preparation of a presentational aid guarantees that it will work for you as you deliver your speech. Keep the following commonsense guidelines in mind as you incorporate the aid into your delivery.

Display the Presentational Aid Only When Appropriate A presentational aid is designed to attract attention and convey information. If it is visible at the beginning of the speech, the audience may focus on it, rather than on what you are saying. Your aid should be seen only when you are ready to discuss the point it illustrates. When you complete your point and it is no longer relevant, cover it again or remove it from the audience's view. You want them to move on to the next idea with you, rather than linger on the presentational aid.

If you are using projections, have someone cued to turn the lights off and the projector on at the appropriate time. If your presentational aid is on poster board, cover it with a blank poster board, or turn the blank side to the audience. If you are using PowerPoint, you may want to include a blank, black slide between your slides to ensure you only display content when it is discussed in the speech.

Occasionally, a speaker will stop speaking, uncover a presentational aid, and then continue. This is where rehearsal can really help you. You want to avoid creating unnecessary breaks in the flow of your speech. With practice, you will be able to keep talking as you uncover or project your aid.

Talk to Your Audience—Not to the Presentational Aid Remember, eye contact is a speaker's most important nonverbal tool. Sustained visual interaction with your audience keeps their attention on you and allows you to monitor their feedback regarding

---

Key Points: Strategies for Using Presentational Aids before the Speech

1. Determine the information to be presented visually.
2. Select the type of aid best suited to your resources and speech.
3. Ensure the correct sizing.
4. Make sure that the aid communicates the information clearly.
5. Construct an aid that is professional in appearance.
6. Practice using your aid.
7. Arrange for safe transportation of your aid.
8. Carry backup supplies with you.
9. Properly position the aid.
10. Test your presentational aid.

your speech. Turning your back to your listeners undermines your impact. For this reason, use prepared graphics rather than a dry erase board.

Refer to the Presentational Aid   Speakers sometimes stand at the lectern using their notes or reading their manuscript, relatively far from their presentational aid. This creates two lines of vision and can confuse your audience. It may also give the impression that you must rely on your notes because you do not fully understand what the presentational aid conveys. If that's the case, your perceived speaker credibility will plummet quickly.

Other speakers carry their notes with them as they move to the aid, referring to them as they point out key concepts. This is cumbersome and again reinforces the image of a speaker unsure of what he or she wants to say.

A well-constructed presentational aid should function as a set of notes. The information represented on the aid should trigger the explanation you will provide without any additional assistance.

Point to your presentational aid with the hand closer to it. (For example, if you stand to the left of your presentational aid—from the speaker's perspective—then use your right hand when pointing to the aid.) This keeps your body open and makes communication physically more direct with your audience. If you use a pointer to refer to the aid, have it easily accessible, use it only when pointing to the presentational aid, and set it down immediately after you are finished with it. Too many speakers pick up a pen to refer to their aid and end up playing with it during the rest of the speech.

Keep Your Presentational Aid in View until the Audience Understands Your Point   Remember that you are more familiar with your speech than your audience is. Too often, a speaker hurries through an explanation and covers or removes an aid before the audience fully comprehends its significance or the point it makes. Just as you should not reveal your aid too soon, do not cover it up too quickly. Give your audience the time necessary to digest the information it conveys. As you discuss and describe the presentational aid, check your audience's response. Many will likely signal their understanding of the presentational aid by nodding their heads or changing their posture.

Use Handouts with Caution   Of all the forms of presentational aids, the handout may be the most troublesome. If you distribute handouts before your remarks, the audience is already ahead of you. Passing out information during a presentation can be distracting, especially if you stop talking as you do so. In addition, the rustling of paper can distract the speaker and other audience members. Disseminating material after the presentation eliminates distractions but does not allow the listener to refer to the printed information as you are explaining it. In general, then, use handouts in a public speech only if that is the best way to clarify and give impact to your ideas.

You will encounter some speaking situations, such as a business presentation, that benefit from, and may demand, handout material. Those audiences are often decision-making groups. During an especially technical presentation, the audience members may need to take notes. Afterward, they may need to study the information presented. Handouts provide a record of the presenter's remarks and supplementary information the speaker did not have time to explain.

Key Points: Strategies for Using Presentational Aids during the Speech

1. Display the aid only when appropriate.

2. Talk to your audience—not to the aid.

3. Refer to the aid.

4. Keep your aid in view until the audience understands your point.

5. Use handouts with caution.

> **SUMMARY**

Using Presentational Aids

The Value of Presentational Aids

14.1 Articulate the five benefits of using presentational aids in speeches.

Presentational aids can add clarity to a speaker's message, reinforce the impact of the message, make a speaker's delivery seem more dynamic, enhance a speaker's confidence, and enhance the speaker's credibility.

Types of Presentational Aids

14.2 Describe, with examples, the nine classifications of presentational aids.

- Presentational aids include objects, pictures, diagrams, graphs, charts, maps, film and video, handouts, and audio/other aids.
- Specific types of graphs are line graphs, pie (or circle) graphs, and bar graphs.

Projection of Presentational Aids

14.3 Use the four types of projected presentational aids.

- When using projected presentational aids (PowerPoint, Breeze or Prezi presentations, and document cameras), *focus* on just a few key points and present them one at a time.
- For graphics that contain text, use horizontal *layout,* with text placed in the top half or two-thirds and with the left margin aligned.
- Slides should have no more than six words per line, no more than six lines per page, with bullets or numbers highlighting key points.
- Use strong, straight *fonts,* with no more than two fonts on each graphic. Finally, select *color and art* that amplify the impact of the graphic without cluttering it.

Strategies for Using Presentational Aids

14.4 Apply the strategies for using presentational aids effectively before and during a speech.

- To use graphics or other presentational aids for maximum impact, take the following steps *before* the speech: (1) determine the information to be presented; (2) select the type of aid best suited to your resources and topic; (3) ensure easy viewing by all audience members; (4) ensure that the aid communicates its information clearly; (5) construct an aid that appears carefully or professionally done; (6) practice using the aid; (7) arrange for safe transportation of the aid; (8) carry backup supplies in case of equipment failure; (9) properly position the aid before beginning the speech; and (10) test the aid before using it.
- While delivering the speech, remember the following: (1) display the aid only when appropriate; (2) talk to the audience, not to the aid; (3) refer to the aid; (4) keep the aid in view until the audience understands the point it makes; and (5) use handouts with caution.

SPEAKING TO INFORM

→ LEARNING OBJECTIVES

After studying this chapter, you should be able to

15.1 Explain, with examples, the three goals of informative speeches.

15.2 Identify, with examples, the eight informative speech categories.

15.3 Apply the five guidelines for developing an effective informative speech.

On September 7, 2016, Tim Cook, CEO of Apple Inc., and his colleagues held an informative event in San Francisco, California. During this event, they revealed new products, described how existing products had been improved, and shared their ideas for the future. In other words, the Apple representatives delivered a series of informative speeches.[1]

We live in an information age—new information is generated and disseminated every minute of every day. The general public has access to a wide range of information through a few simple clicks on their devices. Today, 84 percent of Americans use the Internet, and that percentage is even higher among young adults who are 18 to 25 years old.[2] Worldwide, there were 3,578,000,000 Internet users as of February 28, 2017, and that number increases by approximately 500 new users every minute. In fact, the number of Internet users has increased by more than 860 percent since the year 2000. These 3.5 billion people use the Internet for a variety of reasons, and one prominent reason is to gain information.[3]

Given our human drive to obtain new information, you should view the opportunity to speak informatively as one to help your audience and to meet their needs. This chapter will help you do just that, by teaching you the goals of informative speeches, the categories of informative speeches, and the essential guidelines for developing informative speeches effectively. This information, when combined with all you have learned so far in this course, will help put you on the path to success.

Goals of a Speech to Inform

15.1 Explain, with examples, the three goals of informative speeches.

We seek information for various reasons: We want to *know*, *understand*, and/or *use* information. Therefore, the goals of anyone delivering a **speech to inform** are to impart knowledge, enhance understanding, and/or enable application.

speech to inform
A speech designed to convey new or useful information in a balanced, objective way.

- *To impart knowledge.* Suppose you decided to prepare an informative speech about TIME Slippers (a new type of shoe). Your specific purpose could be: "To inform my classmates about a new type of shoe called TIME Slippers." Because this is a new brand of shoes, your listeners probably know little about this topic, and you can readily assume that your speech would add to their knowledge about TIME Slippers.

- *To deepen understanding.* Alternatively, you could inform the audience about World War II. Your specific purpose could be: "To inform my peers about Sweden's role in World War II as a neutral country." Chances are your audience members have some basic knowledge about World War II, but as you provide new information, you deepen their knowledge.

- *To enable application.* A third specific purpose could be to inform your listeners how to prepare effective, low-cost advertisements when they want to promote an event on campus. In this instance, you would help the audience *apply* basic advertising principles.

Journal: Maintaining an Informative Purpose

If you were to inform your classmates about your favorite vacation destination, what would be your specific informative goal? How could you ensure that you focus on that goal rather than fall into persuasion?

Key Points: Goals of a Speech to Inform

1. Impart knowledge
2. Deepen understanding
3. Enable application

In determining the goal of your speech to inform, remember that both speakers and listeners are active participants in the communication process. Even though you may present your information objectively, listeners will interpret what they hear and integrate it into their frames of reference. Your objectivity as a speaker will not stop listeners from hearing with subjectivity. As a speaker, though, you determine *your* motive for speaking. In a speech to inform, it is not to advocate specific beliefs, attitudes, values, or behaviors on controversial issues. Your goal is to assist your listeners as they come to know, understand, or apply an idea or issue. Thus, when you speak to inform, you assume the role of a teacher. In Section 15.3, we offer guidelines that will help you remain objective as you develop and deliver your informative speech.

SPEAKING WITH CONFIDENCE

Generally, I am more comfortable persuading than informing people. So, the informative speech presented me with a different challenge, which initially increased my nervousness. For my informative speech, I chose a topic that was a current controversial social issue on which I held my own opinions. Therefore, I knew I needed to be careful to avoid being persuasive. However, when developing my speech, I quickly realized that by addressing select issues pertaining to the topic, I was inserting my personal bias into my speech, which made it persuasive. To ensure I remained informative, I had to focus on stressing objectivity and the importance of presenting a balanced view. After taking a step back and reconsidering the angle from which I was addressing the topic, I better understood how to focus my efforts on keeping the speech informative by also discussing points that contradicted my own views. By reconsidering my approach and supporting materials, I was able to redevelop a more balanced and objective speech by accounting for the competing perspectives, which reduced my nervousness because I knew my speech was objective and well balanced.

Drew Norris,
University of North
Carolina-Wilmington

Informative Speech Categories

15.2 Identify, with examples, the eight informative speech categories.

Experts identify several ways of classifying informative speeches into general topic categories. As you read about these topic categories, keep two guidelines in mind. First, approach each category of topics with the broadest possible perspective. Second, recognize that the categories overlap; the boundaries between them are not distinct. Whether you consider St. Peter's Basilica to be an object or a place, for example, is much less important than the fact that it's a fascinating informative speech topic.

The purpose of these categories is to stimulate—not to limit—your topic selection and development. As you begin brainstorming, consider information you could provide your listeners regarding people, objects, places, activities, events, processes, concepts, conditions, and issues.

Speeches about People

People are an obvious and abundant source of topics for an informative speech. A speech about a person gives you the opportunity to expand your knowledge in a field that interests you while sharing those interests with your listeners. If you're an avid photographer, you could discover and communicate something about the life and accomplishments of Ansel Adams, Diane Arbus, or Annie Leibovitz. Of course, you don't need to confine your topic to individuals associated with your major or areas of interest. You could interest and inform audiences by discussing the lives and contributions of people such as Calum Scott, Elvis Presley, Michael Jordan, Beyoncé, Giselle Knowles-Carte, or George Clooney, for example.

You may choose to discuss a group of people, such as the Four Horsemen of Notre Dame, the Red Hat Society, or the Capitol Steps, a political satirist troupe. You could even compare and contrast two or more individuals to highlight their philosophies and contributions, such as Rachel Carson and Ralph Nader, or Malcolm X and Martin Luther King Jr.

In considering an informative speech about a person, you must decide what is important and what the audience will remember. Speeches about people organized so that they resemble biographical entries in an encyclopedia amount to lists of dates. Even the most attentive listener will remember few of the details in such a speech.

Speeches about people are often organized chronologically or topically. In her speech about Mark Zuckerberg, cofounder and CEO of the online social network

We read about, listen to, and watch people who fascinate us. Many of them have unique, interesting stories. Sharing this information with an audience can make an excellent speech.

Facebook, Katherine used a chronological pattern to trace his life and accomplishments. She used parallel wording to help her listeners remember her three key ideas:

I. Growing Up
II. Building Up
III. Leading Up

First, Katherine discussed Zuckerberg's childhood, providing examples of his early predisposition toward technology. Second, she described how he cofounded Facebook during his sophomore year at Harvard University and then dropped out of school to build that enterprise. Finally, Katherine discussed how Zuckerberg's vision for the future of Facebook is reflected in his leadership style, relying not on top-down decision making but on encouraging openness, collaboration, and sharing of information. For example, when you walk into the Facebook headquarters, you see workstations but no individual offices; even Zuckerberg doesn't have a private office although there is a glass-enclosed room for meetings.

Speeches about Objects

An object can be a fascinating topic for an informative speech. Speeches about objects focus on what is concrete rather than on what is abstract. Again, consider objects from the broadest perspective possible so that you can generate a maximum number of topic ideas. Topics for this type of speech could include crop circles, electric cars, performance clothing, smart roads, or volcanoes.

Speeches about objects can use any of several organizational patterns. A speech on the Catherine Palace of Tsarskoye Selo could be organized spatially. A speech tracing the development of cyclones and anticyclones evolves chronologically. A speech on the origins, types, and uses of pasta uses a topical division. If the speech focused only on the history of pasta, however, it might best be structured chronologically.

Alexei used a combination of topical and pro–con organization for his speech on genetically modified (GM) animals, sometimes called *designer animals*:

I. The process of designing animals
II. Benefits of GM animals
III. Problems of GM animals

Speeches about Places

Places are an easily tapped resource for informative speech topics. Speeches about places introduce listeners to new locales or expand their knowledge of familiar places. Topics may include real places, such as historic sites, emerging nations, national parks, and planets. Topics may also include fictitious places, such as the Land of Oz, the Island of the Lord of the Flies, and the Sea of Frozen Words. Speeches about places challenge speakers to select words that create vivid images.

To organize your speech about places, you would typically use one of three organizational patterns: spatial, chronological, or topical. A speech about the Nile river is organized spatially if it discusses the upper, middle, and lower Nile. A presentation about your college could trace its development chronologically. A speech on Poplar Forest, Thomas Jefferson's getaway home, could use a topical pattern discussing Jefferson's architectural style.

If you selected as your informative speech topic Ellis Island, the site of the chief U.S. immigration center from 1892 to 1954, you could choose any of the following patterns of development:

Pattern: Spatial

Specific Purpose: To inform the audience about Ellis Island's Main Building

Key Ideas: I. The registry room
             II. The baggage room
             III. The oral history studio

Pattern: Chronological

Specific Purpose: To inform the audience of the history of Ellis Island

Key Ideas: I. Years of immigration, 1892–1954
             II. Years of dormancy, 1954–1984
             III. Years of remembrance, 1984–present

Pattern: Topical

Specific Purpose: To inform the audience of the history of Ellis Island

Key Ideas: I. The process of immigration
             II. The place of immigration
             III. The people who immigrated

If you choose to speak about a place, avoid making your speech sound like a travelogue. Your speech should identify and develop ideas that contribute to the general education of your listeners.

Speeches about Activities and Events

Activities are things you do by yourself or with others to learn, have fun, relax, or accomplish a required task. Among the sources of speech topics are your hobbies, interests, and experiences. Topics that you already know well and are willing to explore more fully often enhance your credibility and energize your delivery.

If you're interested in dancing, a speech on krumping (sometimes called street dancing or clown dancing) could be lively and informative. You could use a topical pattern, informing your audience on these key points:

  I. The origins of krumping
 II. The purposes of krumping
III. The style of krumping
IV. The face-painting of krumping

Events are important or interesting occurrences. Examples of topics for this type of speech include the sinking of the *Titanic*, the Woodstock festival, and the the release of an American student from a North Korean prison in 2017. For a speech assignment not requiring research, you could speak about an event in your life you consider important, funny, or instructive— for example: "The Day I Deployed to Afghanistan," "The Day My First Child Was Born," or "My First Trip to My Family's Ancestral Village in Ireland."

This tour guide informs students of the issues, events, and leaders of the civil rights movement.

Speeches about events typically use a chronological or topical pattern. For example, if your topic is the daring Great Train Robbery that took place in Britain in 1963, you could organize your speech chronologically, describing what happened before, during, and after those famous 15 minutes.

The Woodstock Music and Art Fair, more commonly referred to as the Woodstock Festival or just Woodstock, was held on a dairy farm in Bethel, New York. A speech on this legendary event of August 15–18, 1969, could be divided into the topical categories of:

    I. The organizers of Woodstock
  II. The audience at Woodstock
 III. The performers at Woodstock

If this topic is too broad, the speaker could focus only on the performers or some other more limited topic.

Speeches about Processes

process
A series of steps producing an outcome.

Much, if not all, of what we do can be considered a **process**—a series of steps producing an outcome. For example, getting ready for school or work in the morning is a process. It may involve taking a shower, getting dressed, fixing your hair, eating breakfast, and brushing your teeth. Your informative speech about a process could explain or demonstrate how something works, functions, or is accomplished. Informative speeches could be on such how-to topics as preventing identity theft, burglar-proofing your apartment, and making a good first impression. Speeches on global positioning systems, nuclear medicine, and cryptography (encoding and decoding messages) are also potentially good informative speech topics about processes.

Because a process is by definition a time-ordered sequence, speeches about processes are commonly organized chronologically. For example, if your specific purpose is to inform your audience of the steps to a successful job interview, you could present these key ideas:

    I. Prepare thoroughly
   II. Arrive promptly
 III. Enter confidently
 IV. Communicate effectively
  V. Follow up immediately

Speeches about processes, however, are not confined to a chronological pattern. The best organization is the one that achieves the purpose of the speech. A student presenting a how-to speech on podcasting would likely choose a chronological pattern if the specific purpose was to explain the steps in the process. Another student might examine the process of podcasting more generally, using a topical pattern to discuss the equipment needed, the most popular file formats, the rapid growth of podcasts, or the effects on traditional broadcasters. Both speeches concern a process, but each uses an organizational pattern suitable for the speaker's specific purpose.

Speeches about Concepts

concepts
Abstract, intangible ideas.

Speeches about **concepts**, or ideas, focus on what is abstract rather than on what is concrete. Whereas a speech about an object such as the Statue of Liberty may focus on

ETHICAL DECISIONS

MANAGING BIAS IN AN INFORMATIVE SPEECH

Leon serves as historian of his campus fraternity. He considers himself an expert on the subject of Greek life at his school, so he decides to use his observations and experiences as the basis for an informative speech on the process of joining fraternities and sororities. However, Leon fears that if he reveals that he is a fraternity officer, his listeners will assume that he is not presenting objective information—so he does not mention it.

Is it ethical for Leon to avoid mentioning his fraternity affiliation and position? Is it possible for him to give an unbiased presentation of the process of joining fraternities and sororities? What obligations does he have to his audience?

the history or physical attributes of the statue itself, a speech about an idea may focus on the concept of liberty. Other topics suitable for informative speeches about concepts include ecotourism, objective music, pirate radio, artificial intelligence, endangered languages, and the bystander effect.

Speeches about concepts challenge you to make something abstract specific. These speeches typically rely on definitions and examples to support their explanations. Appropriate organizational patterns vary. A speech on Norse mythology could use a topical division and focus on key figures. Speeches about theories, particularly if they are controversial, sometimes use a pro–con division.

Drew entertained his listeners with a speech on onomastics, or the study of names. Notice how his introduction personalizes his speech and quickly involves his listeners. You can also see from his preview statement that he used a topical organization for this speech about a concept:

> These are some actual names reported by John Train in his books *Remarkable Names of Real People* and *Even More Remarkable Names*. Let me repeat: These are actual names found in bureaus of vital statistics; public health services; newspaper articles; and hospital, church, and school records: E. Pluribus Eubanks, Loch Ness Hontas, Golden Pancake, Halloween Buggage, Odious Champagne, and Memory Leake.
>
> Train says in *Even More Remarkable Names* that "what one might call the free-form nutty name—Oldmouse Waltz, Cashmere Tango Obedience, Eucalyptus Yoho—is the one indigenous American art form."
>
> We're lucky. No one in here has a name as colorful as any of those. But we all have at least two names—a personal and a family name. Today, I'll tell you, first, why personal names developed, and second, the legal status of names. Finally, I have something to tell each of you about the origin of your name.

Speeches about Conditions

Conditions are particular situations: living conditions in a third-world country or social and political climates that give rise to movements such as McCarthyism, the women's movement, the civil rights movement, and national independence movements.

conditions
The state of something or someone, such as the economy, health, or an infrastructure.

The word *condition* can also refer to a state of fitness or health. Speeches about conditions can focus on a person's physical or mental health, and, indeed, medical topics are a popular source of student speeches. Informative speeches about obsessive-compulsive disorder, progressive supranuclear palsy, and seasonal affective disorder, for example, can educate listeners about these conditions. A speaker could choose as a specific purpose: "To inform the audience about the symptoms, causes, and treatment of diabetes." Topical organization is appropriate for many speeches about specific diseases or health conditions.

Jahweh's mother suffered from rheumatoid arthritis, and seeing his mother struggle with her everyday activities motivated Jahweh to research the disease. After exploring several websites addressing FAQs about rheumatoid arthritis, he decided to address four questions in his speech:

I. What is rheumatoid arthritis?
II. What causes rheumatoid arthritis?
III. How do you treat rheumatoid arthritis?
IV. Is there a cure for rheumatoid arthritis?

Although the fourth question is closed, requiring only a yes or no answer, Jahweh used it as an opportunity to discuss types of experimental research conducted in an effort to find a cure. In the conclusion of his speech, Jahweh referred his classmates to the Arthritis National Research Foundation's website so his audience could continue to learn more about this important topic.

States of health also characterize the economy, individual communities, and specific institutions. *Recession*, *depression*, and *full employment* are terms economists use to describe the health of the economy. Speakers inform their listeners about conditions when they describe the state of the arts in their communities, assess the financial situation of most college students, or illustrate how catch limits have affected the whale population.

Speeches about Issues

issues
Points of controversy in which people hold opposing or multiple opinions, such as abortion.

Speeches about **issues** deal with controversial ideas and policies. The word *controversial* may trigger the question: Isn't this category more appropriate for persuasive speeches? Many times it is; however, controversial topics can also be appropriate for informative speeches. Issues being debated in your school, community, state, or nation can be fruitful topics for a speech to inform.

Suppose your school is considering moving from a letter-grade to a pass–fail grading system. You could give a persuasive speech in support of either approach. You also could deliver an informative speech so that your audience better understands the issue. For example, you could summarize the key arguments of proponents and opponents of the pass–fail approach, or you could discuss different types of pass–fail systems.

Two common organizational patterns for speeches about issues are the topical and pro–con divisions. Speakers predisposed toward one side of an issue sometimes may have difficulty presenting both sides objectively. For example, Carl presented a speech on the issue of school uniforms for public schools. He presented four good reasons for them: Uniforms (1) are more economical for parents, (2) reduce student bickering and fighting over designer clothes, (3) increase student attentiveness in the classroom, and (4) identify the school and promote school spirit. Carl's only argument against public school uniforms was that they limit students' freedom of expression. His speech seemed out of balance, and most of his classmates thought Carl favored school uniforms. Although the assignment was an informative speech, Carl's pro–con approach was ultimately persuasive. If, like Carl, you feel strongly committed to one side of an issue, save that topic for a persuasive speech.

As you begin working on your informative speech, keep in mind this question: "How will the audience benefit from my topic?" What about topics such as the golden age of vaudeville, the origins of superstitions, the effect of music on livestock production, or the psychological aspects of aging? What about a truly bizarre topic like extreme ironing? Maybe you think that such topics are not relevant to your audience. But part of the process of becoming an educated individual is learning more about the world around you. We are committed to this perspective and believe it is one you should encourage in your listeners.

After you select a topic, ask yourself the following three questions: (1) What does the audience already know about my topic? (2) What does the audience need to know to understand the topic? (3) Can I present this information in a way that is easy for the audience to understand and remember in the time allotted? If you are satisfied with your answers to these questions, your next step is to begin developing the most effective strategy for conveying that information.

Key Points: Informative Speech Topics

1. People
2. Objects
3. Places
4. Activities and Events
5. Processes
6. Concepts
7. Conditions
8. Issues

Guidelines for Speaking to Inform

15.3 Apply the five guidelines for developing an effective informative speech.

Before reading this chapter, you already knew several clusters of guidelines for developing excellent informative speeches. This is because some guidelines apply to all speeches: careful audience analysis, adequate research, clear organization, and dynamic delivery, to name a few. We've discussed how to construct an audience profile based on demographic and psychographic analysis of your listeners. We presented guidelines for collecting and evaluating information for supporting the ideas of your speech. We've detailed how to introduce your speech, how to develop the key ideas using the 4 S's strategy in the body of your speech, and how to conclude your speech. You've also learned ways to deliver your speech impressively using your words, your voice, and your body. We encourage you to review these sections of our book to assist you in preparing and presenting an excellent speech, be it informative or persuasive.

Yet there are some guidelines that apply specifically to an informative speech, and we discuss five of them in the remainder of this chapter.

Stress Your Informative Purpose

As noted, the primary objective of your informative speech is to inform, and it's important to be clear about this. Your topic may be controversial or related to other topics that are controversial. For example, if you are discussing the U.S. immigration policy, political correctness, or the role of women in religion, you must realize that some of your audience members may already have very strong feelings about your topic. Stress that your goal is to give additional information, not to change anyone's opinion.

Be Objective

Objectivity is essential in an informative speech. Although both informative and persuasive speakers should support their ideas, informative speakers are committed to presenting a balanced view. Your research should take into account competing perspectives. If, as you develop and practice your speech, you find yourself becoming a proponent of a particular viewpoint, you may need to step back and assess whether your orientation has shifted from informing to persuading. If you don't think you can make your speech objective, save the topic for a persuasive speech.

> **Journal: Staying Objective**
>
> Identify a topic that would challenge your objectivity. How might you work with this topic to ensure that you remain informative rather than falling into persuasion? What, specifically, would you do?

Use an Informative Organizational Pattern for Presenting Your Key Ideas

In this textbook, we have presented, discussed, and given examples of several organizational patterns for dividing the body of your speech into key ideas. Topical, chronological, spatial, causal, and pro–con patterns are appropriate for informative speeches. There is no one best organizational pattern. Choose the pattern that is most appropriate to your topic and specific purpose. However, some patterns are inappropriate for an informative speech. While a pro–con approach is appropriate, a pro–con assessment strategy moves the speech into persuasion. Problem–solution and need–plan patterns are also inherently persuasive.

This chapter's "Theory into Practice: Organizing Informative Speeches" offers suggestions for selecting an appropriate organizational pattern for informative speeches. If you have any doubt that your organization is informative rather than persuasive, check with your instructor.

Limit Your Ideas and Supporting Materials

Because this is a speech to inform, don't make the mistake of thinking that the more information you put into a speech, the more informative it will be. Listeners cannot process all, or even most, of what you present. If you overload your audience with too many facts, figures, and dates, they will stop listening. In Chapter 4, Learning Objective 4.4, we discussed *factual distractions,* meaning information overload, as a common barrier to effective listening. Remember the adage "less is more," and spend more time explaining and developing a few ideas, which will result in greater retention of these ideas by your listeners.

Theory into Practice (TIP)

ORGANIZING INFORMATIVE SPEECHES

Speeches about	Use	If your purpose is to
People	Topical organization	Explain various aspects of the person's life
	Chronological organization	Survey events in the person's life
Objects	Topical organization	Explain various uses for the object
	Chronological organization	Explain how the object was created or made
	Spatial organization	Describe various parts of the object
Places	Topical organization	Emphasize various aspects of the place
	Chronological organization	Chart the history of, or developments in, the place
	Spatial organization	Describe the elements or parts of the place
Activities and Events	Topical organization	Explain the significance of the activity or event
	Chronological organization	Explain the sequence of the activity or event
	Causal organization	Explain how one event produced, or resulted from, another
Processes	Topical organization	Explain aspects of the process
	Chronological organization	Explain how something is done
	Pro–con organization	Explore the arguments for and against the procedure
	Causal organization	Discuss the causes and effects of the process
Concepts	Topical organization	Discuss aspects, definitions, or applications of the concept
Conditions	Topical organization	Explain aspects of the condition
	Chronological organization	Trace the stages or phases of the condition
	Causal organization	Show the causes and effects of the condition
Issues	Topical organization	Discuss aspects of the issue's significance
	Chronological organization	Show how the issue evolved over time
	Pro–con organization	Present opposing viewpoints on the issue

Use Descriptive Language and Nonverbal Cues

Nothing betrays the image of objectivity like the inappropriate use of language. For example, in an informative speech on the pros and cons of juvenile curfew laws, one of our students used language that telegraphed his opinion on the issue. Even when explaining the arguments for such laws, he described them as "silly," "costly," and "unenforceable." In an informative speech, your language should be descriptive, not evaluative or judgmental.

Some speakers have a misconception that vocal and physical delivery are more important for a persuasive speech than for an informative speech. Regardless of the type of speech, your voice and body should reinforce your interest in and enthusiasm for your topic. Your delivery should also reinforce your objectivity. If you find your gestures, body tension, or

If this speaker's gestures and eye behavior undermine her attempts to objectively share the pros and cons of a new proposal, then she is persuading her audience.

voice conveying an emotional urgency, you have likely slipped into persuasion. In an informative speech, you will probably use gestures that are more descriptive and less intense.

Annotated Sample Speech

After reading this chapter, you should know the principles and characteristics of informative speaking, understand how they contribute to effective speaking, and be able to apply them as you prepare your speeches. Our student Melissa Janoske understood and used these principles when she delivered the following speech to her classmates. As you read her transcript, notice how her supporting materials and organization of the introduction, body, and conclusion contributed to a seamless, organic whole. In the marginal annotations, we have indicated the major strengths of Melissa's speech.

Renaissance Fairs: The New Vaudeville[4]

Melissa Janoske, Radford University

1 Imagine you're walking down the street, minding your own business, about to go into a store, when suddenly, someone calls your name. You turn around, and the person advances toward you. Immediately, you find yourself in the middle of a sword fight—right in the middle of the street! As you fight for your life, a crowd gathers, watching and cheering. The fight is treacherous, and your opponent is worthy, but, finally, the fight ends when the gleaming edge of your sword pins your opponent onto the cobblestone path below him. Those who have gathered come up and congratulate you.

2 This seemingly outrageous scene is actually fairly commonplace in certain times and places. The year? Well, either 1521 or today. The place? Any busy street in Renaissance England, or your local Renaissance festival.

3 Elizabethan social historian Mike Bonk captures the excitement and fascination of this era on his current website, www.faires.com. He describes the Renaissance as "a period of intensity in all things: work, play, the arts, world exploration, religion, and superstition. Renaissance faires resurrect [these extremes], both as reenactment and as a way of life."

4 Some people live and die by their ability to re-create pre-seventeenth century Europe. They create elaborate costumes and have entire other personalities that they become on the weekends. Renaissance fairs are both exciting and educational, and anyone with curiosity and imagination can attend, observe, and even participate.

5 It's easy for you to experience present-day Renaissance culture through three easy acts: imagine yourself as a Renaissance figure, affiliate with your local kingdom, and participate in a local Renaissance festival or event.

6 To start on your journey into the Renaissance, imagine yourself becoming a part of the world of a Renaissance fair. This would mean becoming a person from the original world, letting that entire culture become part of who you are, and suspending normal belief about who you are in daily life. Renaissance fair enthusiast Mike Boar proclaims: "Monday through Friday, I'm Mike the Truck Driver. On the weekends, I'm the Barbarian King. Men fear me. Women can't get enough of me. Guess who I'd rather be?" And Mike isn't alone in his love of a personality switch for the weekend. According to Jules Smith, Sr., cofounder of International Renaissance Fairs Ltd., Renaissance fairs are the "new vaudeville," drawing a crowd of 193,000 people to the last fair he held in Maryland. That's a lot of people getting decked out in chain mail and corsets and going out for the weekend. Participants use traditional names and titles, wear period clothing, and even learn about a possible profession from that time period. Events are usually open to the public, and so even if you're not into wearing tights and riding horses, it's still fun to go and watch and learn about the diversity of the culture.

Key Points: Guidelines for Informative Speaking

1. Stress your informative purpose.
2. Be objective.
3. Use an informative organizational pattern for presenting your key ideas.
4. Limit your ideas and supporting materials.
5. Use descriptive language and nonverbal cues.

Melissa's opening comments arouse curiosity about her topic.

This early source citation builds Melissa's credibility on her topic.

In this paragraph, Melissa establishes relevance of her topic.

Paragraph 5 previews the main points Melissa intends to discuss.

Here Melissa begins to apply the 4 S's to her first main point. She signposts ("To start") and states the point: becoming a part of the Renaissance world.

Melissa uses examples and testimony to support her point. Her sources (Boar and Smith) use narration, contrast, and statistics.

Melissa summarizes her first point by stressing the fun and educational value of becoming a Renaissance character.

A complementary transition links Melissa's first and second points. Notice Melissa's creativity in using the archaic phrase "potion from the apothecary."

Melissa signposts ("second") and states her next main point: affiliating with a local kingdom.

Melissa supports this point by providing examples of Renaissance activities.

Melissa summarizes this second point by reiterating the functions of Renaissance kingdoms.

Melissa signposts ("third") and states her final main point: participation in Renaissance fair culture.

Melissa provides examples of many fair activities and of particular fairs held annually.

Melissa summarizes the benefits of participation in Renaissance fairs.

Melissa clearly summarizes her three main points in the first sentence of her conclusion.

Melissa provides an easy-to-remember URL to help listeners extend their exploration of her topic.

Melissa's speech comes to a definite, satisfying close with this vivid, well-worded final image.

7 Learning how to do all of those character-altering activities is important, but the knowledge of all things Renaissance doesn't just come in a potion from the apothecary. It is instead often achieved through the second aspect of Renaissance life: affiliating with your local kingdom. The Society for Creative Anachronism, Inc., an international organization dedicated to Renaissance culture, has divided the world into sixteen kingdoms, spanning the entire globe and allowing everyone in the world in on the fun. A map of these divisions can be found on its website, www.sca.org. Many of these sixteen kingdoms have their divisions within the United States. Virginia is located in the Kingdom of Atlantia, and each kingdom has at least one university in a central location. These universities are run by kingdom officials and offer classes in how to become more immersed in the culture; how to be a goldsmith, or lessons in jousting; or even a lecture on the political methods of King Arthur. You can learn how to fence or ride a horse, cook medieval delicacies, or shop for velvet gowns and leather boots. Each kingdom also allows any of its subjects to gain membership, come to the annual events and fairs, and immerse themselves fully in any events or activities that might help them understand Renaissance Europe.

8 While each kingdom provides the learning opportunities for and access to these festivals, the actual participation in them is the third, and most important, aspect of Renaissance fair culture. Without this participation, all the character changes and kingdom knowledge don't mean nearly as much. It is the practice of Renaissance life that makes it worthwhile, and the actual Renaissance fairs are the easiest and most fun way to do that. There are lots of different types of fair activities to participate in, from jousting festivals to chain mail competitions to cooking parties. You can take classes on spinning and weaving and chain mail or participate in the annual Saint Patty's Day Bloodbath ($5 for a day of swordsmanship and excitement). All aspects of Renaissance culture are available and represented, and all you have to do is go out and look for it. Particular festivals are held around present-day holidays, such as Halloween and feasting days, or events that were important in Renaissance culture. There is a very popular fair held in Pennsylvania every year at Halloween called Renaissance Fright Night that includes renditions of "Frankenstein" and poetry from Poe, goblins and gargoyles that come alive, and street peasants, roasted chestnuts, and fighting for the plenty. This is just one example. There are many websites, such as www.faires.com, that offer detailed information about specific fairs in your area. These festivals are the culmination of the work that people do in learning about the way things were in Renaissance Europe. It's a chance to show off your costumes, present your new persona, showcase your work, or just go and be a part of the festivities. The festivals are a time to enjoy the culture and community that is created and to relax and bask in all the entertainment that is offered through a Renaissance fair.

9 Transforming yourself into a Renaissance figure, affiliating with your local kingdom, and participating in a Renaissance fair are three main ways to experience Renaissance culture today. To get started on your journey, visit www.faires.com. Just make sure you spell it the Renaissance way: f-a-i-r-E-s. Here you will find all sorts of suggestions on integrating Renaissance culture into your life in fun and exciting ways. So take the hint from Mike Boar, the truck driver: lose the college student in you for the weekend, and see how much you like being a Barbarian King with a penchant for chain mail.

Reprinted with permission of the speaker.

› SUMMARY

Speaking to Inform

Goals of a Speech to Inform

15.1 Explain, with examples, the three goals of informative speeches.

Your goals as an informative speaker are to expand listeners' knowledge, enhance their understanding, and/or help them apply the information you communicate.

Informative Speech Categories

15.2 Identify, with examples, the eight informative speech categories.

- Classifying informative speeches by subject gives you an idea of the range of possible topics and the patterns of organization each subject typically uses. Informative speeches can be about people, objects, places, activities and events, processes, concepts, conditions, and issues.

- As you begin to prepare an informative speech, ask yourself three questions: (1) What does the audience already know about this topic? (2) What does the audience need to know in order to understand this topic? (3) Can I present this information in the allotted time so that the audience will understand and remember it?

Guidelines for Speaking to Inform

15.3 Apply the five guidelines for developing an effective informative speech.

- To succeed in public speaking, you should review the sections of this textbook that assist you in preparing and presenting an excellent speech, be it informative or persuasive.

- To capture the essence of informative speaking you should (1) stress your informative purpose, (2) be objective in your approach to the topic, (3) use an informative organizational pattern for arranging your key ideas, (4) limit the ideas and supporting material that you try to include, and (5) use descriptive language and nonverbal cues.

SPEAKING TO PERSUADE

→ **LEARNING OBJECTIVES**

After studying this chapter, you should be able to

16.1 Explain the ethics of persuasion relevant to both speakers and listeners.

16.2 Differentiate among the three types of persuasive speeches.

16.3 Describe, with examples, the three types of influence.

16.4 Explain, with examples, Aristotle's three modes of persuasion: ethos, logos, and pathos.

16.5 Apply the four strategies to establish common ground with your listeners.

16.6 Organize your persuasive speech arguments appropriately for your topic, purpose, and audience.

Every day, we send and receive persuasive messages. Some of these messages may be as simple as influencing a classmate to shoot hoops with you at the gym after class. Other messages are more complicated, like convincing your skeptical parents that studying abroad will enrich your academic experience and distinguish you from other graduates in a tight job market. Still others can be life or world changing, such as inspiring communities to take action against modern-day slavery or advocating for better transportation access for individuals with diabilities.

As you may have guessed based on the above examples, **persuasion** is the process of influencing another person's values, beliefs, attitudes, or behaviors. Delivering a persuasive speech will challenge and benefit you in several ways. It will require you to select an issue you think is important and to communicate your concern to your audience. Approached seriously and researched energetically, a persuasive speech assignment can develop both your critical thinking and speech-making skills, while also providing you with an opportunity to improve your school or community. Change can occur when people speak and audiences act.

As a listener, you also benefit by participating in the persuasive process. A speaker can make you aware of problems and can show you how to help solve them. You have the opportunity to hear other points of view and, consequently, you may better understand why others have beliefs different from yours. Participating as a listener also heightens your critical thinking and improves your ability to explain and defend your own beliefs. Finally, as a listener, you have an opportunity to judge how others use persuasive speaking techniques, thus enabling you to improve your own persuasive speaking by identifying what appears to work well—and not so well—in others' speeches.

Given the tremendous value of persuasion, we dedicate two chapters to the topic. In this chapter, you will first learn about the ethics of persuasion, followed by a discussion about the three different types of persuasive speeches and the three different types of influences. We then offer an overview of Aristotle's modes of persuasion, specific ideas for connecting with your audience in a persuasive speech, and, finally, suggestions about how to organize your key ideas. In Chapter 17, we will examine the specifics of persuasive arguments and reasoning.

persuasion
The process of influencing another person's values, beliefs, attitudes, or behaviors.

The Ethics of Persuasion

16.1 Explain the ethics of persuasion relevant to both speakers and listeners.

In Chapter 2, you learned about the ethical responsibilities of both speakers and listeners. In this section, we extend that discussion by focusing specifically on the ethics of persuasion.

Because persuasion is the process of influencing others, people often incorrectly assume that (1) persuasion requires a power imbalance between the speaker and the audience members, and (2) persuasion involves manipulation and coercion. Although persuasive communication may be more successful when the speaker exerts power over the audience members, persuasion does not necessarily require power.[1] Power implies authority or control over another. For example, your instructor likely encourages you to be on time for class each day. In addition to overtly stating the importance of being on time for class, your instructor has probably included policies in the syllabus that specify the penalties for tardiness, such as a point deduction. In this instance, the power residing in some other person's position shapes your behavior, at least in part. The inherent power imbalance that exists between students and their instructors[2] may enable your instructors to effectively persuade you to engage in certain behaviors while avoiding other behaviors because they have the power to "reward" or "punish" you.

Persuasion, however, is more accurately equated with influence than with power and coercion. As a speaker, you try to influence the audience to adopt your position. You probably have little power over your classmates, and they have the freedom to reject your message. Suppose, for example, that your speech instructor wants your class to attend a lecture given on campus by Ryan Dougherty, founder and CEO of TIME Slippers. You are not required to attend, and there is no penalty or reward. To influence you, however, your instructor emphasizes that Mr. Dougherty is a relatively recent college graduate. She also mentions that Mr. Dougherty's experiences may be of interest to all students, regardless of their majors, because the presentation focuses on pursuing professional dreams and goals in the first few years after graduation. Finally, your instructor mentions that she has several pairs of TIME Slippers and loves them.

In this case, your instructor is using influence rather than power or coercion to persuade you. The concept of persuasion as influence means that you can bring about change (or reinforce) values, beliefs, attitudes, or behaviors whether or not you are the more powerful party in a relationship. You can also see that compared to power, influence requires more effort, creativity, and sensitivity but in the long run is probably more effective than attempting to persuade others by exerting power over them or by manipulation. Most importantly, by relying on influence rather than coercion, you will be perceived as a more ethical speaker.

Media specialist Tony Schwartz combined *manipulation* and *participation* to create a new word: *partipulation*. He argues that voters are not simply manipulated by campaign and advertising strategists. Voters do, after all, have the option of rejecting the messages politicians present to them. So, Schwartz contends, "You have to participate in your own manipulation."[3]

Persuasion is similar to Schwartz's concept of partipulation. As a speaker, you have an ethical responsibility to establish a common perspective and tap into your listeners' values, attitudes, and beliefs. Your goal should not be to manipulate or coerce your audience. As a critical listener, you have a right and an ethical responsibility to choose whether or not you are persuaded. Charles Larson echoes this speaker–listener orientation by stating:

> [T]he focus of persuasion is not on the source, the message, or the receiver, but on *all* of them equally. They *all cooperate* to make a persuasive process. The idea of *co-creation* means that what is inside the receiver is just as important as the source's intent or the content of messages. In one sense, *all* persuasion is *self-persuasion*—we are rarely persuaded unless we participate in the process.[4]

Types of Persuasive Speeches

16.2 Differentiate among the three types of persuasive speeches.

Persuasive speeches are generally classified according to their objectives, whether that is to convince, to actuate, or to inspire listeners. Understanding these divisions can help you determine your primary objective as you work on your speech, but keep in mind that persuasive speeches often include two or more objectives. For example, if your purpose is to get your audience to travel to Belize instead of Mexico for spring break, you must first convince them that Belize is a superior travel destination. We usually act or become inspired after we are convinced.

In a **speech to convince**, your objective is to influence your listeners' beliefs or attitudes. Each of the following specific purpose statements expresses a belief the speaker wants the audience to accept:

- To convince my peers that "hate speech" is constitutionally protected.
- To convince my fellow students that hydrogen fuel-celled cars are commercially feasible.
- To convince classmates that Ben Hogan is the greatest golfer of all time.
- To convince my peers that sealed adoption is preferable to open adoption.

Journal: Influence, not Power

Think of a time when a person who was more powerful than you are was able to use influence rather than power to persuade you. What was the situation and how did the other person persuade you successfully?

speech to convince

A persuasive speech focused on influencing audience attitudes and beliefs, without advocating a specific action.

The speaker's purpose in each of these speeches is to influence belief, not to secure action.

A **speech to actuate** may influence beliefs, but it always calls for the audience to act. The specific purpose statements listed here illustrate calls for action:

- To move, or actuate, my peers to donate old clothes to the Salvation Army.
- To influence my classmates to sponsor an SOS Children's Village child.
- To move the audience to begin a low-impact aerobic workout program.

A third type of persuasive speech is the **speech to inspire**, one that attempts to change how listeners feel. Examples include pep talks and motivational speeches as well as special occasion speeches such as commencement addresses and eulogies. Some specific purposes of speeches to inspire are these:

- To inspire my classmates to honor the service of fallen firefighters.
- To inspire my peers to appreciate those who made their education possible.
- To inspire my fellow students to give their best efforts to all college courses they take.

The purposes of inspiration are usually noble and uplifting. These speeches typically have neither the detailed supporting material nor the complex arguments characteristic of speeches to convince or actuate. Sometimes, speakers may ask their listeners to take a specific action to demonstrate their appreciation—for example, to donate to the National Fallen Firefighters Foundation. In this case, the speech to inspire transitions into a speech to actuate.

Thus far, you have learned what persuasion is, the ethics and importance of persuasion, and the three different types of persuasive speeches. In the next section, you will learn about the three different types of influences persuasive speeches may have and how they are related to the different types of persuasive speeches.

Types of Influence

16.3 Describe, with examples, the three types of influence.

Depending on the type of persuasive speech you deliver—to convince, to actuate, or to inspire—your desired outcome or influence will change. Persuasion can exert three types of influence. You can change, instill, or intensify your listeners' values, beliefs, attitudes, or behaviors. Your desired influence may change based on whether you have determined (via audience analysis; see Chapter 5) that your audience opposes your point of view, is indifferent or unaware, or supports your persuasive message.

Change

First, the most powerful response you can request of your listeners is that they *change* a value, belief, attitude, or behavior. If you think of your listeners' current point of view as a continuum (with those who oppose you at the extreme left end, and those who support you at the extreme right end) you are looking to move people from the left to the right. (See Figure 16.1.) For example, if you discover that the majority of your listeners eat convenience foods, your persuasive speech could encourage them to prepare more meals at home. You would be trying to change their behavior.

Ashton Kutcher, actor and cofounder of Thorn (an antitrafficking organization), testified before Congress in February 2017 to ask for financial support and continued efforts to stop human trafficking. He essentially delivered a speech to actuate.

speech to actuate
A persuasive speech designed to influence audience behaviors.

speech to inspire
A persuasive speech designed to influence listeners' feelings.

Journal: Convince, Actuate, and Inspire

For each of the three types of persuasive speeches (to convince, to actuate, and to inspire), list a speech topic that you would like to discuss in class or elsewhere (e.g., at a community meeting or school event). Write a brief specific purpose for each.

Key Points: Types of Persuasive Speeches

1. Speech to convince
2. Speech to actuate
3. Speech to inspire

Figure 16.1   The Continuum of Persuasion

Oppose			Neutral			Favor
strongly	moderately	slightly		slightly	moderately	strongly
−3	−2	−1	0	+1	+2	+3

Journal: Reasonable Goals

Which of these two specific purpose statements is the most limited and has the most reasonable goal?

To persuade the audience that exposure to violent video games promotes aggression

or

To persuade the audience that habitual exposure to violent video games promotes aggression in children

Explain your answer.

A common mistake many beginning speakers make is to seek dramatic change in their listeners' values, beliefs, attitudes, or behaviors. The speaker who can accomplish this is rare—particularly if the speaker seeks change on highly emotional and controversial issues such as abortion, gun control, capital punishment, religion, or politics. Keep in mind that the more firmly opposed to a position your audience is, the less likely they are to change. So, rather than trying to convince your oppositional audience to support (or oppose) the death penalty, try to convince them of a limited goal, a smaller aspect of the topic; for example, argue that capital punishment deters crime (or does not). Think of this as moving the audience from "strongly opposed" to "moderately opposed" or "slightly opposed" on the continuum—after all, any movement closer to your point of view is effective persuasion. Once a listener accepts that belief, you or another speaker can build on it and focus on a successive objective: support for (or opposition to) the death penalty. After all, complex issues are never tackled or solved in a single speech on a single day. Change takes time and patience.

Instill

Second, you can attempt to *instill* a value, an attitude, a belief, or a behavior. You instill when you address a particular problem about which your listeners are neutral (unaware or undecided). If you persuade your audience that a problem exists, you have instilled a belief. A speaker trying to persuade an audience that intensive care unit psychosis is a serious health problem would first need to define that term for listeners. Then, by documenting cases of "psychotic activity occurring specifically in the intensive care unit among patients . . . that can cause them to fall out of bed, pull out breathing tubes, or . . . pull out central [arterial] lines," the speaker could instill a belief in the audience.[5]

Intensify

Finally, you may try to *intensify* values, beliefs, attitudes, or behaviors. In this case, you must know before your speech that audience members favor your position or behave as you will advocate. Your goal is to strengthen your listeners' positions and actions—to move them even slightly in the direction you advocate on the continuum. For example,

SPEAKING WITH CONFIDENCE

Rather than trying to convince my classmates to tackle a world problem, I wanted to motivate them to begin making simple but important choices to improve their health. I had noticed that some of them (and their friends) had the habit of wearing unsupportive, ill-fitting shoes, such as flip flops. So, I decided to speak on the health benefits of wearing properly fitting shoes. One of my concerns, though, was being taken seriously by my listeners, so I made sure to use sound arguments and credible sources. I presented the medical issues that could result, using expert sources and an accompanying visual aid. After securing agreement on the problems, I then asked my audience to consider healthy options the next time they bought shoes. By keeping my goals focused, limited, and practical, I felt confident that I had made a constructive contribution to the immediate and long-term health of my audience.

Brittney Howell
Radford University

your audience may already believe that recycling is desirable. If your persuasive speech causes your listeners to recycle more frequently, you have intensified their behavior. Your persuasive speech may even encourage them to persuade their family and friends to adopt similar behaviors. When you change believers into advocates and advocates into activists, you have intensified their attitudes and behaviors.

Modes of Persuasion

16.4 Explain, with examples, Aristotle's three modes of persuasion: ethos, logos, and pathos.

As far back as ancient Greece, there is evidence of people giving advice on how to be an effective persuasive speaker. Aristotle, for example, devoted much space to the subject in his classical work, *The Rhetoric*. He discussed three modes of persuasion: ethos, logos, and pathos.[6] These three modes remain an important foundation today for our understanding of persuasive speaking. What do these terms mean, and how can they help you develop and deliver a persuasive speech?

Ethos, or speaker credibility, derives from the character, reputation, and ethical appeal of the speaker. **Logos**, or logical appeal, relies on the form and substance of an argument. **Pathos**, or emotional appeal, taps into the feelings of the audience. It is important to remember that these three modes of persuasion—ethos, logos, and pathos—all work to enhance your persuasive appeal. The best persuasive speeches combine all three. Effective persuaders are credible, present logically constructed and supported arguments, and tap into their listeners' emotions.

Ethos: Speaker Credibility

As a speaker, your first available source of persuasion is your own **credibility**. Aristotle referred to credibility as a speaker's intelligence, character, and goodwill. More recent studies confirm these three components of credibility, although they are now named competence, trustworthiness, and caring.[7] Research indicates that the higher your perceived credibility is, the more likely the audience is to believe you.[8]

Speaker credibility is fluid, varying according to your listeners. If you pepper your speaking with humor, for example, some listeners may see you as lively and interesting, while others may think you are frivolous. You probably have as many different images as you have audience members. To fully understand speaker credibility as it applies to your speeches, it is important to be familiar with the components of credibility and understand how credibility changes over time.

Components of Credibility Studies demonstrate that a highly credible speaker can more successfully persuade than a speaker having low credibility. So, how do you enhance your image with your audience? Communication theorists agree that speakers who appear competent, trustworthy, and caring are viewed as credible.[9] So, if your audience perceives you to possess these attributes, you can be effective in persuading them.

The first component of speaker credibility is **competence**—your perceived expertise. This includes how knowledgeable, skilled, informed, and experienced you are with your topic. In this class, you are among peers, so your audience probably considers you a fellow student rather than an expert. Nonetheless, four strategies will help you establish an image of competence on your subject.

1. *Know your subject.* To speak ethically, you must be well informed about your subject and comprehend both the content and the context of your persuasive message. Persuading your classmates to begin recycling low-density plastics (LDPs) does you little good if your area has no processing plant for LDPs and thus recyclers will not accept LDPs. A well-researched speech increases persuasion by contributing to your image as a well-informed individual. In a public speaking course such as

ethos
Speaker credibility.

logos
Logical appeal.

pathos
Emotional appeal.

credibility
Listeners' perceptions of a speaker's competence, trustworthiness, and caring.

competence
Listeners' views of a speaker's qualifications to speak on a particular topic.

Aristotle (384–322 BC) was a Greek philosopher and scientist who devoted much of his time and writing to examining the strategy of persuasion. His famous book, *The Rhetoric*, is often considered the first public speaking book.

this, the image building you do is cumulative. Thorough, quality research enhances your credibility on the immediate topic and generates positive initial credibility for your next appearance before the same group.

2. *Document your ideas.* You document ideas by using clear, vivid, and credible supporting materials to illustrate them, as we discussed in earlier chapters. Unsupported ideas are mere assertions; providing documentation supports your statements and increases your believability.

3. *Cite your sources.* You need to tell your listeners the sources of your information. Citing sources via oral footnotes enhances the credibility of your ideas by demonstrating that experts support your position. It also requires that your sources be unbiased and of good quality.

4. *Acknowledge any personal involvement or experience with your subject.* Listeners will probably assume that you have an edge in understanding color blindness if you let them know you are color-blind. If you have worked with terminally ill patients and are speaking on hospice care, mentioning your experience will similarly add authority to your ideas.

trustworthiness

Listeners' views of a speaker's honesty, morality, and objectivity.

The second component of speaker credibility is **trustworthiness**, and it tells your listeners that you are honest, moral, genuine, ethical, and objective in what you say. A speaker can demonstrate these attributes in two ways.

1. *Establish common ground with your audience.* If listeners know that you understand their values, experiences, and aspirations, they will be more receptive to your arguments. You increase your persuasiveness when you identify with your listeners.

2. *Demonstrate your objectivity in approaching the topic.* The information and sources you include in your speech should demonstrate thorough, unbiased research. One student gave his speech on cigarette smoking, arguing that its harmful effects were greatly exaggerated. He relied on studies sponsored by the tobacco industry. Very few audience members were persuaded by his evidence. He undermined his image of trustworthiness because he limited his research to sources the audience considered biased.

caring

The extent to which listeners perceive a speaker as understanding, empathetic, and sensitive.

The third component of speaker credibility is **caring**, which refers to having the audience members' best interests at heart by being understanding, empathetic, and sensitive. As a speaker, you can enhance your perceived caring by tapping into your audience members' needs, conveying concern for your audience members, and conveying that your speech is intended to help or benefit your listeners in some way. Research shows that caring speakers are liked by their audience members and the audience members report that they learn a lot from caring speakers.[10] A speaker can demonstrate caring in two ways.

1. *Convey empathy.* Empathy is perceived favorably by listeners of persuasive messages. Being sensitive and understanding to your listeners' concerns and acknowledging their positions will enhance your perceived caring and ability to influence their values, beliefs, attitudes, and behaviors.

2. *Demonstrate that you have your listeners' best interests at heart.* Listeners prefer to be told how your speech can benefit them. As a caring speaker, you should emphasize that you are concerned with your listeners' physical and psychological well-being as well as their academic, financial, personal, and professional success. It is essential that your listeners do not think that you as the speaker will benefit from what you are proposing, but rather that your audience members will benefit from your speech.

As a speaker, present a well-researched and well-documented message and communicate it in an honest and unbiased manner. Your verbal, vocal, and physical delivery should show you to be a fluent, forceful, and friendly individual serious about the issue

ETHICAL DECISIONS

CREDIBILITY: CITING YOUR SOURCES

The competence component of credibility is, in part, dependent on speakers being able to document their ideas and cite their sources. When delivering their speeches, credible speakers cite their sources orally because the listeners don't have access to the speaker's bibliography.

Deciding on what supporting materials to use and what sources to cite in a speech may be quite difficult. For example, research informs us that there are health benefits to eating dark chocolate; there are even health benefits associated with moderate consumption of red wine. However, excessive consumption of either dark chocolate or red wine may be harmful to our health. So, if you are delivering a speech to actuate in which you encourage your listeners to eat more dark chocolate, how do you decide on what supporting materials to use and what sources to cite in your speech? Let's say that you find two excellent articles about dark chocolate consumption published in the *New England Journal of Medicine*. In the first study, the researchers concluded that eating dark chocolate enhances alertness, but it may make it more difficult to sleep. In the second study, the researchers concluded that dark chocolate consumption improves our moods, but it expedites tooth decay.

Would you cite these sources in your speech? Which supporting materials would you include to document your ideas? Will your decisions affect the perception of your character? If so, how?

you address. If listeners perceive you to be competent, trustworthy, and caring, you will have high source credibility and, hence, be an effective persuader.

Stages of Credibility Credibility varies over time. Your credibility before, during, and after your speech may change. These chronological stages of credibility are sometimes referred to as *initial, derived,* and *terminal credibility*.[11]

Initial credibility is your image or reputation prior to speaking. The more the audience knows about you, the firmer your image. Even if your listeners don't know you personally, you can still bring varying images to the speaking occasion. For example, if you are a spokesperson for an organization, your audience may make certain assumptions about you based on what they know about that organization. If a representative from the Family Research Council, the National Rifle Association, or the Sierra Club were to speak to you, you would probably make certain assumptions about the individual based on what you know about that organization. Just as you do with strangers, you form impressions of your classmates based on what they say in class, how they dress, whether they arrive to class on time, their age, and any organization to which they belong.

Derived credibility is the image the audience develops of you as you speak. The moment you enter your listeners' presence, you provide stimuli from which they can evaluate you. As you begin your speech, the number of stimuli multiplies quickly. If you begin your speech with an offensive joke, listeners' images of you will become more negative. When you appeal to your listeners' values and present reasoned arguments to advance your position, you enhance your image. Your information helps your audience judge your credibility. Listeners will also judge your nonverbal behaviors, such as gestures, posture, eye contact, and appearance. If you convey confidence, authority, and a genuine concern for your listeners, you will enhance your credibility.

Terminal credibility is the image the audience has of you after your speech. Even this credibility is subject to change. The listener may be caught up in the excitement and emotion of your speech and end up with an elevated opinion of you. As time passes, that evaluation may change. As you can see, the process of generating and maintaining credibility is ongoing. In this class, for example, your credibility at the conclusion of one speech will shape your initial credibility for your next speech.

Logos: Logical Argument

Aristotle's second mode of persuasion involves the logical reasoning and argument you put forward in your speech. As mentioned, we dedicate Chapter 17 to teaching you how to construct a well-reasoned and logical argument (and how to avoid being

Key Points: Components of Credibility

1. Competence
2. Trustworthiness
3. Caring

initial credibility
A speaker's image or reputation before speaking to a particular audience.

derived credibility
The image listeners develop of a speaker as he or she speaks.

terminal credibility
The image listeners develop of a speaker by the end of a speech and for a period of time after it.

Key Points: The Stages of Credibility

1. Initial credibility
2. Derived credibility
3. Terminal credibility

persuaded by a faulty argument), but the importance of logic to persuasion is worth mentioning here as well.

Consider the following example. Beth Ann grew up in a rural community in which her family had several acres of land on which they raised small farm animals, from rabbits to small pigs. Beth Ann now has a small yard in an urban area, and wishes to raise a few ducks with her children. However, her community has an ordinance against the practice and she cannot do it legally. She attends a town hall meeting and is able to speak for several minutes to present her point of view. She researched her topic thoroughly, providing examples of laws and policies from her childhood community. She shares a thoughtful story of how much she learned by raising animals as a child (e.g., responsibility), and extends goodwill (caring) to her audience by noting the benefits of the practice (e.g., fresh eggs, knowing where food comes from). Her speech is organized clearly, and delivered effectively.

Nonetheless, Beth Ann has entirely failed to persuade her audience. Why? Because her argument is not logical. Raising such animals in a densely populated area is not the same as raising them in a rural environment—the comparison is not effective. She did not refute legitimate concerns about issues like noise or sanitation in a densely populated area. Beth Ann would have improved her chances of persuading her listeners had she acknowledged the concerns about raising small farm animals in her community, and refuted them with evidence from similarly populated communities that allow the practice. Chapter 17 will assist you in constructing your speech from logical arguments and sound reasoning. You should also revisit Chapter 9 for a refresher on the types of supporting materials and tests of evidence that you can use to prove your arguments.

Pathos: Emotional Appeals

Pathos, Aristotle's third mode of persuasion, is the appeal to emotions. Among the emotions speakers can arouse are anger, envy, fear, hate, jealousy, joy, love, and pride. When speakers use these feelings to try to get you to believe something or to act in a particular way, they are using emotional appeals.

Because some of the feelings just listed seem negative, you may consider emotional appeals as unacceptable or inferior types of proof. Perhaps you have even heard someone say, "Don't be so emotional; use your head!" It is certainly possible to be emotional and illogical, but keep in mind that it is also possible to be both emotional and logical. Is it illogical, for example, to be angered by child abuse, to hate racism, or to fear chemical warfare? We don't think so. The strongest arguments combine logic with passion. Logos and pathos should not conflict; they should complement each other.

Jessica began her persuasive speech by relating a personal narrative she remembered from her childhood.

> I was 4 years old; my sister was only 2 [years old]. It was not long after we reached my grandma's house that the phone rang. I could hear ambulance and police sirens head toward the highway as tears were forming in my mom's eyes. There had been a car accident. My dad was rushed to the hospital; his little Fiesta car was totaled. He had been hit on the passenger side by a man driving a station wagon, and, fortunately, both my dad and the other driver survived. Because the other driver fell asleep at the wheel, my dad went to the hospital instead of coming home that night to his family.

Jessica quoted several sources with examples and statistics related to driver fatigue, including these powerful statistics:

> Drowsy driving is estimated to cause about 20 percent of [all vehicle] accidents, 1.2 million a year, more than drugs and alcohol combined. It accounts for an astonishing 5 percent of fatal crashes, and 30 percent of fatal crashes in rural areas.[12]

Did Jessica construct a logical argument? Yes. She presented examples and statis-tics to support her position. Did she construct an emotional argument? Again, yes. She tapped her listeners' need for safety and their compassion for those who have suffered because of drowsy drivers. Logos and pathos coalesced to form a compelling argument. You can use the guidelines in "Theory into Practice: Developing Emotional Appeals" to develop and enhance the pathos of your persuasive speech.

Connect with Your Listeners

16.5 Apply the four strategies to establish common ground with your listeners.

As you learned in the previous section, part of your success in persuading your audi-ence comes from your effective use of ethos, logos, and pathos. We have already offered examples and ideas to build your credibility and use emotional appeals effectively. (We also provided an example of logos, which is discussed in great detail in Chapter 17.) One particularly powerful strategy for enhancing your credibility and engaging with your listeners' emotions is to establish a sense of connection with them. You are prob-ably more easily persuaded by people similar to you than by those who are different

Theory into Practice (TIP)

DEVELOPING EMOTIONAL APPEALS

Thoughtful emotional appeals can engage listeners in both the content and delivery of your message. Use the following four guidelines to connect with your audience and enhance the pathos of your speech.

Tap Audience Values

This guideline requires, first, that you carefully analyze your audience to identify their beliefs, values, and needs. Then, as you construct and deliver your speech, show that what you advocate is consistent with your listeners' values.

Duncan's specific purpose was to persuade his class-mates to become members of Amnesty International. He had joined this organization because he felt that, as an individ-ual, he could do little to help end torture and executions of prisoners of conscience throughout the world. As part of a concerted worldwide effort, however, he saw the opportunity to further social and political justice. Duncan surveyed his classmates and discovered that although many of them knew little about Amnesty International, most strongly supported freedom of expression and opposed governments' actions to suppress this right. Duncan used these shared values to establish common ground with his listeners and to frame what he would propose.

Use Vivid Examples

Vivid, emotionally toned examples illustrate and enliven your message. After presenting testimony of persecution coupled with statistical estimates of the extent of the problem, Duncan paused and then announced, "I want you not only to hear of the plight of these victims but also to see it." He pushed a remote control button and proceeded to show five slides of people brutalized by their own governments. He did not speak but

simply showed each slide for 10 seconds. After the last slide, he spoke again:

> They say a picture is worth a thousand words. Well, these pictures speak volumes about human rights abuse. But these pictures should also speak to our consciences. Can we stand back, detached, and do nothing, knowing what fate befalls these individuals?

Duncan used dramatic visual examples to enhance the pathos of his speech.

Use Emotive Language

Nowhere can words be more powerful than when they work to generate emotional appeals. Near the end of his speech, Dun-can told his listeners, "In the last 4 minutes you've heard about the anguish, the pain, the suffering, and the persecution expe-rienced by thousands of people, simply because they want to be free and follow their consciences." *Anguish, pain, suffering*, and *persecution* are all words Duncan carefully chose to evoke strong feelings among the audience.

Use Effective Delivery

When a speaker's verbal and nonverbal messages conflict, we tend to trust the nonverbal message. For that reason, speak-ers who show little physical and vocal involvement with their speeches usually come across as uninterested or insincere. When you display emotion, you can sometimes generate audi-ence emotion. Throughout his speech, Duncan made effective use of eye contact, gestures, pauses, and vocal emphasis to connect with his classmates. His speech had a powerful effect because his delivery demonstrated his concern for and com-mitment to his topic.

Sales representatives are particularly skilled at establishing common ground with their listeners in order to meet the unique needs of their customers.

from you. We may reason that individuals having backgrounds like ours will view situations and problems as we would. Furthermore, we believe that people who share our beliefs will investigate an issue and arrive at a judgment in the same manner we would if we had the time and the opportunity. Thus, persuasion is more likely if a speaker establishes common ground with the audience.

Sonja, a weekend news anchor for a local television station, was asked to speak to a college television production class on employment opportunities in television. Notice how Sonja established common ground as she focused on experiences she shared with her listeners.

Seven years ago a timid freshman girl sat in a college classroom much like this. Just like you, she was taking a TV production class. And like some of you, I suspect, she dreamed of being in front of a camera someday, sitting at an anchor desk, reporting the news to thousands of families who would let her come into their homes through the magic of television.

There was little reason to predict that this girl would achieve her dreams. In many ways she was rather ordinary. She didn't come from a wealthy family. She didn't have any connections that would get her a job in broadcasting. She was a B student who worked part-time in the university food service to help pay for her education. But she had a goal and was determined to attain it. And then one day, it happened. An instructor announced that a local TV station had an opening for a student intern. The instructor said the internship would involve long hours, menial work, and no pay. Hardly the opportunity of a lifetime! Nevertheless, after class, she approached the instructor, uncertain of what she was getting into. With her instructor's help, she applied for and received the internship. It is because of that decision that I am now the weekend anchor of the city's largest television station.

The rest of Sonja's speech focused on the importance of student internships in learning about the reality of the broadcast media and making contacts for future references and employment. Her opening comments made Sonja a more believable speaker by bridging the gap between her and her listeners. Sonja's suggestions influenced her audience because she had established common ground with them.

Four principles of persuasion should guide how you establish common ground with your audience. Each principle requires you to analyze your audience carefully in order to understand your listeners.

Assess Listeners' Knowledge of Your Topic

Persuasion is more likely if the audience lacks information on the topic. In the absence of information, a single fact can be compelling. The more information your listeners possess about an issue, the less likely you are to influence their perceptions.

Arturo applied this principle in a speech to persuade his audience that auto insurance companies should not be allowed to set rates based on drivers' credit ratings. Few of his listeners knew that the practice occurred. Yet, by citing just a handful of credible sources, Arturo proved that the practice increased beginning in the mid-1990s, had been adopted by 92 percent of insurers by 2001, and was "nearly universal" by March 2002. As a result, drivers with the worst credit ratings paid rates that were, in some cases, 40 percent higher than those with the best ratings.

New and surprising information such as this can have great persuasive impact. Of course, this principle also has significant ethical implications. Ethical speakers will not exploit their listeners' lack of knowledge to advance positions they know are not logically supported.

Assess How Important Your Listeners Consider Your Topic

Persuasion is related to how important the audience considers the topic. The perceived importance of a topic can increase the likelihood of persuasion.

Which of the following speakers do you think had the most difficult challenge? In answering this question, you must consider how important you think the audience considers these topics.

Emilio, Yuna, and Brad gave their persuasive speeches on the same day. Emilio's purpose was to persuade the audience to support the school's newly formed lacrosse team by attending the next home game. Yuna's topic concerned the increasing number of homeless adults and children in the city. She told the class about Project Hope, sponsored by the Student Government Association, and asked everyone to donate either a can of food or a dollar at designated collection centers in campus dining halls or in the Student Center. Finally, Brad advocated the legalization of marijuana, citing the drug's medical and economic potential.

Audience members in this example probably agreed with both Emilio and Yuna, and both may have been successful persuaders. Listeners who viewed combating hunger as a more important goal than supporting the lacrosse team were probably more persuaded by Yuna and may have contributed to Project Hope.

Just as the importance of a topic can work for you as a persuasive speaker, it can also work against you and decrease the likelihood of persuasion. It is surely easier, for example, for someone to persuade you to change brands of toothpaste than to change your religion. The reason is simple: Your religion is more important to you. Brad probably had a tougher time persuading his listeners than did either Emilio or Yuna. Legalizing marijuana probably ran counter to some deeply held audience opinions, and the intensity of those beliefs and values may have made them more resistant to Brad's persuasive appeals. The importance of an issue will vary according to each audience member, and you need to take this into account as you prepare your persuasive speech.

Motivate Your Listeners

Persuasion is more likely if the audience is motivated in the direction of the message. People change their values, beliefs, attitudes, and behaviors because they are motivated to do so. To be an effective persuader, you must discover what motivates your listeners. This requires an understanding of their needs and desires. How can you do this? You can enhance your persuasive appeal by following three steps. First, identify as many of the needs and desires of your listeners as possible. Second, review your list, and select those that your speech satisfies. Third, as you prepare your speech, explain how the action you advocate fulfills audience needs. If you discover that your speech does not fulfill the needs or desires of your listeners, then you have probably failed to connect with the listeners. They may receive your speech with interest, but such listeners will probably not act on your message. What you intended as a persuasive speech may in fact be received as informative.

Relate Your Message to Listeners' Values

Persuasion is more likely if the speaker's message is consistent with listeners' values, beliefs, attitudes, and behaviors. We expect our actions to match our beliefs. In fact, we will call someone a hypocrite who professes one set of values but acts according to another. Your ability to persuade is thus enhanced if you request an action that is consistent with your audience's values.

Use this principle of consistency in constructing your persuasive message. For example, we have had students who persuaded their classmates to oppose the use of animals in nonmedical product testing. They first identified the beliefs that would cause a person to challenge such tests—for example, product testing harms animals and is unnecessary. Next they showed their audience that they share these beliefs. Once they accomplished that, the speakers then asked their listeners to act in accordance with their beliefs and boycott companies that continue to test cosmetics on animals.

Organize Your Persuasive Speech

16.6 Organize your persuasive speech arguments appropriately for your topic, purpose, and audience.

No matter how well you connect with your audience, a poorly organized speech has little chance of surviving in the minds of audience members. Using the organizational strategies discussed in this section can increase your listeners' retention of your message. This is especially important if you seek long-term changes in your audience's attitudes and behaviors. A well-organized speech in which the key ideas are presented in a logical manner boosts your perceived speaker credibility and enhances your argument.

Common organizational patterns for persuasive speeches discussed in Chapter 8, Learning Objective 8.2, are problem–solution, pro–con assessment, need–plan, and causal division strategy. However, sometimes students want to use a topical organizational structure in their persuasive speeches, which is also acceptable.

In this section, we build upon your existing knowledge of organization by considering the order of your key ideas, before moving on to three additional organizational patterns used specifically in persuasive speeches: the comparative advantage pattern, the refutation pattern, and Monroe's motivated sequence.

Primacy and Recency Theories

Once you have determined the key ideas in your speech, you must decide their order. To do that, you must know which of your arguments is the strongest. Assume for a moment that your persuasive speech argues that the public defender system must be reformed. Assume, too, that you are using a topical organization (discussed in Chapter 8, Learning Objective 8.2). Your three key ideas could be:

  I. Public defenders' caseloads are too heavy.
 II. Public defenders have too little experience.
III. Public defenders have inadequate investigative staff.

One of these three key ideas will probably be stronger than the other two. You may have more evidence on one, you may have more recent evidence on it, or you may feel that one argument will be more compelling to your particular audience. Assume that you decide key idea II is the strongest. Where should you place it? You have two options—first or last—but the answer depends on your speech goal and audience analysis.

Primacy theory recommends that you put your strongest argument first in the body of your speech to establish a strong first impression. Because you are most likely to win over your listeners with your strongest argument, this theory suggests that you should win your listeners to your side as early as possible. Primacy theorists tell you to move your strongest argument to the position of key idea I.

Recency theory, on the other hand, maintains that you should present your strongest argument last, thus leaving your listeners with your best argument.

Primacy theory
The assumption that a speaker should place the strongest argument at the beginning of the body of a speech.

Recency theory
The assumption that a speaker should place the strongest argument at the end of the body of a speech.

Recency theorists would have you build up to your strongest argument by making it key idea III.

If your listeners oppose what you advocate, you may want to present your strongest argument first. Moving them toward your position early in the speech may make them more receptive to your other ideas. If your audience already shares your beliefs and attitudes and your goal is to motivate them to action, you may want to end with your most compelling argument. Both the primacy and recency theorists generally agree that the middle position is the weakest. If you have three or more arguments, therefore, do not place your strongest argument in a middle position. When you sandwich a strong argument between weaker ones, you reduce its impact.

Journal: First or Last?

What is your opinion on primacy and recency research? When you listen to others speak, do you tend to remember the first key idea or the final key idea? Or does it depend on the topic? Explain your answer.

The Comparative Advantage Pattern

The **comparative advantage pattern** is appropriate when the speaker wants to illustrate the advantages of one viewpoint, object, or behavior over another viewpoint, object, or behavior. One example of a comparative advantage pattern is to convince your listeners that the advantages of drinking tea far outweigh the advantages of drinking coffee. We call this approach a "pattern" rather than a division because this approach does not inform you of the order in which to present your key ideas. Rather, it informs you of how to structure each key idea. Consider the following example:

comparative advantage pattern
An organizational pattern in which the speaker illustrates the advantages of one viewpoint, object, or behavior over another viewpoint, object, or behavior.

> *Specific Purpose:*   To persuade my peers that swimming provides a better workout than running does
>
> *Key Ideas:*   I. Weight control
>   A. Calories burned per hour when running
>   B. Calories burned per hour while swimming
> II. Joint effects
>   A. Running is a high-impact activity that results in knee, hip, and ankle problems
>   B. Swimming is a low-impact activity that is harmless to your joints

The Refutation Pattern

The **refutation pattern** is used when the speaker attempts to disprove claims and opinions that oppose the speaker's position. Each key idea in the refutation pattern includes two parts. In the first part of the key idea, the speaker addresses a claim that contradicts the speaker's own position. In the second part of the key idea, the speaker refutes (or disproves) the opposing claim. This pattern repeats for each of the speaker's key ideas. As with the comparative advantage pattern, the refutation method is also a pattern because it only informs you of how to structure each key idea, but not the order in which you should present them.

refutation pattern
An organizational pattern in which the speaker attempts to disprove claims and opinions that oppose the speaker's position.

> *Specific Purpose:*   To persuade my fellow students that dogs are not man's best friend, cats are.
>
> *Key Ideas:*   I. Pet loyalty
>   A. Reasons people say dogs are loyal to their owners
>   B. Reasons why cats are even more loyal to their owners than dogs are
> II. Pet training
>   A. Assumption that dogs are easy to train
>   B. Strategies to easily train a cat
> III. Pet affection
>   A. Assumption that dogs are affectionate
>   B. Evidence that cats are more affectionate than dogs

Monroe's Motivated Sequence

In the 1930s, Alan Monroe developed one of the most popular patterns for organizing the superstructure of a speech to actuate—a speech type that proved particularly tricky for speakers.[13] Called "the motivated sequence," this pattern is particularly appropriate when you discuss a well-known or easily established problem. Monroe drew from the conclusions of educator and philosopher John Dewey that persuasion is best accomplished if a speaker moves a listener sequentially through a series of steps. **Monroe's motivated sequence** includes five steps, or stages: attention, need, satisfaction, visualization, and action.

Attention   Monroe argued that speakers must first command the *attention* of their listeners. Suppose your geographic area is experiencing a summer drought. You could begin your speech with a description of the landscape as you approached your campus a year ago, describing in detail the green grass, the verdant foliage, and the colorful, fragrant flowers. You then contrast the landscape of a year ago with its look now: bland, brown, and blossomless. With these contrasting visual images, you try to capture your audience's attention and interest.

Need   Your second objective is to establish a *need*. This step is similar to the problem and need steps in the problem–solution and the need–plan patterns of organizing a speech. For example, your speech on the drought situation could illustrate how an inadequate water supply hurts not only the beauty of the landscape but also agricultural production, certain industrial processes, and, ultimately, the economy of the entire region.

Satisfaction   When you dramatize a problem, you create an urgency to redress it. In the *satisfaction* step of the motivated sequence, you propose a way to solve or at least minimize the problem. You may suggest voluntary or mandatory conservation as a short-term solution to the water shortage crisis. As a longer-range solution, you might ask your audience to consider the merits of planting grasses, shrubs, and other plants that require less water. You could advocate that the city adopt and enforce stricter regulations of water use by businesses or that it develop alternative water sources.

Visualization   Monroe argued that simply proposing a solution is seldom sufficient to bring about change. Through *visualization*, Monroe's fourth step, you seek to intensify your audience's desire to adopt and implement the proposed solution. You could direct the audience to look out the window at their campus and then ask if that is the scenery they want. More often, though, you create word pictures for the audience to visualize. Without adequate water, you could argue, crops will die, family farms will fail, industries will not relocate to the area, and the quality of life for everyone in the area will be depressed. In contrast, you could refer to the landscape of a year ago, the image you depicted as you began your speech. The future can be colored in green, red, yellow, and blue, representing growth and vitality.

Action   The final step of the motivated sequence is the *action* you request of your listeners. It is not enough to know that something must be done; the audience must know what you want them to do, and your request must be within their power to act. Do you want them to join you in voluntary conservation by watering their lawns in the evening when less water will evaporate or by washing their cars less frequently? Are you asking them to sign petitions pressuring the city council to adopt mandatory conservation measures when the water table sinks to a designated level? Conclude your speech with a strong appeal for specific, reasonable action.

Monroe's motivated sequence
A persuasive pattern composed of (1) getting the audience's attention, (2) establishing a need, (3) offering a proposal to satisfy the need, (4) inviting listeners to visualize the results, and (5) requesting action.

Key Points: Organize Your Persuasive Speech

1. Primacy theory
2. Recency theory
3. Comparative advantage pattern
4. Refutation pattern
5. Monroe's motivated sequence

Annotated Sample Speech

Daniel Hinderliter delivered the following persuasive speech and placed fourth at the 2013 Interstate Oratorical Association National Speech Contest. As you read his speech, notice the use of elements of Monroe's motivated sequence to frame his problem–solution discussion of reducing food waste by creating a more sustainable food culture.

Eating Better through Reducing Food Waste[14]

Daniel Hinderliter, West Chester University, Pennsylvania

1 On October 19, 2012, journalist and Bucknell University expert-in-residence Jonathan Bloom performed an experiment: using a large scale, he calculated the amount of food waste thrown out by students in a two-hour lunch period. As reported in his Wastedfood.com blog post of the same day, 1,000 students wasted almost 100 pounds of food *in two hours*. This food waste becomes more staggering when considering the nation as a whole: an August 2012 report from the Natural Resources Defense Council, or NRDC, disclosed that 25 percent of all household food purchases are wasted. That's four slices in the average loaf of bread, one quart of every gallon of milk, three eggs out of each dozen. Ours is a food culture pervaded by waste.

2 It's important at this point to acknowledge that farmers and the food industry suffer from their own wasteful practices. That waste, however, is designed to protect us; consumer waste is not. As a nation, we are attempting to shift to a more sustainable future. Sustainability, however, cannot be legislated or technologically innovated. It takes our own committed collective efforts. In order to truly embody sustainable living, we must make necessary changes in our own individual habits. With over 11 million tons of wasted food in the U.S. since the beginning of 2013, according to the running counter on endhunger.org, something must be done to dramatically curtail our shameful amount of waste.

3 Today, we will grasp the problem of food waste, isolate the causes, and advocate for concrete solutions, to create a more sustainable food culture.

4 Our level of food waste is staggering. The U.S. Environmental Protection Agency estimated on their website epa.gov, last updated April 15, 2010, Americans generated 34 million tons of food scraps. Despite our frequent discounting of this waste through offhanded statements like, "Our wasted food wouldn't be sent to starving children anyway," while true, this everyday behavior of wasting food can have drastic consequences. Effects of food waste are twofold: first, economic and second, environmental.

5 First, our misuse of food has economic consequences in the store and at home. Food waste watchdog Leanpath.com estimates on October 1, 2012, that food prices have risen 42 percent in the past ten years, including an 8 percent price rise in 2011 alone. This means the amount of money we waste in our homes on discarded food rises as well. An Economic News Release dated September 25, 2012, from the U.S. Bureau of Labor Statistics reveals that each dwelling in the U.S. spends $6,500 per year on food. Extrapolating from that number, this means we invest roughly $790 billion in food annually. If the aforementioned National Resources Defense Council is to be believed, roughly $200 billion is to be thrown away.

6 As if the [economic] effects of this food waste are not enough, personal food waste has environmental effects as well, in meal preparation and food disposal. CNN on June 27, 2012, laments that North Americans waste, on average, 230 pounds of food a year per person. In the same report, Richard Swannell, waste prevention director for the Waste and Resources Action Program, warns on CNN of June 27, 2012, "A significant percentage of the household food that is wasted ends up in landfill where it produces CO_2 and methane. Methane is 23 times more potent than CO_2 as a greenhouse gas." Moreover, the previously cited NRDC report opines that 25 percent of the fresh water used for food production is squandered through available food waste. The EPA exposed on their previously cited website that the United States uses 230 billion gallons of water daily for food production, which means we waste 80 billion gallons of water *every single day*.

Attention

In his introduction (paragraphs 1 and 2), Daniel focuses his audience's *attention* on the problem of food waste. He adapts his topic to his listeners by relating one study's estimate of food waste by students. In his second paragraph, Daniel forecasts that later in his speech he will seek his classmates' *action* to "make necessary changes in our own individual habits."

Need

Daniel establishes the *need* for reducing food waste in paragraphs 4–9. He documents the problem in paragraphs 4–6, and he identifies causes of food waste in paragraphs 8 and 9.

7 Jonathan Bloom illustrated through his experiment that students perpetuate the wasted food problem, but why do they waste in the first place? A closer look at personal food waste reveals two causes: the Costco effect and the commoditization of food.

8 First, big bulk food supermarkets such as Costco, Sam's Club, and BJ's can have a huge effect on the way we purchase food. Defined by an April 2012 CNBC documentary as "the routine tendency of its members to succumb to the store's discount-chic allure and spend more than they expect, often buying more than they need," the Costco effect encourages patrons to purchase far more food than they can consume before the food goes bad and needs to be thrown out. In the name of big savings, we end up overbuying big time.

9 Second, the commoditization of food has contributed to our waste of food as well. From the farm to the fork, food has become not a dietary staple, but rather a designer accessory. Food has become a commodity, meaning it's one among any number of products to be merely bought and sold. In our culture we like to buy new. Leftovers are viewed as used food to be thrown away to make room for new food. The January 2012 *Monthly Review* agrees that this commodification means "the farmers producing the bulk of food . . . have become greatly separated from the public that finally purchases their products, not just physically, but also by the long chain of intermediaries between farms and people's tables." We have lost the relationship of producer-consumer and, thus, have lost the ability to see food for what it is—a basic human necessity.

Satisfaction

In paragraphs 10–13, Daniel seeks to *satisfy* the need for a change by presenting a two-step solution of institutional and individual action.

Visualization

In paragraph 11, the first sentence uses *satisfaction* by introducing one solution to the problem. Daniel then uses *visualization* as he describes one university's program to reducing waste. His last sentence moves to the *action* step by encouraging classmates to ask for a similar program at their university.

Action

In paragraphs 11–15, Daniel tells his audience how they can *act* to implement a solution. He lists steps students can take "to reduce our own personal food waste" in paragraphs 12 and 13.

10 With such overarching causes resulting in our wasteful habits, the future does seem bleak. After his experiment, Jonathan Bloom disagrees. Bloom's experiment leads us to see solutions on two levels: the institutional and the individual.

11 First, institutions such as public schools and universities can enact programs to cut down on food waste. Many have started waste collection calculators similar to Bloom's experiment in their cafeterias. University of Notre Dame started a waste calculator in their lunchroom. Program chairperson Anna Gorman explains in an October 30, 2012, article from the *Notre Dame Observer*: "It's mainly just being conscious of what you're picking up," she said. "It's all about making a conscious effort to reduce waste." Programs like these highlight the relationship people have with their food. Ask your own universities about programs you may have in your cafeterias, and inquire about starting them if such programs do not exist.

12 Second, on a personal level, we can all take steps to reduce our own personal food waste in purchase and consumption. When shopping, look for "half price" sales instead of "buy one get one" sales, meaning you get the proper amount of food for a reduced cost instead of twice the amount of food for the regular cost.

13 On the consumer level, Jonathan Bloom admits in his 2011 book *American Wasteland* solutions are easy: the biggest step to take is just to plan. By knowing what we have in our cabinets and refrigerators, we eliminate the need to go grocery shopping for new and redundant foods. Use websites such as supercook.com and myfridgefood.com or comparable phone apps that allow you to scan food on hand, which they convert into tasty recipes. Preserve perishables through proper canning or freezing to increase shelf life and edibility of foods long term. Finally, just eat your leftovers. If you haven't chewed it, it's not used food.

14 Bloom's experiment may have been skewed by an uncontrolled variable: terrible cafeteria food. But this cannot be an excuse for all of us. We have a profound problem. We waste food at an unconscionable level. Yes, part of it is systemic and we can't directly affect that. But every day we each can make a difference that can significantly curtail this shameful waste of our most basic resource.

15 Today, after confronting the problems, isolating the causes, and advocating essential solutions, we understand the magnitude of our waste as well as the magnitude of our ability to change.

› SUMMARY

Speaking to Persuade

The Ethics of Persuasion

16.1 Explain the ethics of persuasion relevant to both speakers and listeners.

- Persuasion does not require a speaker to be more powerful than the audience.
- Ethical speakers who are more powerful than their audience members do not rely on this power imbalance as a means to persuade listeners.
- Ethical speakers do not attempt to manipulate the audience.

Types of Persuasive Speeches

16.2 Differentiate among the three types of persuasive speeches.

- A persuasive speech aimed at changing beliefs and attitudes, but not requesting any overt behavior of listeners, is a *speech to convince*.
- A *speech to actuate* seeks to change behaviors.
- A *speech to inspire* encourages positive changes in the way listeners feel about their beliefs or actions.

Types of Influence

16.3 Describe, with examples, the three types of influence.

- Persuasive speakers must identify the type of influence they seek in their listeners. Do they want to *instill* values, beliefs, attitudes, or behaviors that the listeners may not already possess or practice? Do they seek to *intensify* how the audience already thinks, feels, or acts? Do they want the audience to *change* attitudes, beliefs, values, or behaviors?
- How a speaker answers these questions will determine the specific purpose and the development of the persuasive speech.

Modes of Persuasion

16.4 Explain, with examples, Aristotle's three modes of persuasion: ethos, logos, and pathos.

- Aristotle proposed three modes of persuasion: ethos (ethical appeal—known as speaker credibility), logos (logical appeal), and pathos (emotional appeal).

- Speaker credibility involves perceived speaker competence, caring, and trustworthiness.
- Some speakers have *initial credibility* with a particular audience, based on the listeners' prior knowledge of the speakers. All speakers have *derived credibility*, developed from the ideas they present in their speech and their speech delivery, and *terminal credibility* based on the audience's evaluation of the speaker and the message after the speech.
- Logos is the reasoning and argument a speaker presents. It will be covered thoroughly in Chapter 17.
- Pathos is the emotional appeal that arouses strong feelings and images to persuade the audience. It is best used in conjunction with high credibility and sound logic for successful persuasion.

Connect with Your Listeners

16.5 Apply the four strategies to establish common ground with your listeners.

Persuasive speakers establish common ground with their listeners by (1) assessing listeners' knowledge of their topic, (2) assessing how important their listeners consider their topics, (3) motivating their listeners, and (4) relating their message to the listeners' values.

Organize Your Persuasive Speech

16.6 Organize your persuasive speech arguments appropriately for your topic, purpose, and audience.

- Persuasion is more likely if the speaker's arguments are appropriately placed within the speech. *Primacy theory* asserts that speakers should place the strongest argument first in the body of the speech. *Recency theory* maintains that speakers should build up to the strongest argument, placing it last in the body of the speech. The lesson for public speakers is to avoid placing a strong argument between weaker ones.

- The comparative advantage pattern is appropriate when the speaker wants to illustrate the advantages of one viewpoint, object, or behavior over another viewpoint, object, or behavior.

- The refutation pattern is used when the speaker attempts to disprove claims and opinions that oppose the speaker's position.

- Monroe's motivated sequence is used in speeches to actuate and suggests that the speaker moves the audience sequentially through five steps: attention, need, satisfaction, visualization, and action.

DEVELOPING PERSUASIVE ARGUMENTS

→ LEARNING OBJECTIVES

After studying this chapter, you should be able to

17.1 Apply the specific steps involved in making and refuting arguments.

17.2 Construct five types of arguments.

17.3 Explain, with examples, the 10 fallacies of argument.

17.4 Develop speeches using three types of propositions.

uring the 2016 U.S. presidential election, we heard several people ask: "Are you voting Democrat or Republican?" This is a seemingly natural question, but a highly flawed one. As a voter, you don't have to decide between the Democrats and the Republicans—you have other options. You can vote for the Libertarian Party, Green Party, or the Constitution Party. You can even write in a candidate. Additionally, you have the option not to participate in the election.[1]

Structuring sound arguments and detecting flawed reasoning are important skills for the public speaker. Thomas Gilovich, professor of psychology at Cornell University, explains:

> Thinking straight about the world is a precious and difficult process that must be carefully nurtured. . . . In the words of [paleontologist and evolutionary biologist] Stephen Jay Gould, "When people learn no tools of judgment and merely follow their hopes, the seeds of political manipulation are sown." As individuals and as society, we should be less accepting of superstition and sloppy thinking, and should strive to develop those "habits of mind" that promote a more accurate view of the world.[2]

In the previous chapter, we offered an overview of speaking to persuade. In that chapter, you learned about Aristotle's three modes of persuasion: ethos (credibility), logos (logical appeal), and pathos (emotional appeals). In this chapter, we expand upon our explanation of logos by introducing you to the details of argument and reasoning. We will show you how to construct an argument, refute an argument, and detect faulty arguments. In addition, you will study characteristics and types of persuasive propositions.

Making and Refuting Arguments

17.1 Apply the specific steps involved in making and refuting arguments.

Aristotle argued that the successful persuasive speaker has two basic goals: "[Y]ou state an argument and you prove it."[3] Sounds simple, doesn't it? Well, an argument is more than an assertion or claim. **Argument** is the process of reasoning from evidence to *prove* a claim. Before you can prove your case, however, you must understand the structure of arguments and how those arguments are organized in your speech. Aristotle called this type of persuasive appeal **logos**, or logical appeal. Let's examine how all this works.

argument
The process of reasoning from evidence to prove a claim.

logos
Logical appeal.

Steps of an Argument

Suppose you make the following statement: "I am more confident about public speaking now than I was at the beginning of this course." If someone asked you to justify your statement, you could respond by saying:

> I experience fewer symptoms of nervousness. I seem to worry less about facing an audience. The night before my speech, I sleep better than I used to. I establish eye contact with my audience now, rather than avoiding looking directly at them. I no longer nervously shift my weight from foot to foot, and I have started gesturing.

Together, your statement and response constitute an argument. You have made a claim ("I am more confident about public speaking now") and then supported it with evidence—in this case, examples from personal observation. Aristotle would be pleased.

At its simplest level, an argument includes three steps:

1. Making a claim
2. Offering evidence
3. Showing how the evidence proves the claim[4]

A **claim** is a declarative statement that you intend to prove and persuade your listeners to accept. Some examples of claims include:

claim
A declarative statement that the speaker intends to prove and persuade the listeners to accept.

The New York Rangers are better than the Philadelphia Flyers.

Expressing affection improves our health.

The United States is not a democracy.

The **validity** of any claim depends on whether or not the evidence supports your statement. **Evidence** is the supporting materials you use to prove a point. (See Chapter 9, Learning Objective 9.2, for different types of supporting materials.) As a persuasive speaker, you have an obligation to support your position with valid arguments and supporting materials. Therefore, you must offer your listeners reasons to accept your claim.

validity
The accuracy with which your supporting materials support your claim.

evidence
Supporting materials a speaker uses to prove a claim.

Speakers may introduce a claim and then present supporting materials, or they may introduce evidence and show how that information leads to an inescapable claim. In her persuasive speech, Elvira wanted to encourage her classmates to become organ donors. In her first key idea, she focused on the lack of organs available for transplant surgeries:

> First, there is a lack of organs available for transplant surgeries in the United States.

Elvira has just stated her claim.

> Organdonor.gov reported that, in 2015, 119,000 people were awaiting a new heart, liver, kidney, or other organ, but less than 31,000 organ transplants were performed that year. This discrepancy increases on a daily basis. Every 10 minutes, a new name is added to the organ donation list. However, only 3 out of every 1,000 people who die pass away "in a way that allows for organ donation," as stated on organdonor.gov. The website also states that less than 50 percent of people in the United States are signed up to be organ donors.

Elvira then offers evidence for her claim.

> These statistics clearly demonstrate the demand for organs in the United States. In 2015, almost 90,000 people did not receive their needed organ donations.

Elvira shows how the evidence proves the claim.

Refuting an Argument

When you studied how to organize your speech, we suggested the 4 S's strategy for developing your key ideas in a speech. In a persuasive speech, you signpost your claim, state your claim, support your claim with quality evidence, and summarize, showing how your evidence proves your claim. But how do you refute another person's argument? The question is relevant because topics you and your classmates select for your persuasive speeches will involve a spark of controversy. There is always another side, perhaps several sides, in addition to the one the speaker presents. You may even select

Trial lawyers know that cases—and arguments—cannot be won by eloquent language alone. The validity of any claim depends on the quality of the evidence supporting the claim.

refute

To dispute; to counter one argument with another.

a topic because you read or heard a statement with which you disagreed. Persuasive speakers and critical thinkers must know both how to prove arguments and how to refute them. For each argument you **refute**, you may want to use the following four-step refutation pattern (see also Chapter 16, Learning Objective 16.6):

1. State the position you are refuting.
2. State your position.
3. Support your position.
4. Show how your position undermines the opposing argument.

Seth selected his topic, the importance of language skills for career advancement, after hearing a comment by his roommate. He presented the following argument in his speech. The annotations show how Seth used each of the four steps of refutation.

Seth states the position he plans to refute.

Last week, my roommate stormed into the dorm room shaking a paper he just got back from his English composition teacher. He threw the paper on his bed and screamed, "I can't wait until I get out of college, away from teachers who are obsessed with grammar, and into the real world where people judge you on what you say, not how you say it!" Sound familiar? I bet many of us have felt the same way after getting back a paper with all those picky corrections marked in red ink. As my roommate says, "In the real world, you're not judged on your grammar."

Seth states and supports his position.

Well, my roommate is wrong. Grammar is important in the business world just as it is here in the classroom. How we express our ideas *is* important to our success. At least that's the conclusion of Camille Wright Miller, and she ought to know. She has a Ph.D. and is a consultant on workplace issues. In her January 13, 2002, *Roanoke Times* column, she told about a candidate who was interviewed for an important position in a company, one that would pay more than $100,000. After the interview, one of the owners said, "How many times did he say 'I seen'"? Those two words cost him the job. And this isn't an isolated example. Dr. Miller says, "Many . . . organizations recognize the power of language and the negative impact of grammatically flawed language on their customers and employees." Employers evaluate grammar "in determining an individual's intelligence, capabilities, and fitness to be a manager."

Seth shows how his position undermines the opposing argument.

Using incorrect language can keep us from landing a good job or getting promoted once we're hired. So, I'm going to tell my roommate that he probably should listen to what his English composition teacher says. And all of us should read those picky comments written in red on the papers we get back, too. Because there's some truth in the cliché "Good grammar never goes out of style."

The quality of your decisions—indeed, the quality of your life—depends on what you know and how you use that information.

ETHICAL DECISIONS

TO INCLUDE OR NOT INCLUDE CONTRADICTORY EVIDENCE?

Brian developed a persuasive speech to actuate in which his goal was to influence his audience members to eat more fruit rather than taking vitamin supplements to obtain necessary nutrients. He found an illuminating article that focused on both the pros and cons of eating fruit versus taking vitamin supplements. In the section on the cons of eating fruits, Brian read that many fruits contain fairly high levels of sugar and some also have carbohydrates. This concerned Brian because he knew that many of his fellow students were watching their weight. He knew that he would be less likely to influence his fellow students' behavior if the cons of eating fruits were included in his speech. However, Brian did not want to deceive his audience members by withholding relevant information.

Should speakers include contradictory information if it will be counterproductive to their speech purposes? If yes, how might Brian include this information and still achieve his goals? If no, why not?

Types of Arguments

17.2 Construct five types of arguments.

Speakers can justify their claims by using any of five types of arguments. You may offer proof by arguing from example, analogy, cause, deduction, or authority. The type of argument you select will depend on your topic, the available evidence, and your listeners. You may combine several types of arguments in a single persuasive speech. Knowing how to construct and test arguments will also help as you listen to the speeches of others.

Argument by Example

Argument by example is an inductive form of proof. **Inductive argument** uses a few instances to assert a broader claim. For example, if you have struggled through calculus and analytic geometry, you may conclude that math is a difficult subject. We hear a few friends complain of electrical problems with a particular make of car and decide not to buy that model. A speaker relates several examples of corruption in city hall, and we conclude that political corruption is widespread. Those are all examples of inductive reasoning.

argument by example
An inductive form of argument in which the claim is supported by providing examples.

inductive argument
Use of collected evidence that supports a general claim.

Patrick began his speech using a series of examples to suggest a larger problem. Only then did he ask his audience to consider the cause of the problem. See if you can guess his topic.

> First came a report out of Alabama. The McMillan family found their tap water black, oily, and bubbling. Soon after came Texas. Three ranchers said their water smelled fouled, and two days later, seven of their animals were dead. Ohio. A gas buildup in the Payne family's basement well caused the house to explode, and testing found similar levels in the wells of 22 neighbors. Even now, across the country folks are realizing that with just a match, they can light their tap water on fire.
>
> As the reports mount, a shocking revelation is taking shape. For years, the drinking water of tens of millions of Americans has been systematically poisoned with chemicals like arsenic, formaldehyde, and sulfuric acid. But far from acts of terrorism, this sabotage is not only allowed by our government but subsidized. It's called hydraulic fracturing, a drilling technique that harnesses incredible amounts of natural gas, but at the cost of destroying our most precious resource: our drinking water.[5]

How can you test whether Patrick's or anyone's argument by example is sound? Argument by example is valid only if you can answer yes to each of the following four questions:

1. *Are the examples true?* When you studied supporting materials, you learned that hypothetical or imaginary examples can clarify a point, but they do not prove it. Only when verifiable examples are presented should you proceed to the next question.

2. *Are the examples relevant?* Suppose Susan presents the following evidence in her speech on homelessness: "According to police reports published in yesterday's *News Journal*, city police picked up three individuals who were found sleeping in the park this past weekend. So, you can see that even in our city homelessness is a serious problem." Do these examples really support the claim? Did these individuals not have homes? Had they passed out? Were they there for other reasons? Until you can answer these questions, you cannot assume that they were homeless. The examples must relate to the specific claim.

3. *Are the examples sufficient?* Susan must present enough examples to prove her assertion. In general, the greater the population for which you generalize, the more

examples you need. Three examples of homelessness may be statistically significant in a small town, but that number is far below average for many large cities.

4. *Are the examples representative?* Was the weekend Susan reported typical? How did it compare with other weekends, weekdays, or seasons? To prove her argument, Susan must present examples that are true, relevant, sufficient, and representative.

Argument by Analogy

argument by analogy
An argument that links two objects or concepts and states that what is true in one case is or will be true in another.

An analogy is a comparison. **Argument by analogy** links two objects or concepts and asserts that what is true of one will be true of the other. Argument by analogy is appropriate when the program you advocate or oppose has been tried elsewhere. Some states have some form of "stand your ground" laws; others do not. Some colleges require SAT or ACT test scores for admission; others do not. Some public high schools offer magnet programs; others do not. A speech defending or disputing any of these programs could demonstrate success or failure elsewhere to establish its position.

Jon argued that pharmacists should not have the right to refuse to fill patients' prescriptions, even for moral or religious reasons. Notice how he used argument by analogy to support his position:

> The June 4, 2005, *Ledger Times* reminds us that in many ways pharmacists are like bus drivers and airline pilots. It would be outrageous for a pilot who disapproved of gambling to refuse to transport two Las Vegas–bound passengers who wanted to visit casinos. Or for a bus driver, disturbed [by] tax dollars [that] went to a lavish new football stadium rather than a decrepit public school, to refuse to let sports fans off at the arena. Professional pharmacists hold a state-conferred monopoly on medications. In that respect, they are public servants. Their role calls for neutrality on the job—whether they prefer it or not.[6]

Do you find Jon's argument persuasive? The key to this pattern of argument is the similarity between the two entities. In testing the validity of your argument by analogy, you need to answer this question: "Are the two entities sufficiently similar to justify my conclusion that what is true of one will be true of the other?" If not, your reasoning is faulty. This general question can best be answered by dividing it into two specific questions.

1. *Are the similarities between the two cases relevant?* For example, suppose you used argument by analogy to advocate eliminating Friday classes during summer school on your campus as State U has done. The facts that both schools have similar library facilities and the same mascot would be irrelevant. Equivalent summer enrollments, numbers of commuting students, and energy needs are highly relevant and can be forceful evidence as you build your case.

2. *Are any of the differences between the two cases relevant?* If so, how do those differences affect your claim? If you discover that your college has far fewer commuting students than State U does, this difference is relevant to your topic and will undermine the validity of your claim.

Argument by Cause

argument by cause
An argument stating that one action or condition caused or will cause another.

Argument by cause connects two elements or events and claims that one is produced by the other. Causal reasoning takes two forms—reasoning from effect to cause and from cause to effect. The difference between the two is their chronological order. An *effect-to-cause argument* begins at a point of time (when the effects are evident) and moves back in time (to when the cause occurred). When you feel ill and go to the doctor, the doctor will usually identify the symptoms (the effects) of the problem and then diagnose the cause. The doctor is reasoning from effect to cause. In contrast, *cause-to-effect argument* begins at a point of time (when the cause occurred) and moves forward (to when the effects occurred or will occur). Doctors reason from cause to effect when they tell their patients who smoke that this habit may result in emphysema or lung cancer. If you choose to present an argument by cause, we encourage you to review the causal division strategy you learned in Chapter 8, Learning Objective 8.2.

In his persuasive speech "The Death of Reading," Nicholas used a book metaphor to organize and phrase his message. He previewed his key ideas: "Chapter 1: The Death of Reading; Chapter 2: The Autopsy; and Chapter 3: The Resurrection." Before presenting his solutions, Nicholas argued from effect to cause to explain why children today read less. (The effect is noted in the first paragraph, the cause in the second.)

> Reading leisurely, whether newspapers, magazines, or books, has decreased over 50 percent in today's families since 1975. The American Psychological Association on December 17, 2003, argued that reading is essential to childhood imaginative growth. Modern entertainment, such as television and movies, leaves little room for creative interpretations. "A lack of reading invites Big Brother, preventing our children from being able to create the world themselves. When reading, the children are in control of the reality, not the films."
>
> Now that we have looked at the symptoms, we must next crack open the spine of today's books and run an autopsy to discuss the inherent causes of the death of reading. To children the answer is simple: reading isn't fun anymore. The December 28, 2003, *St. Petersburg Times* tells us that many children believe that the only motivation that they have to read is to pass tests. In 2002 alone, over 85,000 third graders were not allowed into the fourth grade due to an inability to pass their FCAT reading scores, and over 43,000 were forced into summer reading to pass. This form of education is known as "extrinsic motivation." This means that America's schools rely on external rewards, such as grades and test scores. Extrinsic motivation does not teach our children to think independently and critically about situations. Reading, it seems, has fallen prey to this school of thought, because children are taught to read to get good test scores, not because reading is entertaining and intellectual.[7]

Rachel used a cause-to-effect argument in her speech on the lack of safety in nursing homes. (The cause is noted in the first paragraph, the effect in the second.)

> In 1965 the Fire Marshals Association of North America begged Congress to require sprinklers in all nursing homes. Forty years and 12 failed proposals later, Congress has yet to act. On December 16, 2005, *USA Today* reveals that there are 16,000 nursing homes that violate fire safety standards annually. Twenty-three thousand fires are reported every year. Four states—Massachusetts, Minnesota, Montana, and Hawaii—set no fire safety standards, only six states require fire sprinklers, and less than half require smoke alarms that alert authorities.
>
> These statistics lead up to an average of at least one fatal fire every month, much like the one that occurred just before the holidays as reported by the Associated Press on December 13, 2005, where two were killed in a Michigan fire and dozens more injured. Fires in nursing homes are all too common, and with more than 1.6 million residents in need of assisted-living arrangements, the danger is real.[8]

When you argue by cause, test the soundness of your reasoning by asking and answering the following three questions:

1. *Does a causal relationship exist?* For an argument from cause to effect or effect to cause to be valid, a causal relationship must exist between the two elements. Just because one event precedes another does not mean that the first caused the second. One of our students argued that the scholastic decline of American education began with and was caused by the Supreme Court's decision outlawing mandatory school prayer. We doubted the connection.

2. *Could the presumed cause produce the effect?* During a period of rising inflation, one of our students gave a speech arguing that various price hikes had contributed to

the inflation rate. She provided three examples: the cost of postage stamps had increased 87.5 percent, chewing gum 100 percent, and downtown parking meter fees 150 percent. While she was able to document the dramatic percentage increase in the prices of these products, her examples had more interest than impact. They did not convince her audience that these increases could significantly influence the inflation rate by themselves.

3. *Could the effect result from other causes?* A number of causes can converge to produce one effect. A student who argues that next year's increased tuition and fees are a result of the college president's fiscal mismanagement may have a point. But other factors may have made the tuition increase necessary: state revenue shortfalls, decreased enrollment, cutbacks in federal aid, and so on. Speakers strengthen their arguments when they prove that the alleged cause contributed substantively to producing the effect and that without the cause, the effect would not have occurred or the problem would have been much less severe.

Argument by Deduction

Marquis began his speech on time management with the following statement:

> All of us are taking courses that require us to be in class and to study outside class. In addition, many of us are members of social, academic, religious, or career-oriented clubs and organizations. Some of us work. Crowded into our school and work schedules are our responsibilities to friends and family members. In short, we're busy!
>
> College is a hectic time in our lives. Sometimes it seems that we're trying to cram 34 hours of activity into a 24-hour day. In order to survive this schedule and beat the stress, college students need to develop effective time-management skills. You are no exception! If you listen to my speech today, you will learn how to set realistic goals, meet them, and still have time to socialize with friends and get a good night's sleep. Sound impossible? Just listen closely for the next 8 minutes.

deductive argument

An argument stating that what is true generally is or will be true in a specific instance.

syllogism

The pattern of a deductive argument, consisting of a major premise, a minor premise, and a conclusion.

major premise

A claim about a general group of people, events, or conditions.

minor premise

A statement placing a person, an event, or a condition into a general class.

conclusion

The deductive argument that what is true of the general class is true of the specific instance.

Marquis used two types of argument in his introduction. He opened by arguing from example, providing several instances to make his case that college life is busy. He then used deductive reasoning to make the speech relevant to each member of the audience. A **deductive argument** moves from a general category to a specific instance. In this sense, deductive arguments are the reverse of argument by example. To see why that's true, consider the structure of a deductive argument.

Deductive arguments consist of a pattern of three statements: a major premise, a minor premise, and a conclusion. This pattern of deductive argument is called a **syllogism**. The **major premise** is a claim about a general group of people, events, or conditions. Marquis's major premise was this: "College students need to develop effective time-management skills." The **minor premise** places a person, event, or condition into a general class. Marquis's minor premise could be phrased like this: "You are a college student." The **conclusion** argues that what is true of the general class is true of the specific instance or individual. Marquis concluded that each college student in his audience needed to develop effective time-management skills.

Use the following steps to check the structure of your deductive argument:

1. State your major premise.
2. Say "because," and then state your minor premise.
3. Say "therefore," and then state your conclusion.

The resulting two sentences should flow together easily and make sense. Marquis could have said the following: "College students need to develop effective time-management skills. *Because* you are a college student, *therefore* you need to develop effective time-management skills." Notice that if the two premises are true and relate to each other, the conclusion must also be true. Should Marquis have stated his argument that way in his speech? Probably not. The words *because* and *therefore* may sound forced, and his minor premise (You are a college student.) is obvious to his classmates. Nevertheless, using the because–therefore structure when preparing your speech allows you to check the logical flow of your argument.

For deductive arguments to be valid, they must meet certain tests. Whether you are listening to others' arguments or evaluating arguments in your own speech, keep in mind three questions.

1. *Are the premises related?* "All men are created equal. Equal is an artificial sweetener. Therefore, all men are artificial sweeteners." This statement doesn't make much sense, does it? The first sentence uses the word *equal* to mean "equivalent." The second uses *Equal* as a product name for a sugar substitute. For an argument to be valid, the premises must relate to each other. In this case, they clearly do not.

   Let's construct another example. Suppose Bayani prepares a speech trying to persuade his classmates to apply for a new academic scholarship named after his father, Arvin Ocampo. In his speech, Bayani makes the following statement:

   > Any student enrolled in State U who is a rising sophomore can apply for the Ocampo Scholarship. That includes everyone in this class. Just think, next year you could have your entire tuition and fees paid, and you can spend your money on something you've been wanting but were unable to afford. Maybe even that new tablet or laptop.

   Before Bayani convinces his classmates to apply for the scholarship, he first tells them that they are eligible. His argument may be depicted as follows:

   Major premise: Any State U student who is a rising sophomore can apply for the Ocampo Scholarship.
   Minor premise: Every student in this class is a State U student who is a rising sophomore.
   Conclusion: Therefore, every student in this class can apply for the Ocampo Scholarship.

   The terms in the minor premise fall within the scope of the major premise. The two premises are related, and the conclusion seems logical.

2. *Is the major premise true?* Before Bayani's classmates begin filling out a scholarship application form, they should ask the question, "Is the major premise of the argument true?" Suppose two prerequisites for application are full-time student status and good academic standing. The statement "any State U student who is a rising sophomore can apply for the Ocampo Scholarship" is then false. Part-time and probationary students cannot apply. The conclusion of the argument ("Every student in this class can apply for the Ocampo Scholarship.") would therefore not necessarily be true. You must be able to prove your major premise before you draw a conclusion.

3. *Is the minor premise true?* A false minor premise is just as damaging to an argument as a false major premise. Let's suppose that Bayani's major premise is true and that any State U student who is a rising sophomore can apply for the Ocampo Scholarship. What if his class includes some current sophomores? His minor premise ("Every student in this class is a State U student who is a rising sophomore.") is then false. Those students are not eligible for the scholarship, and Bayani's conclusion is false. Arguing a position entails ethical considerations. You must know your facts and reason logically from them.

Journal: Argument by Deduction

Identify the major premise, minor premise, and conclusion in the following group of statements:

Inquiring Minds should be aired on the Trashy Cable Network.
Inquiring Minds is a fluffy news show.
All fluffy news shows should be aired on the Trashy Cable Network.

Argument by Authority

argument by authority

An argument using testimony from an expert source to prove a speaker's claim.

Argument by authority differs from the four other forms of argument we have discussed. To see how it is different, consider the following example from Rashad's speech:

> I believe that our campus needs a new football stadium, and I'm not alone in my opinion. Last month, our athletics director, Mr. Croucher, discussed the need for a new football stadium after we won the last game of the season. Additionally, the chancellor recently announced that our school spirit would be enhanced if more students were able to attend the football games. That would require a new, bigger stadium, which I support.

Argument by authority uses testimony from an expert source to prove a speaker's claim; its validity depends on the credibility the authority has for the audience. In this example, Rashad did not offer arguments based on example, analogy, cause, or deduction to explain the validity of his position. Instead, he asserted that both the athletic director and the chancellor are supportive of a new football stadium. He asked the audience to support his position based on the credentials of the authority figures (athletic director and chancellor) who endorsed his claim. His rationale was that his sources had access to sufficient information and had the expertise to interpret it accurately; thus, we should trust their conclusions.

Theory into Practice (TIP)

TESTING YOUR ARGUMENTS

Mario Cuomo, noted speaker and former governor of New York, encouraged leaders to persuade others "not so much with speeches that sound good, as with speeches that are good and sound."[9] As you select and develop the arguments for your speeches, ask and answer the questions that we discussed in this chapter. Remember to use these same guidelines when you listen to the speeches of others.

To construct an *argument by example*, ask yourself:

- Are the examples true?
- Are the examples relevant?
- Are the examples sufficient?
- Are the examples representative?

To construct an *argument by analogy*, ask yourself:

- Are the similarities between the two cases relevant?
- Are the differences between the two cases relevant?

To construct an *argument by cause*, ask yourself:

- Does a causal relationship exist?
- Could the presumed cause produce the effect?
- Could the effect result from other causes?

To construct an *argument by deduction*, ask yourself:

- Are the premises related?
- Is the major premise true?
- Is the minor premise true?

To construct an *argument by authority*, ask yourself:

- Is the source an expert?
- Is the source unbiased?

An argument based on authority is only as valid as the source's credibility. To test your argument, ask and answer the following two questions:

1. Is the source an expert?
2. Is the source unbiased?

Our discussion of these questions and other tests of evidence in the supporting materials section of this book will help you select the best authority for your claim. (See Chapter 9.)

Testing the arguments you use and hear others use is crucial to effective, ethical speaking and listening. The "Theory into Practice" feature summarizes these tests. When you analyze the arguments you use, you strengthen them and can save yourself the embarrassment of being caught using illogical or invalid proof. However, it is just as important to check the validity of persuasive arguments you hear. By doing this, you avoid being duped into misguided thoughts and actions.

In spite of these tests, persuasive speakers sometimes incorporate certain errors of proof into their speeches. These errors are so widely used that they have been named and studied. In the following section, we examine some of these arguments that appear—but only appear—to say something authoritative. If you can identify these errors, you can avoid them.

Fallacies of Argument

17.3 Explain, with examples, the 10 fallacies of argument.

A **fallacy** is "any defect in reasoning which destroys its validity."[10] Fallacies can be dangerous and persuasive for the same reason: Because they resemble valid reasoning, we often accept them as legitimate. They can produce bad decisions leading to harmful consequences.

fallacy
A flaw in the logic of an argument.

Speakers who value civility respect the credibility of their ideas and the welfare of their listeners. As you construct your persuasive speech, ensure that the arguments you encounter in your research are valid. Then, use your research to develop sound arguments to support the ideas in your speech. As a listener, you have an ethical responsibility to critically evaluate the ideas other speakers present to you. Be alert for those arguments based on sound versus flawed reasoning. Consider the valid arguments and reject fallacious ones.

How can you tell the difference? We will discuss 10 of the most common fallacies. As you read them, notice how many resemble the patterns of argument we have just discussed.

Hasty Generalization

People who jump to conclusions commit the fallacy of **hasty generalization**, a faulty form of argument by example. What distinguishes valid from fallacious inductive proof is the quantity and quality of examples. When speakers make claims based on insufficient or unrepresentative instances, their reasoning is usually flawed. For example, a speaker uses examples of three students convicted of plagiarism and concludes that cheating is widespread on campus. Or, a student argues that three of his four professors this semester are international faculty members, so most of the professors at his university must be from outside the United States. People who rely too heavily on first impressions, who do not read widely, or who spend little time researching are prime candidates for reasoning from hasty generalization.

hasty generalization
A fallacy that makes claims from insufficient or unrepresentative examples.

False Analogy

Speakers argue by analogy when they link two items and assert that what is true of one will be true of the other. If the two items are sufficiently similar, the speaker's claim may

false analogy
A fallacy that occurs when an argument by analogy compares entities that have critical differences.

be valid. However, if the items differ in critical ways, the persuader may be guilty of using a **false analogy**, and the claim may be fallacious. You've probably heard someone respond to an argument by saying, "That's like comparing apples and oranges." That person just detected a faulty comparison. Consider some of the arguments we've heard in students' speeches and see if you can detect some faulty reasoning:

> We license drivers; why shouldn't we license parents? You can't take to the road until you learn how to drive and pass a test. Aren't children more important than cars?

> Investing in the stock market is no different than playing the lottery. Each is risky and there's no guarantee you won't lose money.

What do you think of these arguments? Which comparisons are valid arguments by analogy? Which are fallacies? You need to exercise your critical thinking skills as you read, listen to, and develop arguments by analogy.

Post Hoc Ergo Propter Hoc

post hoc ergo propter hoc
A chronological fallacy that says that a prior event caused a subsequent event.

This fallacy uses the Latin title and literally means "after this, therefore because of this." A chronological fallacy, **post hoc ergo propter hoc** (often called post hoc) assumes that because one event preceded another, the first caused the second; it is an improper application of the argument by cause. Perhaps you have heard a friend comment, "I knew it would rain; I just washed my car!" Your friend is probably making a joke based on the post hoc fallacy. People exhibit post hoc reasoning when they expect something good to happen if they carry a lucky charm while gambling, wear a lucky shirt to a football game, or cross their fingers as a teacher returns an exam.

These flaws in reasoning may seem obvious. Yet other examples of confusing coincidence with causation are more subtle and potentially more damaging. For instance, a person rejects medical treatment, relying instead on a cure that has not yet been researched, because someone else tried it and subsequently got well. An incumbent mayor takes credit for every city improvement that occurred since she took office; her opponent blames her for everything bad that happened during this time. An event may have more than one cause. It is also preceded by occurrences having no effect on it whatsoever. As a result, determining the relationship between two events or conditions is often difficult. You must examine that relationship if you are to avoid the post hoc fallacy.

slippery slope
A fallacy of causation stating that one action inevitably sets a chain of events in motion.

Slippery Slope

The slippery slope fallacy typically warns of a dangerous outcome that will be inevitable if certain events take place, although the conclusion is not logical.

Envision yourself at the top of a hill on a wintry day. You take one step, slip on a patch of ice, lose your footing, and begin sliding down the hill. You try to regain your balance, but you continue your slide, stopping only when you reach the bottom of the hill. This visual image depicts the slippery slope fallacy. **Slippery slope** asserts that one action inevitably sets in motion a chain of events or indicates a trend; it is an example of the faulty use of argument by cause. This defect in reasoning is exemplified in the following argument:

> If we begin to control the sale of guns by restricting the purchase of handguns, where will it end? Will shotguns be next? And then hunting rifles? Soon the right to bear arms will disappear from the Constitution, and sportsmen and sportswomen will be denied one of their basic freedoms.

This speaker's argument implies that a single act will set in motion a series of events that no one will be able to stop, but that's not necessarily the case. Just because legislators support one constitutional amendment or one law doesn't mean that

they must support subsequent reforms. Usually, a slide down the slope is preventable. Each journey involves a series of decisions, and it is possible to retain or regain your footing.

Red Herring

The name of the **red herring** fallacy apparently originated with the English fox hunt. When the hunt was over, the hunt master would drag a red herring—a type of fish that is smoked and salted—across the path of the hounds. The pungent scent would divert the dogs from their pursuit of the fox, and they could then be rounded up.

A red herring fallacy is an example of a faulty argument by deduction. A speaker makes a claim based on an irrelevant premise. In essence, a speaker guilty of the red herring fallacy introduces an irrelevant issue to deflect attention from the subject under discussion. Both of the following speakers attempted to divert discussion from germane issues to irrelevant concerns:

> A politician answers charges that she accepted illegal campaign contributions by noting her service on the state's ethics advisory board.

> A student responds to a charge of plagiarism with the statement, "I was a Boy Scout throughout high school."

When you present a persuasive speech, you are an advocate for the position you present. As such, you have an ethical responsibility to defend your arguments. Answer criticisms of your argument with evidence and logic; don't deflect criticism by diverting your audience to another track.

red herring
A fallacy that introduces irrelevant issues to deflect attention from the subject under discussion.

Appeal to Tradition

This fallacy is grounded in a respect for traditional ways of doing things. On the surface, respect for tradition seems reasonable. But the fallacy commonly called **appeal to tradition** defends the status quo and opposes change by arguing that old ways are superior to new ways; it is an improper use of an argument by authority. A speaker who argues against admitting men to her college because of the school's history as a women's school commits this fallacy unless she offers additional support for the claim. Its most common form of expression—"We've always done it that way"—is merely descriptive. It discourages discussion and reevaluation of our traditions.

As important as many traditions are to us, they should not be used to thwart needed change. The Constitution of the United States gave people many of the freedoms they enjoy. Yet it also precluded non-European Americans and women from full participation in society. The fight to secure the right to vote for all citizens challenged that tradition. Old ways are not always the best ways.

appeal to tradition
A fallacy that opposes change by arguing that old ways are always superior to new ways.

False Dilemma

When forced to choose between two alternatives, you face a dilemma. Dilemmas can be actual or false. In an actual dilemma, the alternatives you face are real; there is no room for compromise. Suppose you are asked to choose between going to a movie with friends and attending a review session for an upcoming test. If the review and theater hours coincide, your dilemma is real and you must forfeit either entertainment or study.

A **false dilemma** presents only two options when, in reality, there are more. For example, if there is a late showing of the movie, perhaps you can convince your friends to meet you at the theater after you attend the review. In this instance, the dilemma is false because you do not have to choose between studying and seeing the movie; you can do both.

The fallacy of false dilemma is sometimes called the *either–or fallacy*. The dilemma usually polarizes issues into two mutually exclusive categories, such as "Stand with

false dilemma
A fallacy that confronts listeners with two choices when, in reality, more options exist. (Sometimes called the either–or fallacy.)

America or stand for terrorism" and "When guns are outlawed, only outlaws will have guns." Neither slogan allows for middle-ground positions.

Listeners should be especially attentive to all "either–or" and "if–then" statements they hear. These grammatical constructions lend themselves to the fallacy of false dilemma, as in the following examples:

> The issue is very simple: Either you support the Constitution on which this nation was founded, or you're not a patriotic American.

> I don't support a cutback in defense spending. I don't want to see a weakening of America's strength.

Each of these examples presents the listener with only two choices. However, they disregard other legitimate options. We can exhibit patriotism and still question a nation's laws and policies. Eliminating unnecessary defense spending does not necessarily weaken the country. Using that money for other important projects—like major road and bridge repair—may make America stronger.

False Authority

false authority
A fallacy that uses testimony from sources who have no expertise on the topic in question.

The fallacy of **false authority** is an invalid form of argument by authority. This fallacy occurs when advocates support their ideas with the testimony of people who have apparent but not real expertise. Before deciding to accept someone's opinion or testimony, ask the question, "Is the person an objective expert on this topic?" Celebrity endorsements of commercial products frequently illustrate this fallacy. Advertisers often use celebrities more for their popularity than their credibility.

It is important to exercise your critical thinking skills to avoid using the fallacy of false authority. If you cite information from a website without checking its authority and accuracy or if you quote from authors without knowing their credentials, you have used the fallacy of false authority, most likely unintentionally. The statement "I couldn't find any information about the author" is a recipe for irresponsibility. You can avoid the fallacy of false authority by using only information from experts and credible sources.

Bandwagon

In the 1800s and early 1900s, political candidates held parades to meet the people. A band rode on a wagon leading the parade through town. As the wagon passed, local leaders would jump on the bandwagon to show their support. The number of people on board was considered a barometer of the candidate's popularity and political strength.

bandwagon
A fallacy that determines truth, goodness, or wisdom by popular opinion.

The **bandwagon** fallacy is also a faulty argument by authority. It assumes that popular opinion is an accurate measure of truth and wisdom. Frequently referred to as the "everybody's doing it" fallacy, bandwagon arguments commonly use phrases such as "everyone knows" or "most people agree."

Speakers who defend their positions by pointing to polls showing popular support exploit the bandwagon fallacy. While agreement regarding a belief or action may be reassuring, it is no guarantee of accuracy or truth. "Truth is not always democratic."[11] History is cluttered with popularly held misconceptions. Remember, most people once believed that the world was flat and that the sun revolved around Earth. You should decide the validity of an argument by its form and substance, not merely by how many people agree on it.

Ad Hominem

ad hominem
A fallacy that urges listeners to reject an idea because of the allegedly poor character of the person voicing it; name-calling.

Ad hominem, literally meaning "to the man," arguments ask listeners to reject an idea because of the allegedly poor character of the person voicing it. Political speeches often are peppered with ad hominem arguments. These statements may evoke applause, cheers, and laughter, but they provide little insight into issues. When Donald Trump called Hillary Clinton a "nasty woman," and Hillary Clinton called Trump's supporters a "basket of deplorables," they were making ad hominem attacks rather than engaging in reasoned discourse. A club member commits this fallacy when he argues that Bryan's proposal for an alcohol-free party should not be taken seriously because Bryan has two DUI (driving under the influence) convictions.

In its most obvious form, this fallacy is name-calling. For some people, simply knowing that a speaker is liberal, conservative, feminist, or fundamentalist is sufficient to close their minds. They disregard the merits of an idea because of the person delivering the message. An ethical listener has a responsibility to give all ideas a fair hearing.

To speak ethically and with civility, you must know how to construct valid arguments and avoid defective ones such as those we have just discussed. Once you have mastered this ability, you can use your arguments to achieve the overall goal of your speech.

Selecting Propositions for Persuasive Speeches

17.4 Develop speeches using three types of propositions.

Earlier, you learned that your first steps in constructing a speech are to select your topic, focus or narrow it, determine your general purpose, formulate your specific purpose, and construct a central idea. In persuasive speaking, you can add one additional step: to state your proposition.

A **proposition** is a declarative sentence expressing a judgment you want the audience to accept. If you speak on the topic of improving education, you may narrow this broad subject and select as your specific purpose to persuade the audience that teacher salaries should be increased. Your basic position—"teacher salaries should be increased"—can be thought of as a proposition. Notice that this proposition *expresses a judgment* that *is debatable* and that *requires proof*. We will discuss these three characteristics of propositions in the next section.

Your central idea, in contrast, lists the reasons you offer to prove your proposition. In the preceding example, your central idea could be: "Higher teacher salaries would recruit better teachers, retain better teachers, and improve student learning." The following example illustrates the similarities and differences among the proposition, specific purpose, central idea, and key ideas of a speech.

> *Proposition:* The new campus classroom building should be named Richter Hall.
>
> *Specific Purpose:* To persuade the audience that the new classroom building should be named for Louise Richter
>
> *Central Idea:* The new classroom building should be named for Louise Richter, an outstanding teacher, advisor, and friend.
>
> *Key Ideas:* I. The name of the new classroom building should honor an outstanding educator.
> II. Louise Richter deserves this recognition.

Notice that this proposition expresses a judgment, while the central idea includes the reasons the speaker will offer to prove the proposition.

Characteristics of Propositions

If you formulate a well-worded proposition early in preparing your persuasive speech, you will be sure of your persuasive goal and can keep it firmly in mind. Your proposition also helps you focus your persuasive speech and test the relevance of supporting ideas as you develop them. Devising your proposition can be relatively easy. Propositions are marked by three characteristics.

Journal: Fallacies

Corey tells his audience the incident of Chicago firefighters who discovered sacks of undelivered mail in the home of a mail carrier. From this example, he argues that there is a need for national reform of the U.S. Postal Service. Identify the fallacy that is illustrated by Corey's argument and explain your answer.

Key Points: Fallacies of Argument

1. Hasty generalization
2. False analogy
3. Post hoc ergo propter hoc
4. Slippery slope
5. Red herring
6. Appeal to tradition
7. False dilemma
8. False authority
9. Bandwagon
10. Ad hominem

proposition
A declarative sentence expressing a judgment or an opinion a speaker wants listeners to accept.

Propositions Express a Judgment   A proposition for a persuasive speech states the position you will defend. Consequently, it should be worded as a declarative sentence expressing your position. If you advocate statehood for Puerto Rico, your proposition could be worded like this: "The United States should grant Puerto Rico statehood." This simple declarative sentence clearly states your position on the issue.

Sometimes, however, you may be interested in a topic but lack enough information to have developed a position on it. In this case, you may first want to phrase a question to guide your research. Once you answer the question, you can then develop your proposition. Mark, a criminal justice major, worded the following question to guide his research: "Is the death penalty for juveniles cruel and unusual punishment?" He researched the topic, reading articles by scholars and jurists on both sides of the issue. He made a list of arguments for and against capital punishment for juveniles. Although Mark supported capital punishment for adult offenders, his research convinced him to oppose it for juveniles. The proposition he subsequently decided to defend was: "The death penalty for juveniles is cruel and unusual punishment." By phrasing his position statement, writing it out, and keeping it in front of him as he continued researching and assembling his arguments, Mark was able to keep his speech focused on arguments against capital punishment for juveniles.

Propositions Are Debatable   Propositions are appropriate for persuasive speeches only if they are debatable. In other words, the judgment must include some degree of controversy. The proposition "Earth revolves around the sun" is not a good proposition for a persuasive speech because you are unlikely to find any qualified authority today opposing that statement. We now accept it as fact. Once we accept a proposition as fact, it ceases to be an appropriate topic for persuasive speeches.

Propositions Require Proof   A proposition is an assertion, and assertions are statements that have not yet been proved. Your objective as a persuasive speaker is to offer compelling reasons for listeners to accept your proposition. As we discussed earlier in this chapter, you may support your proposition with arguments from example, analogy, cause, deduction, or authority.

> **Key Points: Requirements of Propositions**
>
> 1. Propositions express a judgment.
> 2. Propositions are debatable.
> 3. Propositions require proof.

Types of Propositions

Propositions for persuasive speeches are of three types: fact, value, and policy. The type of organization and supporting materials you will use depends on the type of proposition you defend.

proposition of fact
An assertion about the truth or falsity of a statement.

Propositions of Fact   A **proposition of fact** focuses on belief. You ask the audience to affirm the truth or falsity of a statement. The following are examples of propositions of fact:

> Access to math tutors increases students' grades in mathematics courses.
> An aspirin a day can reduce the risk of heart disease.
> Antimatter-powered space travel is technologically feasible.

In her speech on random drug testing, Lourdes defended this proposition: "Random drug testing on the job decreases workplace drug use." Her specific purpose and key ideas were as follows:

> *Specific Purpose:*   To convince the audience that random drug testing decreases workplace drug use
> *Key Ideas:*   I. Random drug testing deters casual drug use.
>   II. Random drug testing helps decrease drug addiction.

proposition of value
An assertion about the relative worth of an idea or action.

Propositions of Value   A **proposition of value** requires a judgment on the worth of an idea or action. You ask the audience to determine the "goodness" or "badness" of something, as in this proposition: "Corporal punishment in schools is wrong." Propositions of value can also ask you to compare two items and determine which is better, as in Sir William Blackstone's statement, "It is better that ten guilty persons escape than one innocent suffer." Other propositions of value include the following:

Deterrence is a more important goal of criminal justice than rehabilitation.

Censorship is a greater evil than pornography.

Minority rule is morally indefensible.

Suppose you decided to persuade your audience that free agency is bad for professional sports. You could develop your speech on this value proposition as follows:

Specific Purpose: To persuade the audience that free agency is hurting professional sports

Key Ideas: I. It destroys the competitive balance of teams.
II. It undermines the financial solvency of teams.
III. It creates bad role models for kids.

Propositions of Policy   A **proposition of policy** advocates a course of action. You ask the audience to endorse a policy or to commit themselves to some action. These statements usually include the word *should*. Here are some examples of policy propositions:

College athletes should be paid.

Nonviolent offenders should be excluded from "three strikes and you're out" sentencing.

Students should be able to repay student loans through community service.

Duane wanted to persuade his audience to support the student government association's proposal to change from a quarter to a semester academic calendar. Organizing his speech topically, he presented three benefits of a semester system.

Specific Purpose: To persuade the audience that our college should adopt a semester calendar

Key Ideas: I. Semesters allow more time for research in theory courses.
II. Semesters allow more time for skill development in performance courses.
III. Semester credits are easier to transfer to other institutions.

proposition of policy

A statement requesting support for a course of action.

> **Journal: Types of Propositions**
>
> Determine whether the following statement is a proposition of fact, value, or policy and explain your answer:
>
> "The FDA should reduce required testing for experimental drugs to fight life-threatening illnesses."

> **Key Points: Types of Propositions**
>
> 1. Propositions of fact
> 2. Propositions of value
> 3. Propositions of policy

Acclaimed singer/songwriter Elton John, who established the Elton John Aids Foundation in 1992, testified before Congress in May 2015 to advocate a proposition of policy—that the United States should continue to lead the fight against the AIDS epidemic.

SPEAKING WITH CONFIDENCE

When I chose my persuasive speech topic, I was nervous about how to organize my speech in a manner suitable for a persuasive speech. I started by choosing a type of argument, which happened to be an argument by example. This helped me refine my use of evidence to assert my claims while relying on inductive reasoning. As I developed my speech, I found it important to address my claims and present statistical evidence in order for my audience to understand my argument without using hasty generalizations. I also knew I had to organize my speech to ensure it would make sense to my audience. I was able to organize my key ideas and arguments using Monroe's motivated sequence. Because I was confident that my speech was well organized and easily understood by my audience, I was able to deliver my speech with confidence.

Stephanie Spencer
University of North
Carolina–Wilmington

> ## SUMMARY

Developing Persuasive Arguments

Making and Refuting Arguments

17.1 Apply the specific steps involved in making and refuting arguments.

- To be an effective persuader, you must know how to structure a valid argument, detect flaws in reasoning, and word propositions.

- The three steps of structuring an *argument* are to (1) make a claim you want the audience to accept, (2) supply evidence supporting that claim, and (3) explain how the evidence proves your claim.

- The act of countering one argument with another is called *refutation*. To refute an argument, follow this refutational strategy: (1) state the position you are refuting, (2) state your own position, (3) support your position with evidence, and (4) show how your position undermines the argument you oppose.

Types of Arguments

17.2 Construct five types of arguments.

- Speakers must justify their claims or give listeners a reason to accept the claim.

- Five types of argument in a persuasive speech are: (1) *argument by example*, which uses specific instances to support a general claim; (2) *argument by analogy*, which links two concepts, conditions, or experiences and claims that what is true of one will be true of the other; (3) *argument by cause*, which links two concepts, conditions, or experiences and claims that one causes the other; (4) *deductive argument*, which employs a pattern called a *syllogism*, which consists of a major premise, a minor premise, and a conclusion; and (5) *argument by authority*, which uses testimony from an expert source to prove a speaker's claim.

Fallacies of Argument

17.3 Explain, with examples, the 10 fallacies of argument.

- Fallacious arguments are dangerous because they may resemble sound reasoning.

- Ten fallacies of argument are common. (1) *A hasty generalization* makes claims based on insufficient or unrepresentative examples. (2) *False analogy* compares entities that have critical differences. (3) *Post hoc ergo propter hoc* falsely confuses chronology with causation, arguing that because event A preceded event B, A caused B. (4) *The slippery slope* fallacy asserts that one event inevitably unleashes a series of events. (5) *Red herring* introduces irrelevant issues to deflect attention from the true question under discussion. (6) *Appeal to tradition* asserts that old ways of doing things are correct or best, simply because they are traditional. (7) *False dilemma* argues that we must choose between two alternatives, when in reality we may have a range of options. (8) *False authority* uses testimony from sources who have no real expertise on the topic in question. (9) The *bandwagon* fallacy argues that we should behave or think a particular way because most people do. (10) Finally, *ad hominem* urges listeners to reject an idea because of allegations about the character, politics, religion, or lifestyle of the person voicing the idea.

Selecting Propositions for Persuasive Speeches

17.4 Develop speeches using three types of propositions.

- All persuasive speeches advocate *propositions*, position statements the speaker wants listeners to accept. A persuasive proposition must be stated as a declarative sentence that expresses a judgment, is debatable, and requires proof in order to be accepted.

- The three types of persuasive propositions are propositions of fact (focusing on belief), value (requiring a judgment on the worth of an idea or action), and policy (advocating a course of action).

SPEAKING ON SPECIAL OCCASIONS

→ LEARNING OBJECTIVES

After studying this chapter, you should be able to

18.1 Apply the five guidelines for a speech of introduction.

18.2 Apply the four guidelines for a speech of presentation.

18.3 Apply the four guidelines for an acceptance speech.

18.4 Apply the specific guidelines for two types of tribute speeches.

18.5 Apply the five guidelines for a speech to entertain.

We can all count on being called on to deliver a speech on some special occasion—for example, introducing a guest speaker at a club meeting, accepting an award from a civic group, or delivering a eulogy at the memorial service of a relative or friend. To speak your best on any of these occasions, you must consider the customs and audience expectations in each case.

In this chapter, we discuss five special occasions or special circumstances for public speaking: the speech of introduction, the speech of presentation, the acceptance speech, the speech of tribute, and the speech to entertain. You will learn guidelines for and read examples of these types of speeches. This information can serve you well beyond the classroom and prepare you for any occasion when you are requested, invited, or expected to speak.

The Speech of Introduction

18.1 Apply the five guidelines for a speech of introduction.

One of the most common types of special-occasion speeches is the **speech of introduction**. Some people use that phrase to indicate speeches by people introducing themselves to an audience. We use the phrase in this chapter to mean a speech introducing a featured speaker. The following five guidelines will help you prepare a speech of introduction:

- *Keep the focus on the person being introduced.* The audience has not gathered to hear you, so don't upstage the featured speaker. Keep your remarks short, simple, and sincere.

- *Be brief.* If you can, request and get a copy of the speaker's résumé or curriculum vita. This will give you information to select from when preparing your introductory remarks. The key word in that last sentence is *select*. Your listeners will tune out quickly if your introduction is a lengthy chronology of jobs or events in a person's life. Highlight key information only.

- *Establish the speaker's credibility on the topic.* You do this by presenting the speaker's credentials. As you prepare, ask and answer questions such as these: What qualifies the speaker to speak on the subject? What education and experiences make the speaker's insights worthy of our attention?

- *Create realistic expectations.* Genuine praise is commendable; just be careful not to oversell the speaker. Can you imagine walking to the microphone after the following introduction? "Our speaker tonight is one of the greatest speakers in this country. I heard her last year, and she had us laughing until our sides hurt. Get ready for the best speech you've heard in your entire life!"

- *Establish a tone consistent with the speaker's presentation.* Would you give a humorous introduction for a speaker whose topic is "The Grieving Process: What to Do When a Loved One Dies"? Of course not, but if the evening is designed for merriment, your introduction should help set that mood.

Communication professors should certainly know how to introduce a featured speaker. In the following example, Professor Don Ochs of the University of Iowa did an exemplary job of introducing his longtime colleague Professor Samuel L. Becker, the keynote speaker at a Central States Communication Association convention. You'll see that Ochs uses some communication jargon because he was speaking to a group of communication professionals. Notice, though, how Ochs's brief, cordial remarks focus on Becker, establishing Becker's credibility and setting the tone for his informative and inspirational speech.

> Thirty years ago I walked out of an Iowa City store onto the main street and noticed Sam Becker walking about 20 feet ahead of me. His youngest daughter was alongside Sam but she was terribly upset about something, crying, and

speech of introduction

A speech introducing a featured speaker to an audience.

Key Points: Guidelines for the Speech of Introduction

1. Focus on the featured speaker.
2. Be brief.
3. Establish the speaker's credibility.
4. Create realistic expectations.
5. Set the tone for the speech.

speech of presentation

A speech conferring an award, a prize, or some other recognition on an individual or group.

Key Points: Guidelines for the Speech of Presentation

1. State the purpose of the award or recognition.
2. State the recipient's qualifications.
3. Adapt your speech's organization to audience knowledge.
4. Compliment all finalists for the award.

obviously hurt about something. Sam put his arm around his daughter and, in the space of two blocks, said something that comforted and fixed the problem. She was smiling when they parted company.

I share this snapshot of Sam with you because, for me, it captures Sam's approach to life, higher education, scholarship, and our profession.

Sam Becker has figuratively put his arm around difficulties and problems for his entire career. He's made all of us as teachers and scholars better persons and better professionals with his intellect, his vision, his energy, and his instinctive willingness to help.

As a rhetorician, I would much prefer to introduce Sam with figures and tropes, with synecdoche, litotes, and hyperbole. But Sam is a social scientist, so I will be quantitative instead.

How much has Sam helped us? Sam has taught at four universities, written six books, been active in eight professional associations, authored 10 monographs, served on 12 editorial boards, worked on evaluation teams for 32 colleges and universities, served on 36 university committees, lectured at 50 colleges and universities, directed 55 Ph.D.s, and authored 105 articles. Without doubt, he has helped and assisted and supported all of us. Our speaker today, Sam Becker.[1]

The Speech of Presentation

18.2 Apply the four guidelines for a speech of presentation.

The **speech of presentation** confers an award, a prize, or some other form of special recognition on an individual or a group. Such speeches are typically made on special occasions: after banquets or parties, as parts of business meetings or sessions of a convention, or at awards ceremonies.

When you give a speech of presentation, let the nature and importance of the award being presented as well as the occasion on which it is being presented shape your remarks. The following four guidelines will help you plan this special-occasion speech:

- *State the purpose of the award or recognition.* If the audience is unfamiliar with the award or the organization sponsoring the award, begin by briefly explaining the nature of the award or the rationale for presenting it. This is especially important if you represent the organization sponsoring the award. In contrast, an award having a long history probably needs little if any explanation.

- *Focus your speech on the achievements for which the award is being made.* Don't attempt a detailed biography of the recipient. Because you are merely highlighting the honoree's accomplishments, the speech of presentation will be brief, rarely more than 5 minutes long and frequently much shorter.

- *Organize a speech of presentation primarily according to whether your listeners know the name of the recipient in advance.* If they do not know the honoree, capitalize on their curiosity. Begin by making general comments that could refer to several or many people; as the speech progresses, let your comments become more specific. Use gender-neutral descriptions ("this person" or "our honoree"), rather than using "he" or "she." In this way, you keep your audience guessing and allow them the pleasure of solving a puzzle. If the audience knows in advance the name of the person being recognized, begin the speech with specifics and end with more general statements that summarize the reasons for the presentation.

- *Compliment all finalists for the award.* If a group of individuals has been nominated and you are announcing the winner with your speech of presentation, briefly compliment the entire group of people who have been nominated for the award.

Some public speaking instructors assign speeches of presentation as a fun, final speaking assignment. Typically, each student delivers a speech of presentation in which he or she presents a fellow classmate with an award. In "Theory into Practice: Liu Presents an Award," Liu gives Beth an award for being "The Greenest Student," because she spoke about both global warming and recycling in their public speaking class.

Theory into Practice (TIP)

LIU PRESENTS AN AWARD

Notice how Liu follows the guidelines for a speech of presentation as he speaks about his classmate, Beth, and her accomplishments.

It is with great honor and excitement that I am here today to present the 2017 "Greenest Student Award." This award was first established in 2000 when former student Karl Bader, an environmental science major, developed the "Students for Clean Air" organization on our campus.

Since its inception in 2000, one student has been recognized annually for her or his passion for, and work toward a more environmentally friendly world. Some of the past award winners include Garret Huck, class of 2004, Denish Patel, class of 2010, and most recently Emma Moore, class of 2016.

This year's honoree has demonstrated great passion for protecting our environment. For instance, this person always uses a refillable water bottle in class and encourages other students to recycle their plastic, glass, and aluminium bottles. This individual has used public transportation or even walked to campus each day this semester to protect and conserve our environment. The honoree has delivered two outstanding speeches about global warming and recycling to encourage all of us to protect our environment and also serves as the president of the "Students for Clean Air" organization on campus.

This year, we had five outstanding nominees for the "Greenest Student Award": Anita, Beth, Alishah, Josh, and Romeo. These five nominees have done a great job advocating for environmental preservation. However, one of them stood out above and beyond the rest. I would like to congratulate this year's "Greenest Student Award" recipient, Beth Rosen. Congratulations, Beth!

Notice how Liu clearly states the purpose of the award and provides a brief historical overview of the award.

Here Liu points to specific evidence that qualifies Beth for the award. Note that Liu begins with general statements that could apply to many students before becoming more specific. In doing so, he organizes his speech according to the listeners' knowledge about the recipient.

In this final paragraph, Liu compliments all the finalists before bestowing the award to Beth.

SPEAKING WITH CONFIDENCE

In our public speaking course, our final assignment was to deliver a speech of presentation and an acceptance speech. The speech of presentation involved each student presenting another student with an award. I felt intimidated and I worried I wouldn't adequately celebrate the student assigned as my award winner. However, once I thought about my assigned classmate's personality, interests, and involvement around campus, I felt more confident about what I would say. After that, I simply went back and reviewed the guidelines for speeches of presentation—stating the purpose of the award, focusing my speech on the achievements for which the award is being made, organizing my speech according to what my audience members know about the award winner, and finally complimenting the finalists before bestowing the award to the recipient. By following the four guidelines for speeches of presentation, I was able to be more experimental and original in crafting my speech. In doing so, I felt confident when I delivered my award speech and I earned a perfect grade on this fun, final assignment.

Derrick Peña
Penn State Hazleton

ETHICAL DECISIONS

HOW (AND WHETHER) TO POLISH A BAD APPLE

Russell King is president of the Porridge Players, an organization that stages musical comedies on his campus. This season, the Players have performed *South Pacific*, and the actress who played Nelly Forbush is Maria MacIntosh, an enormously talented singer, dancer, and actress with a horrible temper and an insufferably arrogant attitude. As president of the Players, Russell has been called on time after time to mediate disputes between Maria and other members of the cast and crew. By the time the season is over, he has little respect for her, despite her considerable talents.

At the end of each season, the faculty advisory board for the Porridge Players votes on awards for the best performers,

director, technical people, and so forth. No one is very surprised when Maria is chosen to receive the award for best actress. Russell, however, is dismayed to learn that he has to present it, along with a short introductory speech. He wonders what to do.

Should Russell simply praise Maria's performance and not mention the difficulties she caused, or is it his responsibility to make the faculty board aware of her negative impact on the company? What kind of information do you think Russell should include in his speech?

The Acceptance Speech

18.3 Apply the four guidelines for an acceptance speech.

At some point in your life, you may be commended publicly for service you have given to a cause or an organization. You may be presented a farewell or retirement gift from your friends or coworkers. You may receive an award for winning a sporting event, an essay contest, or a speech contest. Although these are different occasions, they have at least one thing in common—each requires a response. To accept a gift or an award without expressing appreciation is socially unacceptable. An **acceptance speech**, then, is a response to a speech of presentation. When a recipient acknowledges the award or tribute, he or she provides closure to the process. A gracious acceptance speech usually includes the following four steps:

- *Thank the person or organization bestowing the award.* You may wish to name the group sponsoring the award and the person who made the speech of presentation. In addition, you may want to commend what the award represents. Your respect for the award and its donor authenticates your statement of appreciation.

- *Compliment your peers as a group rather than individually.* If you are accepting a competitively selected award and especially if your competitors are in the audience, acknowledge their qualifications and compliment them.

- *Thank those who helped you achieve the honor.* Whether you are an accomplished pianist, vocalist, artist, athlete, or writer, you have usually had someone—parents, teachers, or coaches—who invested time, money, and expertise to help you achieve your best. Thank them in your speech.

- *Accept your award graciously.* Whether you are a novice or an experienced award winner, you should emphasize how valuable the award is to you and how honored you are to receive it.

In response to Liu's speech of presentation, Beth delivered an acceptance speech, presented in "Theory into Practice: Beth Accepts an Award."

The Speech of Tribute

18.4 Apply the specific guidelines for two types of tribute speeches.

A **speech of tribute**, or commemorative speech, honors a person, a group, or an event, and it can be one of the most moving forms of public address. In this section we focus on two very common speeches of tribute—the eulogy and the commencement speech.

---

acceptance speech

A speech responding to a speech of presentation by acknowledging an award, a tribute, or recognition.

Journal: Acceptance Speech

If you were given the "Student of the Month Award" within your major, who would you thank for helping you achieve this award and why?

Key Points: Guidelines for the Acceptance Speech

1. Thank the person or organization bestowing the award.
2. Compliment the other nominees.
3. Thank those who helped you attain the award.
4. Accept the award graciously.

speech of tribute

A speech honoring a person, group, or event.

Theory into Practice (TIP)

BETH ACCEPTS AN AWARD

Notice how Beth incorporates the four guidelines we've discussed when she accepts the award Liu presented to her.

I'd like to begin by thanking Liu for the "Greenest Student Award." I'd also like to extend a special thanks to our campus administrators who support an environmentally friendly campus and continue to recognize one student each year for her or his efforts to preserve and protect our environment. Receiving this award will serve as a constant reminder for me to continue to reduce, reuse, and recycle to protect our environment.

Beth not only thanks Liu for the award, she also acknowledges the sponsoring organization—her campus.

I was so pleased to know I was nominated for this award. Anita, Alishah, Josh, and Romeo—the other nominees—are also environmental science majors, and they are all equally worthy of this award in my opinion.

Notice how Beth compliments her fellow nominees.

I would like to thank professor Rick Olsen for not only teaching us about our precious environment, but also for encouraging us to live "green lives." Also, my parents taught me the value of reusing toys, reducing the time I spent in front of the TV, and drinking filtered water rather than bottled water. Thanks to their efforts, I am committed to living an environmentally friendly life.

Beth thanks those who helped her achieve this award.

Lastly, I would like to note that I am so very proud to receive this award. Ever since I came to our campus, I have worked diligently to make our campus even more environmentally friendly and I look forward to taking those motives and achievements with me to my next stop in life. Again, thank you very much, Liu.

Here Beth emphasizes the value of this award and accepts it graciously.

The Eulogy

A special form of a speech of tribute is the **eulogy**, a tribute to someone who has recently passed away. Vivid and memorable examples include Abraham Lincoln's *Gettysburg Address*, Ronald Reagan's tribute to the crew of the Challenger after the shuttle explosion in 1986, and Barack Obama's eulogy for human rights advocate and former South African President Nelson Mandela on a rainy Tuesday in December 2013 in Johannesburg, South Africa.

eulogy
A speech of tribute praising a person who has recently passed away.

The following five guidelines will help develop a eulogy:

- *Establish noble themes.* As you begin developing a eulogy, ask, "Why was this person worthy of my respect and praise?" Answer this question by developing themes you want the audience to remember. Focus on the positive. A eulogy celebrates what was good about a person; it is not an occasion for a warts-and-all biography. You must be careful, however, not to exaggerate a person's accomplishments. To do so may undermine your speech by making it seem insincere or unbelievable.

- *Provide vivid examples.* Anecdotes, stories, and personal testimony are excellent ways of making your speech more vivid, humane, and memorable.

- *Express the feelings of the audience assembled.* The audience needs to be a part of the occasion for a eulogy. If you are honoring Mr. Crenshaw, a former teacher, you may speak for yourself and for all students who studied under him. The tribute should express more than one person's view.

- *Create a memorable image of the person being honored.* You can accomplish this by combining noble themes, vivid examples, and audience feelings. Your speech not only honors someone but also helps audience members focus on that person's importance to them.

On June 10, 2016, in Louisville, Kentucky, Billy Crystal delivered a eulogy for his friend, boxing legend and activist Muhammad Ali. The actor and comedian recounted numerous personal accounts of Ali's courage, calling him " . . . a tremendous bolt of lightning created by Mother Nature out of thin air, a fantastic combination of power and beauty."[2]

Journal: The Speech of Tribute

Imagine you were to give a eulogy for a favorite celebrity. What are two or three noble themes you could develop about this person in your speech? What is one story or anecdote you might develop into a vivid example about the person?

Key Points: Guidelines for the Eulogy

1. Establish noble themes.
2. Provide vivid examples.
3. Express audience feelings.
4. Create a memorable image.
5. Be genuine.

commencement speech
A brief, often witty graduation speech intended to emphasize the occasion, education, and skills of the speaker and her or his peers.

- *Be genuine.* If you are asked to deliver a eulogy about someone you did not know well, you may want to decline respectfully. The personal bond you developed and the interaction you had in getting to know someone is essential for a eulogy.

Peggy Noonan, presidential speechwriter, captures the power of eulogies:

> They are the most moving kind of speech because they attempt to pluck meaning from the fog, and on short order, when the emotions are still ragged and raw and susceptible to leaps. It is a challenge to look at a life and organize our thoughts about it and try to explain to ourselves what it meant, and the most moving part is the element of implicit celebration. Most people aren't appreciated enough, and the bravest things we do in our lives are usually known only to ourselves. No one throws ticker tape on the man who chose to be faithful to his wife, on the lawyer who didn't take the drug money, or the daughter who held her tongue again and again. All this anonymous heroism. A eulogy gives us a chance to celebrate it.[3]

The Commencement Speech

At this point, you may think to yourself: "It is nice to be done with my public speaking class." Yes, you should be proud of your accomplishments this semester, but wouldn't it be great if you got to use the skills you have refined to deliver another common speech of tribute—the **commencement speech**—during your graduation? While that may be an intimidating idea, it is also an empowering prospect:

> To be selected as the student speaker for the . . . commencement ceremony is a great honor and carries great responsibility. The individual chosen represents the graduating class and entire . . . student body. This is a once-in-a-lifetime opportunity.[4]

To prepare for a commencement speech, we offer four guidelines adapted from the Cowell College at the University of California, Santa Cruz:[5]

- *Be brief.* As with most special occasion speeches, brevity is a plus. During your graduation ceremony, you and your peers will likely be tired and ready to go celebrate your accomplishments with your friends and family. So, keep your commencement speech short, no more than 5 minutes.

This student commencement speaker pays tribute to her undergraduate experience during her recent graduation.

- *Emphasize the occasion.* When people get married, the officiant might say, "We are gathered here today to . . . ." Just like an officiant, you should emphasize the occasion—your graduation. What does a graduation ceremony represent? Where do people go from here? Who enabled you to complete your education? What does it mean to have completed a college education? Answering these and other questions will enable you to hone in on the occasion and stay focused.
- *Reflect on your education.* Take the audience members on a journey through your college career. Emphasize various events (new student orientation, homecoming, sporting events, severe weather conditions, challenging courses or qualifying exams, etc.) that you experienced during your college career.
- *Play the part.* As a college graduate, your audience will expect that you use proper language and present your ideas intelligently. However, graduations are also festive occasions, so incorporate appropriate humor to energize your audience.

> **Key Points:**
> **Guidelines for the**
> **Commencement Speech**
>
> 1. Be brief.
> 2. Emphasize the occasion.
> 3. Reflect on your education.
> 4. Play the part.

The Speech to Entertain

18.5 Apply the five guidelines for a speech to entertain.

The **speech to entertain** makes a point through the creative, organized use of the speaker's humor. The distinguishing characteristic of this speech is the entertainment value of its supporting materials. It is usually delivered on an occasion when people are in a light mood: after a banquet, during an awards ceremony, or other festive occasions.

A *speech to entertain* is different from *speaking to entertain*. In their opening monologues, Chris Rock, Ellen DeGeneres, and Stephen Colbert speak to entertain. Their purpose is to relax the audience, establish some interaction with them, and set the mood for the rest of the show. Their remarks are usually not organized around a central theme, something essential to a speech to entertain.

The following five guidelines along with what you already know about developing a public speech will enable you to construct a speech to entertain:

- *Make a point.* Frequently, the person delivering a speech to entertain is trying to make the audience aware of conditions, experiences, or habits that they take for granted. We have heard students present successful speeches to entertain on topics

speech to entertain
A speech designed to make a point through the creative, organized use of humorous supporting materials.

While Ellen DeGeneres speaks to entertain, the woman to the right delivers a humorous toast at a wedding in South Africa. This is a speech to entertain.

ranging from our interest in tabloid news stories to routine, expensive dates versus creative, less expensive dates. In some of these speeches, the speaker stated the main point fairly bluntly by the end of the speech (e.g., "You do not have to spend a fortune to have an interesting time on a date"). In other speeches, speakers simply implied their central idea.

- *Be creative.* To be creative, your speech to entertain must be *your* product and not simply a replay of an Ellen DeGeneres or a Jimmy Kimmel monologue. A replay is not creative, even if you do a great job of delivering the other person's lines. Your speech to entertain should give your audience a glimpse of your unique view of the world.

- *Be organized.* Your speech must have an introduction, a body, and a conclusion, just as informative and persuasive speeches do. The speech to entertain must convey a sense of moving toward some logical point and achieving closure after adequately developing that point. Failure to organize your materials will cause you to ramble, embarrassing both you and your audience. You will feel like the novice comic caught without a finish, a sure-fire joke that makes a good exit line. The audience will sense that you are struggling and will have trouble relaxing and enjoying your humor.

- *Use appropriate humor.* The speech to entertain is difficult to do well for a simple reason: Most people associate entertainment with lots of laughter and feel that if the audience is not laughing, they are not responding favorably to the speech. But consider the range of things that entertain you, from outrageous antics to quiet, pointed barbs. Your humor should be adapted to your topic, your audience, the occasion, and your personal style. The following four suggestions should guide your use of humor:
  - *Be relevant.* Good humor is relevant to your general purpose and makes the key ideas of your speech memorable. For example, one of our former students delivered a speech to entertain by discussing the ways we label products and people. One of his points was that the product warnings printed on packaging tell us about various companies' views of their customers. His examples were relevant to that main idea and added humor to his speech by helping him show the absurdity of many product labels.

- *Be tasteful.* Audience analysis is vital for a speech to entertain (see Chapter 5). Taste is subjective. What delights some listeners may offend others. Do your best in analyzing your audience, but when in doubt, err on the side of caution. Remember, humor that is off-color is off-limits.

- *Be tactful.* Avoid humor that generates laughter at the expense of others. There may be times when good-natured ribbing is appropriate, but humor intended to belittle or demean a person or group is unethical and unacceptable.

- *Be positive.* The tone for most occasions featuring speeches to entertain should be festive. People have come together to relax and enjoy one another's company. Dark, negative humor is usually inappropriate, as it casts a somber tone on the situation.

- *Use spirited delivery.* We have often heard good speeches to entertain and looked forward to reading transcripts of them later. We were usually disappointed. The personality, timing, and interaction with the audience that made the speech lively and unforgettable could not be captured on paper. We have also read manuscripts of speeches to entertain that promised to be dynamic when presented, only to see them diminished by a monotonous, colorless, and lifeless delivery.

Journal: Using Humor

If you were asked to give a speech about your favorite actor, musician, athlete, or artist, how might you incorporate appropriate humor in that speech?

Key Points: Guidelines for the Speech to Entertain

1. Make a point.
2. Be creative.
3. Be organized.
4. Use appropriate humor.
5. Use spirited delivery.

CHAPTER 18

› SUMMARY

Speaking on Special Occasions

The Speech of Introduction

18.1 Apply the five guidelines for a speech of introduction.

- The *speech of introduction* presents a featured speaker to an audience.
- When giving such a speech, be brief, focus your remarks on the featured speaker, establish that person's credibility, create positive but realistic audience expectations, and match the tone of the featured speech.

The Speech of Presentation

18.2 Apply the four guidelines for a speech of presentation.

- The *speech of presentation* confers an award, prize, or special recognition on an individual or group.
- Such a speech should state the purpose of the award or recognition, particularly if it is new or unfamiliar to the audience, and reveal why the person deserves the award. If the audience does not know the name of the recipient in advance, create suspense, revealing the recipient's name only late in the speech. If the person being honored has been selected from nominees known to the audience, compliment those other individuals.

The Acceptance Speech

18.3 Apply the four guidelines for an acceptance speech.

- The *acceptance speech* is an honoree's response to a speech of presentation.
- In accepting an award, thank the people bestowing it. You should also compliment your competitors if you know them. Then thank those who helped you attain the award, and accept the award graciously.

The Speech of Tribute

18.4 Apply the specific guidelines for two types of tribute speeches.

- The *speech of tribute*, or commemorative speech, honors an individual, a group, or a significant event.
- A eulogy, spoken to honor a person who has recently died, is one of the most familiar speeches of tribute. In delivering a euology, you should establish noble themes built on vivid examples from the subject's life. In addition you should express the collective feelings of the audience, create a memorable image of the subject, and be genuine.
- The *commencement speech* is a speech delivered during a graduation ceremony. When delivering a commencement speech, be brief, emphasize the occasion, reflect on your education, and play the part.

The Speech to Entertain

18.5 Apply the five guidelines for a speech to entertain.

- The *speech to entertain* seeks to make a point through the creative, organized use of the speaker's humor.
- Usually delivered on a light, festive occasion, your speech to entertain should make a point, be creative, be well organized, use appropriate humor, and be delivered in a spirited manner. The humor you use should be relevant to your point, tasteful, tactful, and positive.

GIVING AND RECEIVING FEEDBACK

LEARNING OBJECTIVES

After studying this appendix, you should be able to

A.1 Use the model of criticism by articulating judgments, reasons, and norms.

A.2 Apply the 10 guidelines for critiquing speeches.

A.3 Apply the four guidelines for acting on feedback to improve your speeches.

ppropriate feedback is crucial to your development as a public speaker. What you learn from your instructor and classmates about distractions caused by language, voice, or body will help you polish your speaking skills. You, in turn, want to be an incisive and sensitive critic when you write or speak about others' speeches. **Criticism** is information given to others in a way that enables them to use it for self-improvement.[1]

This information includes both positive comments that reinforce what a speaker did well and negative comments that point to areas for improvement. If you say, "Your speech was well within the 7-minute time limit," you spotlight a positive aspect of the speech. If you write or say, "I liked your speech," you are also providing feedback. This last comment, however, doesn't really teach the speaker anything. There is nothing wrong with saying, "I enjoyed your speech," or "I didn't care for this speech as much as your last one." Just don't stop there. Explain why.

criticism

Feedback offered for the purpose of improving a speaker's public speaking skills.

A Model of Criticism

A.1 Use the model of criticism by articulating judgments, reasons, and norms.

All criticism contains three parts: *judgments*, *reasons*, and *norms*.[2] Figure A.1 illustrates the relationships between these parts. The most familiar and superficial level of criticism consists of **judgments**. We make them frequently about many different subjects: "I loved the movie *La La Land*," "Dr. Venkat is an excellent teacher," or "I always enjoy your speeches."

Underlying those judgments, whether we voice them or not, are **reasons**: "*La La Land* had a great cast and I really enjoyed the music," "Dr. Venkat is an excellent teacher because her lectures make a course I dreaded lively and interesting," or "I always enjoy your speeches because you choose such unusual topics." Statements such as these specify reasons for the critics' judgments.

The statements in the preceding paragraph are instructive and useful because they help others infer your **norms**—the values you believe make something good, effective, or desirable. Such statements tell us that the critics enjoy well-crafted movies, appreciate liveliness in class lectures, and like unusual topics in public speeches. We may, of

judgments

A critic's opinions about the relative merits of a speech; the most common and superficial level of speech criticism.

reasons

Statements that justify a critic's judgments.

norms

The values a critic believes necessary to make any speech good, effective, or desirable.

Figure A.1   A Model of Criticism

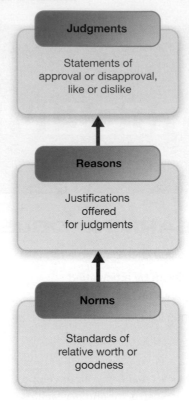

course, argue with the critics about whether these norms are valid. That is healthy and productive. As speech critics we must provide reasons for our judgments; only by doing so do we tell the speaker the basis of our reactions.

Here are some examples of helpful comments made by students about their classmates' speeches:

> Anna, your concern for children certainly shows in this speech on rating day care centers. Your personal examples really helped make the speech interesting.

> John, your speech on how to improve study habits was the best I heard. It was appropriate and beneficial to everyone in the class. Your language was simple and coherent. You explained just what we needed to know in the time you had.

> Amav, one problem I saw was your use of visual presentational aids. Once you have finished with the visual aid, you should put it away rather than leave it where the audience can see it. That way, the audience will focus their attention on you rather than on the object.

One value of receiving well-written or thoughtful oral comments about your speeches is that repetition of feedback will reinforce it. If one person tells you that you need to speak louder, you may dismiss the advice. If 12 people say that they had trouble hearing you, however, you are more likely to pay attention.

A second value of receiving feedback from many people, especially people from various cultures, is that different people value different aspects of a speech. Some may put a premium on delivery, others on content, and still others on organization. With such a variety of perspectives and values, it would be a shame if all feedback were reduced to "Good job!" or "I liked it." To provide the best feedback you can, remember to specify the reasons for your judgments; ask yourself why a speech affects you and then try to communicate those reasons to the speaker.

We should also make a final note about the spirit in which you give feedback in this class. You should never make criticisms that are designed to belittle or hurt the speaker. *Target the speech, not the speaker*. Focus on specific behaviors rather than the person exhibiting those behaviors. You will probably never hear a speech so fine that the speaker could not make some improvement, and you will never hear a speech so inept or ill prepared that it does not have some redeeming value. *Listen evaluatively* and then *respond empathetically*, putting yourself in the speaker's place, and you should make truly helpful comments about your classmates' speeches.

Critiquing Speeches

A.2 Apply the 10 guidelines for critiquing speeches.

To help you become a better critic, we offer 10 guidelines you can use as you evaluate speeches. One of our students, Susan, delivered an informative speech on three major tenets of the Amish faith. We asked some students to critique Susan's speech, and we have used their comments to illustrate our suggestions.

Begin with a Positive Statement

Do you remember being told, "If you can't say something nice, don't say anything at all"? Well, that's good advice to follow when you critique your classmates' speeches. Public speaking is a personal experience. You stand in front of an audience expressing *your* thoughts in *your* words with *your* voice and *your* body. When you affirm the positive, you establish a healthy climate for constructive criticism. Fortunately, you can always find something sincerely helpful to say if you think about it.

Two of our students began their critiques of Susan's speech with these opening statements:

> I found your speech on the Amish to be very interesting; their beliefs are fascinating. They seem very simple but very committed to their group—what a unique way of living.

> I have lived near the Amish in Pennsylvania. Your speech explained the reasons for their behavior. You clearly explained why they do what they do.

Notice that while both critics compliment the speaker, the second critic also demonstrates her involvement in the topic.

Target a Few Key Areas for Improvement

Imagine how you would react if you were told, "There are 17 areas you need to work on for your next speech." You'd probably feel overwhelmed. Susan's critics focused on the most important strengths and areas of improvement. In doing so, they provided her with manageable goals for her next speech. After accomplishing them, she could begin to improve other aspects of future speeches.

Organize Your Comments

A critique, just like a speech, is easier to follow if it is well organized. You can select from several options to frame your comments, and you should select the one that is most appropriate to you, the speaker, and the speech.

For example, you can organize your comments topically into the categories of speech *content*, *delivery*, and *organization*. A second option is chronologically; you can discuss the speech's *introduction*, *body*, and *conclusion*. A third option is to divide your comments into speaking *strengths* and *areas of improvement* (remember, give positive comments first). You could even combine these options. You could discuss the speaker's introduction, body, and conclusion and within each category discuss first the strengths and then areas for improvement.

Be Specific

For speakers to become more proficient, they need to know *what* and *how* to improve. One student told Susan, "I liked the way you presented the speech as a whole." That statement provides a nice pat on the back, but it doesn't give Susan much direction. The qualifying phrase "as a whole" seems to suggest that the listener noticed small problems that were minimized by the generally positive effect of Susan's speech. What were those problems, and what could Susan have done to minimize them? Remember to provide reasons for your judgments. In the two statements below, the listeners' comments are specific.

> I was really impressed with the fact that you did not use your notecards while you delivered the introduction or the conclusion. That suggests that you were confident and well prepared.

> Susan, you used good transitional phrases or words to move from subtopic to subtopic within each main point. An example of this was when you said, "Not only do the Amish have simple ways of dressing, but they also provide very simple toys for their children."

Be Honest but Tactful

Phrasing suggestions for improvement tests your interpersonal skills. At times you may be reluctant to offer criticism because you think it may offend the speaker. If you are not honest, the speaker may not know that the topic was dull, the content superficial, and the delivery uninspiring. Still, you must respect the speaker's feelings. The statement "Your speech was dull, superficial, and uninspiring" may be honest, but it is hardly tactful. It may provoke resistance to your suggestions or damage the speaker's self-esteem.

One student thought Susan's speech content and organization were excellent but that her delivery was mechanical and lifeless. The student could have said, "Your delivery lacked excitement." Instead, she wrote, "The only problem I saw with your speech was a lack of enthusiasm. Maybe the speech was too rehearsed. I think it needed some humor to break the monotony."

Personalize Your Comments

The more interest and involvement your critique conveys, the more likely the speaker is to believe in and act on your advice. You can personalize your comments in three ways. First, use the speaker's name occasionally, as in "Susan, your hand gestures would be more effective if you used them less. I found myself being distracted by them."

A second way of reducing a speaker's defensiveness and establishing speaker–critic rapport is by using I-statements in place of you-statements. Explain how the speech affected you. Instead of saying, "Your organization was weak," say, "I had trouble following your key ideas," and then give some examples of places where you got lost. The following is an example of what one of our students could have said and what she actually did say in her critique of Susan's speech:

> *She could have said:* "You lost my attention during the first part of your speech because you spoke so fast that I couldn't keep up with you."

> *Instead, she said:* "I had difficulty following your words at first because your rate seemed fast to me. After you settled down into the speech, though, I could listen with more attention."

A third way of personalizing your comments is by stating how you have benefited from hearing the speech. The following statement from a student critique let Susan know that her use of presentational aids to illustrate Amish artifacts was interesting and helpful:

> Your speech . . . especially caught my attention when you showed the toys, the quilt, and the artwork. And putting the visual aids down after explaining them helped in keeping me interested in the next area.

Reinforce the Positive

Sometimes we want so much to help someone improve that we focus on what the speaker did wrong and forget to mention what the speaker did well. As you enumerate how speakers can improve, don't forget the things they did well and should continue doing. One student, impressed with Susan's language and vocal delivery, offered the following comment:

> Susan, your delivery was excellent. You used your voice to emotionally color your message. I really felt as if I was living in the pictures that your descriptions created.

Problem Solve the Negative

If you are serious about wanting to improve your speaking, you will want to recognize areas of improvement for your speech. Only then can you improve. As a critic, you have a responsibility to help others become better speakers. Don't be afraid to let them know what went wrong with a speech.

As a rule, though, do not criticize behaviors that the speaker cannot correct. On the day she spoke, Susan was suffering with seasonal allergies. As a result of antihistamines she was taking, her throat was dry. Even if this had detracted significantly from her message, it would have been inappropriate for a student to comment, "I had trouble listening to what you said because your mouth seemed dry. Avoid that in your next speech." Such a request may be beyond the speaker's control. On the other hand, it would be useful to suggest that Susan take a drink of water immediately before speaking.

You will help speakers improve their speaking skills if you follow two steps in your feedback. First, point out a specific problem and, second, suggest ways to correct the problem.

One student was impressed with Susan's presentational aids but offered her the following advice about one of the aids:

> You said that the Amish don't like to have their pictures taken, and yet you used a picture of an Amish man as a visual aid. Next time, if you'd explain how or where you got the picture, it wouldn't leave picky people like me wondering during the rest of your speech how you got that picture.

Provide the Speaker with a Plan of Action

When you give your comments, include a plan of action for the speaker. What should the speaker concentrate on when presenting the next speech? One student focused Susan's attention on her next speaking experience by suggesting the following action plan:

> Susan, your overall speech and style of presentation were very good. However, I detected two minor things that could be improved. First, except when you were moving toward or away from a visual aid, you remained in one place. I believe that taking a few steps when you begin a subtopic would emphasize your transitions and enhance your message. Second, take more time to demonstrate and talk about the boy's toy that you showed us. You said, "It has marbles and fun moving parts," but I didn't really get a chance to see how it operates. Your organization, your vocal emphasis and inflection, your eye contact, and your knowledge of the topic were all terrific. You're an effective speaker, and if you use these suggestions for your next speech, you will be even more effective.

End with a Positive Statement

Conclude your critique on a positive note. Remind speakers that both you and they benefited from this experience. One of the best compliments you can give a speaker is that you learned something from the speech. One of our students concluded her critique of Susan's speech as follows:

> Susan, you did an outstanding job. Your speech was well organized and very informative. You showed some signs of nervousness, but more practice will alleviate most of them. Whenever and wherever you will be speaking next, I'd like to be there.

Acting on Feedback

A.3 Apply the four guidelines for acting on feedback to improve your speeches.

Many of us dislike receiving criticism, yet such feedback is important to our development and success as public speakers. If you want to communicate more effectively, you must seek feedback from your listeners. Ethical speakers respect their audiences. Consideration for the audience means, in part, trusting their opinions and advice. If you respect your listeners, you will value their questions and advice about your speech. The following four guidelines will enable you to get the most out of this process.

Focus on *What* Your Critics Say, Not *How* They Say It

Listen to the content of the feedback, not the way it is presented. Too often, we become defensive when someone critiques us. Remember that offering criticism is not easy, and your critic may not have mastered the guidelines we've presented in the previous section. Avoid reacting emotionally to feedback, even if it is poorly worded and insensitive. Instead, focus on the content of the suggestions you receive.

Seek Clear and Specific Feedback

To improve your speaking, you must be aware of specific areas for improvement. Suppose a critic says, "Your organization could be improved." That may be an honest and valid statement, but it isn't very helpful because it lacks specific areas for improvement. Ask the critic to be more specific. Is the problem with the introduction, body, or conclusion? What specific strategies could you use to improve your organization? It may take some good interpersonal communication to elicit the feedback you need to become a better public speaker.

Sometimes you may receive conflicting feedback. Don't dismiss criticisms simply because they seem contradictory. For example, one critic may comment that your eye contact was good, another that it was poor. Both may be right. Perhaps you spoke only to those in the center of the room; they may have liked your eye contact, while others felt excluded. Or a critic's reaction may have been based on cultural norms; some cultures value eye contact more than others. It's important to learn the reasons behind a critic's judgment before you can improve your public speaking skills.

Evaluate the Feedback You Receive

It's not enough to receive and understand feedback. You must use your critical thinking skills to analyze and evaluate that feedback. Repetition is one standard of judgment. If only one classmate thought your attention-getting step was weak, don't be too concerned. However, if your instructor and the majority of your classmates thought it was deficient, you should target that as an area for improvement.

Develop a Plan of Action

After receiving feedback, summarize and record those comments. Then rank those areas needing improvement according to their importance. Rather than tackling every criticism, select a few to work on for your next speech. Write a plan of action that states your goals and the strategies you will use to achieve them.

Remember that your goal as you move from one speech to the next is not consistency but consistent improvement. So, rather than defending what you said or did in your speech, listen carefully and act on those suggestions for improvement that you receive most frequently. If you have doubts about the validity of suggestions your classmates are making, discuss the matter with your instructor. You will make the most accelerated improvement if you graciously accept the compliments of your peers and your instructor and then work quickly to eliminate problems that they bring to your attention.

Key Points: Guidelines for Acting on Feedback

1. Focus on *what* your critics say, not *how* they say it.
2. Seek clear and specific feedback.
3. Evaluate the feedback you receive.
4. Develop a plan of action.

USING AN AUDIENCE QUESTIONNAIRE

→ **LEARNING OBJECTIVES**

After studying this appendix, you should be able to

B.1 Design a questionnaire to elicit information about your audience and their views on your topic.

B.2 Gather your data in a manner that ensures anonymous and confidential responses.

B.3 Interpret questionnaire responses as you develop the supporting materials in your speech.

---

questionnaire

A set of written questions designed to elicit information about listeners' knowledge, beliefs, attitudes, or behaviors regarding your specific speech topic.

A questionnaire is a set of written questions designed to elicit information about your listeners' knowledge, beliefs, attitudes, or behaviors regarding your specific speech topic.[1] If you're unable to learn enough about your listeners through informal means such as observation and discussion, you have another option. If you need precise, measurable information and have the luxury of ample time and opportunity to collect it, consider administering a questionnaire. When you administer a questionnaire, you conduct *survey research*. The following guidelines will help you construct and administer a questionnaire and then interpret the responses.

Construct a Questionnaire

B.1 Design a questionnaire to elicit information about your audience and their views on your topic.

First, determine what you need to know about your audience. Do not ask unnecessary questions. What do they already know about your topic? If you're trying to persuade them, do they agree or disagree with you, or are they undecided? How strongly do they hold these positions?

Second, construct your questions depending on the type and amount of information you seek, how long respondents will have to complete your questionnaire, and how you plan to compile and use the information you gather.

You can ask two types of questions in your questionnaire: closed questions and open-ended questions. **Closed questions**, which are ideal for gathering demographic information, offer respondents a finite set of responses that are either categorical or in a scale format that asks people to place themselves along a continuum. The following are examples of demographic questions using a closed categorical response format.

closed questions

Questions with a finite set of responses that are either categorical or in a scale format that asks respondents to place themselves along a continuum.

- What is your sex?   [ ] Female   [ ] Male
- Are you currently employed?   [ ] Yes   [ ] No
- What's your academic status?
  [ ] First-year student   [ ] Sophomore   [ ] Junior   [ ] Senior   [ ] Other

Closed questions that are scaled ask respondents to place themselves at a particular point along a continuum. This type of question is useful when assessing attitudes, beliefs, values, and frequency of behaviors. Generally, ratings for scaled questions ascend from left to right or move from lowest to highest ratings. The following are examples of scaled closed questions that assess attitudes, beliefs, values, and frequency of behaviors.

- I enjoy watching college football games on TV. (Attitude)
  [ ] Strongly disagree   [ ] Disagree   [ ] Neutral   [ ] Agree   [ ] Strongly agree
- The honor code at our school is too strict. (Belief)
  [ ] Strongly disagree   [ ] Disagree   [ ] Neutral   [ ] Agree   [ ] Strongly agree
- It is important to earn a college degree. (Value)
  [ ] Strongly disagree   [ ] Disagree   [ ] Neutral   [ ] Agree   [ ] Strongly agree
- I talk to my instructors to get clarification on assignments. (Frequency of behavior)
  [ ] Almost never   [ ] Rarely   [ ] Sometimes [ ] Often   [ ] Almost always

Open-ended questions invite respondents to answer questions about their attitudes, beliefs, values, and behaviors in their own words. Though they take more time to answer, compile, and interpret, open-ended questions often provide unexpected but helpful information or specific examples a speaker may include in a speech. The following are examples of open-ended questions:

- What do you think are the qualities of a good supervisor? (Belief)
- How do you feel about the general education requirements at our school? (Attitude)
- What are some activities in which you participate that contribute to a healthy lifestyle? (Behavior)
- What are some important attributes of a good friend? (Value)

Your questions, whether open-ended or closed, should be clear, objective, and focused. Each question should focus on one item or issue. Avoid emotional language that may "lead" respondents to a particular response. Pilot test your questionnaire on friends who are similar to your intended audience. Time how long it takes to complete the questionnaire. Ask for clarity and objectivity of your questions, and then revise your questions accordingly.

During his sophomore year in college, James enrolled in an ethics class that required him to write a midterm paper on a current ethical issue. James had seen a televised news story about People for the Ethical Treatment of Animals (PETA) and decided to research the issue of animal rights. Always an animal lover, James was shocked when he accessed PETA's website and read accounts of how beef cattle and poultry are housed, injected with hormones, and slaughtered. During his junior year, James started to attend PETA meetings on campus and decided to stop eating meat products and become a vegetarian. For his persuasive speech, James wanted to convince his classmates that it was unethical to eat meat products and to persuade them to become vegetarians. To help him learn more about his audience, he constructed the questionnaire shown in Figure B.1.

open-ended questions

Questions that enable respondents to answer questions about their attitudes, beliefs, values, and behaviors in their own words.

Figure B.1 James's Audience Questionnaire

Please take a few minutes to answer the following questions. The information gathered will be used to assist me in preparing for my persuasive speech. To maintain anonymity, do not include your name. Thank you for your assistance.

1. What is your sex?   [ ] Female   [ ] Male

2. Do you live on or off campus?   [ ] On campus   [ ] Off campus

3. How would you describe your current state of health?
   [ ] Very healthy   [ ] Healthy   [ ] Neutral   [ ] Unhealthy   [ ] Very unhealthy

4. How would you describe your eating habits?
   [ ] Very healthy   [ ] Healthy   [ ] Neutral   [ ] Unhealthy   [ ] Very unhealthy

5. I believe that eating animals is unethical.
   [ ] Strongly disagree   [ ] Disagree   [ ] Neutral   [ ] Agree   [ ] Strongly agree

6. Would you consider changing your eating habits if it would improve your health?
   [ ] Yes   [ ] Maybe   [ ] No

7. A vegetarian diet is a healthy diet.
   [ ] Strongly disagree   [ ] Disagree   [ ] Neutral   [ ] Agree   [ ] Strongly agree

8. Are you a vegetarian?   [ ] Yes   [ ] No

9. What do you think are the benefits of a vegetarian diet? (Please explain your answer.)

10. What do you think are the drawbacks of a vegetarian diet? (Please explain your answer.)

Administer a Questionnaire

B.2 Gather your data in a manner that ensures anonymous and confidential responses.

After you have constructed your questionnaire, you need to give it to your intended audience. Because the information you gather will shape your speech, administer any questionnaire at least a week before your speech is due. Your written and oral directions should ensure respondent anonymity and confidentiality; people are more likely to provide truthful responses if they think the information cannot be used to embarrass them. You have an ethical responsibility to consider your listeners' interests, respect their privacy, and not mislead them. Remember, asking people to reveal their values, beliefs, attitudes, or behaviors implies an ethical commitment on your part. James ensured respondent anonymity and confidentiality; he also thanked his classmates for their participation, both orally and on his written questionnaire. To ensure that you do not violate any ethical guidelines, ask your instructor or search your campus's website for information about your school's Office of Research Compliance.

Interpret Questionnaire Responses

B.3 Interpret questionnaire responses as you develop the supporting materials in your speech.

After you have administered your questionnaire, you will need to analyze the responses and interpret the results so that you can incorporate the information into your speech. The first step is to organize the responses to each question. For closed questions, simply count the number in each response category. This is called a **frequency count**. James tallied responses for Question 3 (How would you describe your current state of health?) as follows:

How would you describe your current state of health?

Very healthy = 2

Healthy = 16

frequency count

A measure of the number of times that a certain event or response occurs.

Neutral = 1

Unhealthy = 5

Very unhealthy = 0

Compiling responses to open-ended questions is more subjective and time consuming than compiling responses to closed questions. One method is to summarize responses on separate pieces of paper and then tabulate those according to common themes. For example, James identified poor taste, inconvenience, and a lack of protein as common responses to the open question concerning the drawbacks of a vegetarian diet (Question 10).

Once you have organized the questionnaire responses, you are ready to answer the important question: *What does all this information tell me?* Do your listeners agree or disagree with your position on the topic, or are they neutral? Do their attitudes, beliefs, values, and behaviors vary widely? Do these differences vary according to age, sex, ethnicity, or academic classification? Are there well-worded answers to open questions that you can attribute to the anonymous respondent and use as supporting material in your speech?

The payoff for all the work you put into constructing, administering, analyzing, and interpreting the results of your questionnaire is that you have specific information about your audience to help you construct your speech.

Before he administered his questionnaire, James had planned to persuade his audience to become vegetarians by arguing that eating meat supports and sustains poor treatment of animals. After compiling and analyzing his classmates' responses, James discovered that only two students believed that eating animals is unethical; however, twenty said they would consider changing their eating habits if it would improve their health. James used this information to adapt his speech to his audience. Instead of focusing on the ethical issue of eating meat, he emphasized the health benefits of a vegetarian diet. Because a slight majority had listed the lack of protein as a drawback of a vegetarian diet, James explained how protein-rich foods such as beans and tofu could ensure proper nutrition. Next, he outlined some simple steps for selecting tasty vegetarian foods. Because three-fourths of the class lived on campus, he provided several menu selections available in the dining halls and fast-food venues on campus.

James's hard work paid off. He delivered a speech that was adapted to his specific audience, and his classmates were impressed that he made the effort to include them in his speech.

DEVELOPING AND DELIVERING TEAM PRESENTATIONS

→ **LEARNING OBJECTIVES**

After studying this appendix, you should be able to

C.1 Apply the 10 individual and collaborative steps of preparing a team presentation.

C.2 Apply the 10 strategies for delivering a team presentation.

Successful athletic teams recognize the importance of working together as a group to accomplish their goals. Business and professional organizations are increasingly using work teams to accomplish their objectives. Communication scholars Thomas Harris and John Sherblom argue that "teams differ substantially from many small groups, because the teams, rather than the leader, control the group process." Teams rely on individual responsibility and shared leadership.[1]

For most of your work in this public speaking class, you have operated alone. You have selected, researched, and organized your speech topics. You have practiced and delivered these speeches standing alone in front of your classmates. Team presentations will tap many of the skills you have already learned while also testing your ability to work productively with others toward a shared goal. International management consultant Ken Blanchard offers a simple, compelling benefit of working in teams: "None of us is as smart as all of us."[2] To be successful, team members must interact and support one another as they prepare and deliver cohesive team presentations.

Preparing a Team Presentation

C.1 Apply the 10 individual and collaborative steps of preparing a team presentation.

Although there is no one correct way to prepare for a team presentation, the following 10 suggestions will help you work efficiently and effectively. Those steps requiring team interaction are underlined; the other steps can be completed individually.

- **Brainstorm about the topic.** Through brainstorming, you will discover what team members already know, and you will uncover numerous ideas for further research. In addition to providing content, brainstorming also serves a relationship function. By giving all members an opportunity to participate, brainstorming gives you a glimpse of your peers' personalities and their approaches to team interactions. Maintaining an atmosphere of openness and respect during this first meeting gets the team off to a good start.

- **Conduct exploratory research.** The second phase of your team process is individual research. While there may be some merit in each person selecting a different topic to research, your research roles should not be too rigid. Rather than limiting yourself by topic, you may wish to divide your research by resources. One member may do a general Internet search while another interviews a professor who is knowledgeable on the topic, and so forth. It is important that you don't restrict your discovery to the list of topics you have generated. Exploratory research is also a form of brainstorming. As you look in indexes and read articles, you will uncover more topics. Each team member should try to find a few good sources that are diverse in scope.

- **Discuss and divide the topic into areas of responsibility.** After exploratory research, your team should reconvene to discuss what each member found. Which expectations did your research confirm? Which were contradicted? What topics did you find that you had not anticipated? Your objective at this stage of the team process is to decide on the key areas you wish to investigate. Each person should probably be given primary responsibility for researching a particular area. That person becomes the content expert in that area. While this approach makes research more efficient, it has a drawback. If one person serves as a specialist, the team gambles that he or she will research thoroughly and report findings objectively. If either assumption is not valid, the quantity of information may be insufficient and its quality contaminated. An alternative approach is to assign more than one person to a specific area.

- **Research your specific topic area.** Your focus should be on the quality of the sources you discover, not on quantity. While your primary goal should be to gather information on your topic, you should also note information related to your colleagues' topics. Share sources that may help another team member. Team members who support one another in these and other ways make the process more efficient and enjoyable.

- **Draft an outline of your content area.** After you have concluded your initial research but before you meet again with your team, construct an outline of the ideas and information you've found. This step is important because it requires you to make sense of all the information you have collected, and it will expedite the next step when you will share information with the team.

- **Discuss how all the information interrelates.** You are now ready to meet with your team. Members should summarize briefly what they have discovered through their research. After all team members have shared their ideas, they should decide which ideas are most important and how these ideas are related. There should be a natural development of the topic that can be divided among team members.

- **Finalize the team presentation format.** The speaking order should already be determined. There are, however, certain procedural details that the team must decide. Will the first speaker introduce all presenters or will each person introduce the next speaker? Where will the participants sit when they are not speaking: facing the audience or in the front row? The more details you decide beforehand, the fewer distractions you will have on the day you speak.

- **Plan the introduction and conclusion of the presentation.** As previously stated, a presentation should appear to be that of a team and not that of four or five individuals. Consequently, you must work on introducing and concluding the team's comments, and you must incorporate smooth transitions from one speaker's topic to the next. An introduction should state the topic, define important terms, and establish the importance of the subject. A conclusion should summarize what has been presented and end with a strong final statement.

- **Prepare and practice your presentation.** Most of our earlier suggestions on these topics also apply to your team's presentation. Some differences are worth noting, however. For example, as part of a team presentation, you will need to refer to your colleagues' comments and perhaps even use some of their supporting materials. The team presentation may also impose physical requirements you have not encountered as a classroom speaker, such as speaking to those seated around you in addition to making direct eye contact with the audience, or speaking from a seated position.

- **<u>Rehearse and revise the presentation</u>.** Independent practice of your portion of the presentation is important, but that is only one part of rehearsal. The team should practice its entire presentation in order to make participants more confident about their individual presentations and give the team a feeling of *cohesion*, meaning "togetherness."

Delivering a Team Presentation

C.2 Apply the 10 strategies for delivering a team presentation.

A team presentation is more than just a collection of individual speeches on the same topic. By coordinating your team's content and delivery, you will enhance your collective credibility and message impact. Consider the following 10 guidelines to create a polished and proficient team presentation.

- **Dress appropriately.** All presenters should be well groomed and dressed appropriately for the topic and occasion. To enhance your team's cohesiveness, you should consider dressing similarly. When athletic teams travel to tournaments and games, they dress alike to bolster the athletes' team spirit.
- **Introduce the presentation and team members.** Provide an agenda for your presentation. What will listeners learn and who will present each section? Will one person introduce all team members at the beginning, or will each person introduce the next presenter?
- **Organize and deliver the team's ideas.** Throughout the presentation, use all the strategies you've learned in this class. Review Chapter 8 and Chapter 10 for suggestions about how to organize your presentation, and see Chapter 13 for effective delivery strategies.
- **Incorporate smooth transitions from one person to the next.** A seamless presentation requires planning and practice. Just as you used transition statements to enhance the flow of your individual speeches, it is essential that the transitions from one speaker to the next are smooth in your team presentation.
- **Have one person design and produce all presentational aids.** This will ensure that the design and appearance of your presentational aids are consistent.
- **Have one person display all presentational aids except when he or she is speaking.** Assigning one person to handle and project all the aids will help make the presentation flow smoothly and consistently.
- **Assign someone to keep time and provide other signals to the team.** Use subtle but clear time signals so that team members do not exceed their time limits. This person may also signal when presenters are speaking too softly or too rapidly.
- **Conclude the main part of your presentation.** Often the person who introduced the presentation also concludes the presentation.
- **Conduct a question-and-answer session.** If you are allowed a Q & A period, decide who will manage it. Will one person or several answer questions from the audience? Who will recognize those who want to ask questions? Review the guidelines discussed in Appendix D.
- **Practice, practice, practice.** Successful team presentations require that you practice both individually and as a team. Practicing may not guarantee perfection, but it can enhance your mastery of public speaking, both in this class and in the future.

Following the procedures we have described should result in a carefully planned, conscientiously researched, adequately supported, and well-delivered team presentation. More than that, however, your presentation should also demonstrate the spontaneity, goodwill, and camaraderie that will likely have developed if members of your team have functioned effectively and productively together.

THE QUESTION–ANSWER PERIOD

After studying this appendix, you should be able to

D.1 Apply the four guidelines for an effective question–answer session.

Alison Gopnik once said: "Asking questions is what brains were born to do, . . . seeking explanations is as deeply rooted a drive as seeking food or water."[1] But have you ever asked a question only to receive an unsatisfactory or incomplete answer, or even an answer unrelated to your question? The answer is most likely *yes.*

Holding a question–answer period following your speech or team presentation gives you the opportunity to interact directly with your audience. This usually results in a natural, lively delivery and makes for better speaker–listener rapport.

If questions are friendly, that is a high compliment: The audience is genuinely interested in you and your topic. If questions stem from audience confusion about your presentation, you have an opportunity to clarify. If someone asks you a combative and contentious question, you've just been given a second chance to win this person over to your point of view.

You will find the following four guidelines helpful when you stand in front of an audience and ask, "Are there any questions?"

1. **Restate or clarify the question.** When you take a moment to restate or clarify the question to ensure you understood it correctly, you are engaging in perception checking. This is important for three reasons. First, repetition ensures that the entire audience has heard the question. Second, repeating the question gives the questioner the opportunity to correct you if you misstate it, saving you the embarrassment of beginning to answer a different question. Third, if the question seems confusing to you or somehow misses the point, you can rephrase the question to make it clearer, more focused, and more relevant. Never answer a question you don't understand.

2. **Compliment the question whenever possible.** We have all heard speakers say, "I'm glad you asked that." Of course, you cannot repeat that same remark after each question. But you can say, "That's a good (or perceptive or interesting) question" or "I was hoping someone would ask that." This applies even to hostile questions. Sincerely complimenting a hostile questioner can defuse a tense situation and focus attention on issues rather than on personal antagonism.

3. **Answer the question.** Of course, the content and the form of your answers depend on the specific questions; nevertheless, the following five suggestions may be helpful to ensure you answer the questions correctly and completely:

    •   **Know your topic thoroughly.** Your success during the question–answer period will depend in large part on your research and preparation for your speech.

You should always know more than you include in your speech. Most of the time, poor answers reflect poor preparation. If you attended a lecture about the dangers of excessive sun exposure and asked the speaker if the same principals apply to tanning beds, you would likely think the speaker had a limited understanding of the larger topic of UVA and UVB rays' relationship to skin cancer if he or she said, "I don't know."

- **Be as brief as possible.** Obviously, some questions require longer, more thoughtful answers than others. The question, "How much did you say it will cost to complete Phase II of the new library?" can be answered simply, "Two and a half million dollars." The question, "What will that $2.5 million provide?" will require a much longer answer.

- **Be methodical when giving lengthy answers.** When you need to give a detailed answer, use the organizational strategies that you've already learned and practiced: Preview, signpost, state, and explain what you want the audience to remember. For example, if you were to detail the above question, "What will that $2.5 million provide?," you might state: "This sum of money would provide four major benefits for the campus community." Then list the four benefits as a preview statement. After that, discuss each benefit by saying, "The first benefit is, ..." Follow this with an explanation, and then say, "The second benefit . . . " and so on.

- **If you don't know an answer, admit it.** Making up an answer is unethical. Fabricated answers not only undermine your credibility, but the audience may also act on incorrect information you have provided. There is nothing wrong with saying, "I don't know" or "I don't know, but I'll check on it and let you know." If you give the second response, make sure you follow up promptly.

- **Be careful about what you say publicly.** Remember that in a public gathering there is no such thing as an off-the-record statement. If the press is present, what you say may indeed be reported. As a rule, never say anything that would embarrass you or slander others if it were to appear in the next morning's paper. (Think back on the 2016 presidential campaign. Both Hilary Clinton and Donald Trump were "caught" using less than proper language for a presidential candidate.)

4. **Check the response with the questioner.** Did you answer the question to her or his satisfaction? Is there a follow-up question? Remember two drawbacks to this approach, however. If each person is allowed a question and a follow-up, you will be able to answer fewer people's questions. Second, if questioners are argumentative, asking them if you answered the question to their satisfaction gives them an opportunity to keep the floor and turn the question–answer period into a debate. If that happens, we suggest that you politely acknowledge and appreciate the questioner's perspective, by noting that you are happy to discuss this further at a later time, but for now you wish to give some of the other audience members an opportunity to ask their questions as well.

On a practical level, the question–answer period is one sure test of how well you know the topic of your speech. Handled effectively, a question–answer period gives you a final chance to clarify questions audience members might have, to reinforce your key ideas, and to cultivate the image you want to leave with your listeners.

SAMPLE SPEECHES

Flash Mobs[1]

Jennell Chu, San Antonio College

Jennell Chu delivered the following classroom speech in the spring of 2011. Notice her simple structure and her use of examples that would be familiar to many of her listeners.

1 On June 3, 2003, over 100 people gathered in New York City's Macy's department store, on the ninth floor, around an expensive rug. When asked what they were doing, they would each respond that they all lived together on the outskirts of town and were buying a rug. Then they just left. Later that day about 200 people gathered in the lobby of the Grand Hyatt New York and clapped for 15 seconds. Then, once again, they just dispersed.

2 According to Kenneth Baldauf, who studied these and other such occasions for his ebook *Emerge with Computer Concepts*, these are part of a growing trend called flash mobs, which is what I will be talking about today.

3 According to Baldauf, a flash mob is a group of people who assemble suddenly in a public place, do something unusual, and then disperse in order to gain attention or to create confusion and sometimes amusement. Now, I've actually participated in a few flash mobs myself and they have always been a lot of fun without any ill intent behind them. And as flash mobs are a trend that you're seeing more and more today, it is good to know common types of flash mobs and why these occasions are becoming so common.

4 Now, first I will be speaking about the common types of flash mobs. Dance flash mobs are one of the most common types of flash mobs that you will see. And what happens in them is that a group of people get together and learn how to do choreography to set to music. And a lot of the times these are done as tributes to the artists themselves, such as the group Flash Amsterdam who does Michael Jackson tributes. So they would go out and do things to his classic songs such as "Beat It" and "Billie Jean" and so many others.

5 Now freeze flash mobs are another type of common flash mob. These began when the group Improv Everywhere started, filmed at the Grand Central Station in New York. You can read more about this at their website www.improveverywhere.com underneath "Frozen Grand Central." What they did [was] a group of people just went to the station and then they just froze. It didn't matter if they were talking, whether they were taking a picture, or even one man I remember dropped his notes on the floor and was starting to pick them up. They just froze and did not move for a certain amount of time. Then, afterwards, by some certain signal, they just once again started going on with their daily lives. Now according to Baldauf, the largest freeze flash mob ever done was in Paris, where over 3,000 people participated.

6 And another type of common flash mob that you've seen doesn't have a set method, as [do] dance and freeze flash mobs; it's more general, one that you can come up with for yourself. These flash mobs are done in support [of] or opposition to a certain idea. The World News Network picked up on a flash mob done by a group, United Way, in Washington Station.

What this group did [was] they went into the station and then they just began undressing. And when they undressed, you could see across their T-shirts a slogan that said, "Live United." This was to show support of how all people in the world should live together in harmony, without any prejudice. So whether it's a dance flash mob, a freeze flash mob, or a flash mob to show your support for or opposition [to] something, these are just some of the common types that you will see today.

7   Now the second thing I will be speaking about is why flash mobs are becoming so common in today's society. The Internet is a big reason why flash mobs are so common nowadays. Thanks to the Internet we have social networking sites such as Facebook, Twitter, MySpace, and so many others that it is just so easy for a large group of people to come together for one purpose. And of course there's also YouTube. With YouTube, if you search the words "flash mob," you can come up with thousands of videos that you just spend hours watching because [they are] very entertaining to watch. And once on to these videos, people watch them, think they're fun, then they eventually want to be part of one or they want to start their own. And that, of course, just helps spread the trend all over the world.

8   Cell phones are another big reason why flash mobs are so common. Nowadays, cell phones are basically mini-computers. Everywhere you go, you have the Internet, so once again you have those social networking sites. Then you also have your instant access to your email, and there's also text messaging. So now it's just so easy to get the news spread out to everyone. And you can even make [a flash mob] up as soon as [you] get the idea because you can just send it out to everyone in your phone book, and they can send it out to more people [who can send it on to] more people. And you can just have a huge group.

9   And, of course, flash mobs are themselves just becoming more mainstream these days. There are businesses around the world [that] are using flash mobs as a way of advertising. And then, of course, there are television shows which are becoming more used to the idea of flash mobs and are incorporating them in [their programs]. Erica Futterman even stated in the *Rolling Stone*'s February 9th edition that the popular show "Glee" used a flash mob in order for one of the show's characters to attempt to get a date on the Valentine's episode. So as you can see, the Internet, cell phones, and just by flash mobs becoming more mainstream [are] reason[s] why these occurrences are becoming so much more common in today's society.

10   So by now you should know some of the common types of flash mobs and why they are becoming so common. And, like I said, flash mobs can be anything—they can be complex like a dance flash mob, where you have hundreds of people learning choreography. Or, you can just get people to start a pillow fight in a random street. Or, if you're like me, you'll wind up downtown with a group of girls and start singing the "Sailor Moon" theme song. But any way you start, while each individual flash mob will appear and then quickly disappear, the trend of flash mobs themselves doesn't appear to be disappearing quite as quickly.

Gum Chewers[2]

Austin Willis, Penn State Hazleton

Austin delivered this informative speech in a Communication Arts & Sciences class at Penn State Hazleton. Notice Austin's use of a pro–con division strategy and internal signposts within each key idea.

1   By a show of hands, how many of you in this room chew gum? [20 of 23 students raised their hands.] Now, how many of you don't chew gum? [3 students raised their hands.] My point exactly.

2   In fact, researchers Britt, Collins, and Cohen confirmed that this class is similar to the rest of the college student population. In a survey consisting of American undergraduate students, "nearly 87 percent confirmed that they chew gum at least occasionally." Based on this research, it is no surprise that chewing gum has grown into a popular pastime, as stated by the International Chewing Gum Association. Yes, there really is an International Chewing Gum Association.

3 "[C]hewing gum has grown into being one of the world's oldest candies [and] has even become a billion dollar industry" as stated by Wrigley, a leading gum production company, in a statement on Statisticbrain.com.

4 Today, I will inform you first on the positive effects of chewing gum, and second, I will inform you on the negative effects of gum chewing.

5 First, let's uncover the positive effects of chewing gum. Specifically, we will focus on the ideas that chewing gum can help enhance persons' ability to focus, maintain their stress, and even enhance their memory.

6 First, we'll consider the notion that chewing gum helps us focus. In *Psychological Reports* 2009, Tänzer and colleagues reported the results of their study of gum chewing and the abilities of 8- to 9-year-old students to maintain focus during a 16-minute test. Although students who chewed gum didn't perform so well in the first 12 minutes, they outperformed the no-gum control group in the last 4 minutes. The authors concluded that chewing gum "had a significant and positive effect on concentration performance." Similar results have been reported in more recent studies. Specifically, in 2011, Tucha and Simpson reported that chewing gum has a positive effect on healthy adults' abilities in maintaining focus during extended periods of time. After understanding how gum affects our ability to focus, let us go over how chewing gum may positively impact our stress levels.

7 Second, let's review how chewing gum may help us manage our stress. Chewing gum is believed to relax the mind. When it comes to dealing with stress, two studies were conducted by researchers Zibell and Madansky [who] compared frequent and infrequent gum chewers to see how both manage their stress. "Fifty-six percent of frequent gum chewers and 42 percent of infrequent [gum] chewers stated that managing their stress is a reason why they chew gum." Following this survey, the State-Trait Anxiety Inventory was administered, which is one approach of assessing stress. Studies revealed that in abstaining of chewing gum resulted in higher levels of anxiety and stress among all participants. Not only may chewing gum relieve stress, it may also enhance our memory.

8 Third, chewing gum may enhance our memory. While studying, chewing gum can help people focus, and apparently, if people chew the same flavor of gum during an exam as when they studied, it can even boost their memory. In fact, "an increase of learning performance of at least 30 percent was claimed following chewing gum" as stated in an August of 2012 article titled "Gum Chewing and Cognition: An Overview" by researchers Tucha and Koerts. Moreover, there's a difference between *immediate* and *delayed memory*. Researchers Wilkinson and colleagues published a study revealing significant improvements in both immediate and delayed memory. In order to test this study, participants had to remember a list of 15 words, and the delayed recall was within less than an hour. This study indicated that a recall of information improved when people chew[ed] gum during the learning period. In addition to the positive effects of chewing gum, it should be noted that chewing gum has also been found to have negative effects on people, or even no effects at all.

9 Second, let's discuss the negative implications of chewing gum.

10 First, let's go over the questionable belief that chewing gum has the ability to enhance our abilities to focus. A plethora of experiments found no connection between chewing gum and people's ability to focus. According to a *Journal of Behavioral and Neuroscience Research* article titled "A Review of the Evidence that Chewing Gum Affects Stress, Alertness and Cognition," two experiments found "alertness reaction time was significantly slower for a spearmint gum control group compared to not chewing [gum]" at all, indicating that chewing gum slows down and inhibits a person's full potential to focus. Researcher Smith in 2010 challenged this claim by concluding that gum led to a prolonged attention rate by using a choice reaction time task. Unfortunately, studies only showed the relationship between a person's positive mood and their attention spans rather than the physicality of chewing gum and their attention rates. Not only has chewing gum been found to have no impact on a person's ability to focus, but it also showed no improvement on controlling stress.

11 Second, I will discuss the inconsistent relationships found between chewing gum and stress. Stress has become a major reason why people chew gum, but how much stress does

this habit truly relieve? The answer to this question could be none at all. For instance, in 2009, researchers Torney, Johnson, and Miles were unable to find a benefit of chewing gum related to self-reported stress. In order to test this, they utilized an anagram in which participants had to solve and were hoping that this would cause stress through embarrassment if participants were unable to solve the anagram. However, no increased stress was found, which suggests that gum has no effect on the different levels of acute stress. After discussing the relationship between chewing gum and stress, we can continue by discussing how gum affects our memory.

12   Third, does chewing gum really enhance our memory? Researchers Johnson and Miles conducted two separate experiments in 2008 to test the effects of chewing gum on people's memory. Their results included the following statement: "Although flavorless gum and mint-flavored strips reported change in current mouth activity . . . [t]hey didn't [show signs] that induce context-dependent memory." This indicates that neither the type of gum nor the sensation of chewing aids a person's ability to recall information. Further research showed that chewing gum during a learning period actually may cause *poorer* recall. Researchers are continually attempting to discover connections between chewing gum and maintaining our memory. However, the phenomenon of gum chewing is very robust and it is unclear to determine whether or not chewing gum is actually beneficial.

13   Today, I have talked about both the positive and possibly the negative effects that gum chewing can have on people's ability to focus, maintain their stress, and even strengthen their memory. I hope I provided all of you with a unique perspective on the contradicting beliefs of gum chewing.

14   With the difficulty of proving whether or not the pros or cons of gum chewing are stronger, researchers will continue to study the effects of chewing gum. But in the meantime, for those of you who are fans of the product, if you desire to, keep on chewing.

Student Involvement[3]

Derrick Peña, Penn State Hazleton

Derrick Peña delivered the following persuasive speech in his Public Speaking course at Penn State Hazleton during the Fall of 2016. Notice how Derrick makes his arguments relevant to his audience and works to establish common ground with his listeners.

1   Imagine yourself at an interview with a representative from the graduate, medical, or law school that you've always dreamed of attending, or at an interview with the boss of your "dream work-place," when you are suddenly asked: "What did you do throughout your undergraduate years, aside from going to class?" What if you have nothing to say? Would you reflect back on your college career and think, "Maybe I should have joined that club?" Notably, we will discuss why you should get involved on campus. According to Penn State's website, only 65 percent of students are involved in an intramural or a student organization. I would like to influence you all to either stay involved or become involved. Here at Penn State Hazleton, it is relatively easy to become involved around campus. Personally, I am involved in many different student activities. For instance, I am the President of the Lion Ambassadors, I am an active THON member, and I partake in a faculty/student research project focusing on the biochemical aspects of Alzheimer's disease. From my involvement on campus, I have seen myself transcend into a stronger leader, which has allowed me to grow as an individual.

2   Being involved in student organizations, as told by Educational Quest, increases the chances of earning more scholarships and allows you to build your résumé. Finances play an important role in attending college and most organizations do have some sort of scholarship tied in to them. If not, by being involved, applying for a scholarship may allow you to be a stronger candidate. Many of us will be heading to University Park [Penn State's main campus] within the next few months, where there are more clubs, and more people to interact with—and I hope that from listening to my speech, you will all be excited to become involved on campus in the near

future. Today, we will discuss how to get involved in various activities, clubs, and organizations on campus and the student-instructor relationship as a form of student involvement.

3 First, let's discuss how to get involved in various activities, clubs, and organizations on campus. Getting involved on campus is one of the easiest things you can possibly do. It all begins with the school setting a date for a campus club fair, to inform and encourage you all to attend the fair. Attending a campus club fair allows you to interact with students like yourself, and possibly make new friends.

4 According to Mayfield and Mayfield, two of the main reasons for getting involved in college are: it allows students to have a connection to their school and it allows them to build community. I often hear many students claim that there is not much to do around campus. Honestly, I do believe it is because those students tend to not be involved. For a commonwealth campus, we have more than 15 student organizations, including research opportunities. Sure, it may be a small campus, but there is always something to get involved in. You may also decide to start your own club if you see our school does not offer something that interests you. By joining or starting a club, you can build new relationships, network, and make a name for yourself on campus and show that you are more than just a student who goes to class.

5 Although the idea of getting involved on campus and meeting new people seemed frightening at first, I overcame those fears by talking with my friends on campus who were involved in various groups and organizations. Overall, aside from succeeding academically while being involved, I have seen myself transcend into a strong individual. Being engaged around campus has allowed me to make a name for myself on campus and to enhance my communication skills further.

6 Another way to get involved other than joining a club is by rooting for your school's sport's teams. Even if you do not play the sport, grab a group of friends and show spirit—show that you have pride in your school, make your college experience more memorable. Or, even join an intramural. These clubs are designated to keep you healthy, reduce stress levels, and to simply have a fun time all while completing your schoolwork. So, attend the campus club fair, you never know what may happen. Learn about the different opportunities, engage in conversations with club representatives, and once you feel that connection, all you have to do is sign up. From then, you are one step closer to becoming the epitome of an involved student. Although there are many clubs and organizations in which you can get involved, including academic, athletic, and special purpose clubs and organizations, among others; they may not all be for you. In that case, you can get involved in your learning by getting to know your instructors.

7 In addition to knowing how to get involved in various activities, clubs, and organizations on campus it is important to know that the student-instructor relationship is an essential component of student involvement.

8 Second, let's discuss the student-instructor relationship as a type of student involvement. Often times we run into situations where we are unsure about a concept from class, or we need a letter of recommendation, or we simply need some guidance, and that is when the student-instructor relationship plays a vital role. Two studies conducted by Dr. Daniel Mansson and his colleagues from West Virginia University explored the relationship between student communicative attributes and out of class communication with their instructors. These studies focused on which student attributes, such as assertiveness and argumentativeness, are related to how frequently, and the reasons, students talk with their professors outside of class. However, the most important point in this article is that students who interact with their instructors are more likely to succeed in college than students who don't interact outside of class with their instructors.

9 I know it may seem difficult to ask questions in front of your classmates, but do not remain taciturn. Vocalize your concerns and questions and do not let your education be hindered because you are too fearful of what others may think. If not, attend office hours to make sure your instructor knows who you are. A study conducted by Martin, Myers, and Mottet in 1999 indicates that students talk with their instructors for five reasons: to get to know their instructor, to seek important class-related information, to participate in class, to make excuses, and to "brown-nose" the instructor, which is known as sycophantic communication. I recommend talking with your instructors primarily to get to know them, to seek class information, and to participate in

class, because in a follow-up study by the same authors a year later, they found that doing so enhances students' learning.

10 Another study conducted by a senior student Emily Gallagher from NYU's Applied Psychology program showed that developing a positive student-teacher relationship results in academic improvement due to the student's new derived motivation and excitement to learn. The more excited and prepared we are for a particular subject, the better we will perform, thus, the better academic outcome and benefit for us, as students. Having a positive outlook on a class can definitely allow you to succeed more than you expected, since you are putting in more of an effort.

11 As college students, establishing a one on one connection with an instructor is essential due to the rigor of many of our courses. A student-instructor relationship allows the professor to better get to know the student, too. I relish communicating with my instructors outside of the classroom because it shows that I am willing to excel beyond measure and improve my academic outcomes, and I have in fact seen improvements in my own performance from attending office hours. Remember to establish that connection, ask questions, let instructors know who you are, and you will enjoy many positive outcomes.

12 Today we've discussed student involvement. Specifically, we discussed how to get involved in various activities, clubs, and organizations on campus and the student-instructor relationship as a form of academic involvement. Getting involved on campus allows you to improve your communication skills, make new friends, attain leadership responsibilities, and, succeed academically. Imagine yourself at University Park wondering whether or not to attend the campus club fair, and think about all that I have mentioned. Wouldn't you rather have something that sets you apart from other students in addition to your grades? If you find yourself struggling in a class, establish that one–on–one connection with your instructor or TA, show that you are willing to get involved and work harder to achieve your goal. Keep in mind that college is what you make of it; do not let the years go by and later on regret not joining a club, or getting to know your instructors. So get involved, be proactive, and make a change! People rarely regret what they have done—they regret what they didn't do. So, don't leave our campus with regrets. Take advantage of all opportunities and get involved on campus.

Mental Illness[4]

Ashley Burdick

Ashley Burdick delivered the following topically organized informative speech on mental illness. Note how Ashley shares her personal experience—increasing her credibility—and establishes common ground with her listeners.

1 Would you all believe me if I told you that at least 4 of us in this room today were suffering from some kind of mental illness? Well, you should, because it's true.

2 1 in every 4 adults in the U.S suffers from some type of mental illness. That's a total of 43 million people. And what if I told you that out of that 43 million people, not even half receive the help that they need? Mental illness costs America $193 billion in lost earnings per year. One-half of all chronic mental illness begins by the age of 14; three-quarters by age 24. Suicide, mainly attributed to mental health issues, is one of the top 10 leading causes of death in the U.S., and is more common than homicide.

3 Well, in case you haven't already guessed it, I'm here to talk about the prevalence of mental illness with you. A topic that is near and dear to my heart not just because I have personal experience with it, but because it affects so many people.

4 I'll first talk about a few of the most common mental illnesses. I'll then touch base on why mental health comes with such a negative stigma. And lastly, I'll cover what to do if you need help, or someone you know needs help.

5 Why listen to me? I'll tell you. Because someone you know and love is living with mental illness. Hey, you could be living with it too. And that's not always a bad thing. Many illnesses

are completely manageable or barely noticeable, so you may not even know that you have one. But don't worry; you're not literally crazy. But now is the time to educate yourselves about the issue of mental health, which continues to be an increasing problem, not only in our society, but the entire world

So, let's begin.

6   One of the most common types of mental illness is anxiety. While there are many different variations of anxiety, the core concept and symptoms are the same across the board. Anxiety is when a person responds to certain objects or situations with fear and dread, and is usually accompanied by an array of physical symptoms. Those symptoms can include:

- Nausea/vomiting
- The "shakes"
- Rapid heartbeat
- Excessive sweating
- Impending sense of doom
- Panic attacks

7   Anxiety is a natural, biological response of our bodies. It's healthy to feel anxiety before a test or presentation, or in social situations, because it keeps us alert to our surroundings. It also helps us keep a handle on what's right and wrong.

8   Another common mental illness is depression. Depression is a mood disorder that causes a persistent feeling of sadness and loss of interest. Symptoms of depression can include:

- Feelings of worthlessness
- Sleep disturbances
- Loss of interest in everyday activities (sex, hobbies, sports, school)
- Loss of appetite or over-eating
- Unexplained physical problems
- Frequent/recurrent thoughts of suicide or suicide attempts

Everyone has felt depressed after losing a loved one, after a break-up, or even after failing a test. Depression, like anxiety, is a normal emotion to feel at times throughout our lives.

9   But when these things start interfering with everyday life, that's when they become a problem. When depression gets so severe that you can't get out of bed anymore because you feel like your life isn't worth living, or when anxiety gets so intense, that you lose sight of reality while shaking a mile a minute with a racing heartbeat, dry heaving in the bathroom, something needs to change.

10   A recent research article found that those two mental illnesses are very prevalent in the teenage – mid twenties population. That may include a lot of you in the audience today. Remember, if you suffer from either aforementioned mental illness, or any other disorder, it's not a bad thing.

11   When most people hear the term "mental illness" they immediately think "sick," "crazy," "messed up in the mind," etc. Although mental illness is a medical condition, it doesn't mean that there's something wrong with you. This is the negative stigma I mentioned in the beginning of this talk. People associate mental illness with negative things. A study conducted by Dr. Crisp et. al found that the majority of people hold negative stigmatizing beliefs of mental illness regardless of whether they know someone with a mental health problem, or even have mental health issues themselves. The negative stigma comes from when mental illness was first recognized as an issue. The mentally ill were excluded, taunted, and even brutalized. Early beliefs attributed mental illness to demonic possessions. Later beliefs stated that the mentally ill couldn't function normally in society, so naturally they were ostracized. The stigma is now openly addressed, and strides are being made to get rid of it for good. But it's very difficult to erase it completely because that's what everyone has believed for so long.

12   So, what do you do if you need help, or someone you know needs help? If you even suspect that you might be suffering from some type of mental illness, seek out professional help

as soon as possible. It's better to get a definitive diagnosis and start to get the problem under control, instead of denying that there's anything wrong, and letting it get the better of you.

13 Primary care doctors are a good first source to contact. They can help lead you in the right direction, whether you need a therapist, medication, or just someone to talk to about what is going on. The first step of the healing process is to admit that there is something wrong. A study found that those who ignored their symptoms were more likely to engage in some kind of self-harming behavior. Do not live in denial!

14 I hope I've familiarized you enough with the different types of mental illness, why they come attached to such a negative stigma, and how to handle a situation where you or someone you know needs help. Maybe now we can begin tackling this issue in our society.

15 Not so long ago I was struggling, like so many people out there, with some depression and anxiety. It negatively impacted my life in numerous ways to the point where I didn't think that things would ever look up. But by educating myself, learning therapeutic techniques, and finding a support system, I made it through.

16 I know that mental health is a topic that isn't broached easily, but I thank you for bearing with me. It's a topic that needs to be talked about more openly, and today, we've started to put that into motion.

As Gandhi so gracefully once said, "be the change you wish to see in the world."

The Problem with Food Aid[5]

Chiwoneso Beverley Tinago, William Carey University

Chiwoneso placed second at the 2009 Interstate Oratorical Association contest. Notice how she reveals her personal commitment and connection to the topic near the end of her persuasive speech.

1 Muna is an eight-year-old girl from Mulonda, Zambia. Every morning she walks to a food distribution point set up by the World Food Program at a nearby hospital. She holds tightly to her battered tin cup as she waits in line for hours to receive the mixture of corn and soy powder, but the stocks are running low and like every other day, she walks home empty-handed.

2 Muna's reality is that she is an AIDS orphan who struggles to stay alive, but she will not die from AIDS; more than likely she will die of hunger. This story is becoming all too common and was taken from *The New York Times* of January 17, 2009. The latest estimates from the UN Food and Agriculture Organization (FAO) show that another 40 million people were pushed into hunger in 2008 as a result of higher food prices. The FAO warned that the ongoing economic crisis could tip even more people into hunger and poverty.

3 Since the late 1960s, wealthy countries have been obligated by the Food Aid Convention to feed the hungry. However, a major part of the problem that the hungry face today is the nature of the food aid itself. This is not a new issue, but as the world's remaining arable farmland comes under increasing pressure from climate change and the development of biofuels, it is an issue that policy makers, humanitarian workers, and politicians need to resolve if widespread world hunger is ever to be alleviated.

4 Today, we will reveal the current problems inherent in the global food aid policy, then examine some of the causes before finally providing some workable and desperately needed solutions.

5 In August 2007, one of the biggest and well-known American charity organizations, CARE, announced that it was turning down $45 million a year in food from the U.S. government. According to the USAID [United States Agency for International Development] website updated daily, the U.S. provides nearly 60 percent of the world's food aid—that's nearly double the amount provided by European countries combined. Until this day, CARE claims that the way U.S. aid is structured causes, rather than reduces, hunger in the countries where it is received. Let's assess their claims by revealing the current problems in the food aid policy. These problems are threefold: ineffective use of aid money, monetization, and undercutting of local economies.

6   First. Transporting thousands of tons of food from the United States is a costly and timely process. The *Bloomberg News* of December 8, 2008, told the story of how a bag of corn stamped "US Aid from the American people" took more than 6 months to reach Ethiopian native Haylar Ayako. The corn had traveled more than 12,000 miles by rail, ship, and truck. Warehouse-stays punctuated each leg of the journey until the corn finally arrived in the village of Shala-Luka. But by that time Haylar had buried seven of his grandchildren. According to the *World Politics Review* of December 19, 2008, transporting the food drains needed funds from the actual provision of food aid. By the time all the costs are figured in, it's like every dollar worth of food ends up costing three dollars to get [the food] to the people who need it.

7   Second. Most of us view food aid as simply free food given to needy people. This is not entirely true. The *Seattle Times* of November 11, 2008, states that some food that is transported falls into the hands of aid agencies who in turn sell the grain to local communities and use the revenue to finance their development programs. This means that a large portion—even a majority—of food donated as project food aid is not used as food at all but is converted to cash. This is known as monetization. More than likely, food ends up going to those who can afford it instead of whose who desperately need it.

8   Third. The introduction of imported food in certain regions removes farmers' incentives to produce. According to the WTO [World Trade Organization] website updated daily, the grain that the agencies are selling is undercutting local farming since the aid grain is cheaper than the local grain. This puts local farmers out of business and deeper into poverty and, in the long run, becomes part of a process by which those countries lose the means to develop.

9   Now, the U.S. does not stand alone in the food aid problem. Countries like Canada and South Korea also sell food aid; however, more attention has been placed on the U.S. because it has a larger sphere of influence since it provides the most food aid. So with that in mind, having outlined the problem, let us move on and examine some of the causes. These problems are twofold: current U.S. legislation and lack of regulation.

10   First. According to the aforementioned *Seattle Times* article, U.S. legislation requires that 75 percent of all food aid shipments be sent aboard U.S.–flagged carriers. The U.S. also buys grain used for food aid from U.S. farms. But these are far from being family farms. A U.S. Government Accountability Office study released last year in April noted that just 18 U.S. companies were deemed eligible to bid for food aid contracts, with two of the country's largest agribusinesses, Cargill and Kalama Export Company, earning $28 million in food aid contracts in March and April 2008 alone.

11   Second. Another cause is [the] lack of regulation. The Food Aid Convention is the main international agreement governing food aid. According to the WFP website updated daily, the convention has no mechanism for determining food aid effectiveness or for evaluating performance of individual donors. Moreover, it operates with little transparency, providing remarkably little public information on its deliberations. Thus, this lack of effectiveness and transparency allows for practices like monetization to take place.

12   By no means are we denying the positive accomplishments of food aid programs, but it is obvious that the current policy on food aid is both self-interested and politicized; thus, action needs to be taken on the international, governmental, and personal levels. First and most important, donor countries need to negotiate a new global food aid compact to replace the languishing Food Aid Convention. The new agreement would strengthen effectiveness and accountability by officially doing away with monetization of food aid and requiring that donors purchase food aid locally or closer to the needy region whenever possible. Programs like Purchase for Progress, which was formed by the World Food Program and the Bill and Melinda Gates Foundation in September 2008, now buy 70 percent of all their food aid in developing countries like Malawi and India. This allows countries to develop their own agriculture economies and allows food to move more quickly and cost-effectively to the people who need it most.

13   Second. Change is needed in the current U.S. food aid legislation. In January 2008, American growers, processors, and transporters fought off a proposal before Congress that would speed deliveries of food aid by buying at least 25 percent more food closer to needy regions. This proposal must be reconsidered under the new Obama administration, and it is

essential to point out that the proposal does not ask for more money, but rather, asks that the 2 billion dollars that is currently available for food aid be utilized wisely in order to feed the most people.

14 Finally, on a more personal level, if you donate money to any aid organizations, be more aware of how your money is being used. I recently started an initiative on campus called students turning hunger into hope, which encourages the other 44 organizations on campus to use the 2008–2009 school year as a food aid platform by supporting organizations that use cost-effective food aid programs. At the end of my speech, I will be handing out a card with a list of some of these organizations. Now if you are unable to donate money, then I encourage you to visit www.thehungersite.com. Click on the orange Give box on the main page, and the site sponsors led by Mercy Corps International will pay for cups of food to be given to children at numerous schools in developing countries at no cost to you. Last year the site fed over 72 million children.

15 Today, we have revealed the current problems inherent in the global food policy, then examined some of the causes before finally providing some solutions. The plight of the hungry is sometimes difficult to fathom. I have been a recipient of food aid after my country suffered a severe drought in the 90s, but unlike Muna, Haylar, and the other 25,000 people who die from hunger every day, the food arrived just in time. When President John F. Kennedy named the Food for Peace program in 1961, he said, "Food is strength, and food is freedom, and food is a helping to people around the world whose goodwill and friendship we want." That may be true, but it would be imprudent of us to forget that food is food. As governments and aid agencies worry about losing money if an overhaul of the global food aid policy is achieved, it is essential to remember now more than ever that losing once had a kinder, nobler name—giving.

Special Occasion: Eulogy[6]

Nick Guardi

Nick Guardi delivered the following speech to eulogize his close friend, Ben. As you read, consider how well Nick utilizes the suggestions for preparing an effective eulogy offered in Chapter 18, Learning Objective 18.4.

1 Good afternoon. My name is Nick — and Ben was my loyal friend, my confidante and my mentor for the past six years.

2 He was more like an older brother. We had many experiences during that time. We laughed, we cried, we fought and we laughed again. I can go on for hours talking about the kind of person he was, but I think many of you already know Ben was the friendliest, sweetest, most comprehensive and humble person I ever met in my life, always worrying about the welfare of others.

3 I have good memories of my friend, one of which was the day we met. Just thinking about it, I can feel the mid-August summer heat. It was the start of two-a-days, when I found myself playing linebacker next to him on the football field my sophomore year of high school and then I got to know Ben as a brother throughout the next couple years.

4 Ben was a great athlete and even better leader, which made him a formidable captain for both the football and the basketballs teams at Fairfield High School. In addition to his athletic success, Ben also excelled academically. He wanted to follow in his father's footsteps and work in the business field after he finished school. Most recently, Ben was a junior at his dream school, the University of Connecticut, and only months away from earning his business degree. He had already lined up a job for after graduation with IBM and he was on his way to living out the rest of his dream.

5 In these short six years of friendship, I can only remember one fight, if you don't count the brotherly bickering. It was over nothing, too. Ben and I shared many personality characteristics and, unfortunately, we were both very stubborn. It was two summers ago, when we were getting ready to hit the lake for the afternoon. Ben came to pick me up, which right there, I knew he'd be in a foul mood because he was a designated driver. So when he arrived, I came outside and he

stayed at the top of my driveway as he always did. I didn't feel like walking up my driveway that day, so I texted him to come down. After about 10 minutes of childish stand-off, after he refused, he actually just left me there. I wound up having to drive myself and we exchanged some words when we saw each other, but that was our friendship. We fought like brothers.

6 I remember the last day I saw Ben so vividly. I dropped him off at the airport as he was off to Cancun, Mexico, for yet another spring break experience. I couldn't go with him, so I offered to drive him, and as little of a favor as it seemed at the time, that hour and a half car ride to JFK [national airport] will be ingrained in my mind forever.

7 Just eight days ago, my best friend passed away. He left an empty space in my heart, a place that nobody can fill. March 17th was the saddest and most painful day I've ever had in my life until now. It is a memory that cannot be erased from my mind, neither my heart. Although I told him lots of times that I loved him, you know, in a manly way, I would give anything to turn back time and tell him I loved him one more time, and to tell him just how important he was to my life.

8 People say that time heals all wounds, but today, I can tell you that is not true. Until today, I feel the same pain in my heart that I felt that Thursday evening. I know he is closer to me and there is no more distance or time difference that separates us now. I thank you, Ben, for all those years of friendship that you gave me. Thank you for everything you did for me. I want you to know, my friend, that I love you and that I'll always remember you. You'll always be my friend, Ben.

Thank you.

Endnotes

Chapter 1

1   For excellent discussions of the benefits of public speaking, consult the following three sources: Stephen K. Hunt, Cheri J. Simonds, and Brent K. Simonds, "Uniquely Qualified, Distinctively Competent: Delivering 21st Century Skills in the Basic Course," *Basic Communication Course Annual* 1, no. 1 (2009), 1–29; Sherwyn P. Morreale, Michael M. Osborn, and Judy C. Pearson, "Why Communication Is Important: A Rationale for the Centrality of the Study of Communication," *Journal of the Association for Communication Administration* 29, no. 1 (2000): 1–25; Sherwyn P. Morreale and Judy C. Pearson, "Why Communication Education Is Important: The Centrality of the Discipline for the 21st Century," *Communication Education* 57, no. 2 (2008): 224–240.

2   Thomas M. Scheidel, *Persuasive Speaking* (Glenview, IL: Scott, Foresman, 1967), 2.

3   C. K. Ogden and I. A. Richards, *The Meaning of Meaning*, 9th ed. (New York: Harcourt, Brace, 1953), 10–12. Chapter 1, "Thoughts, Words and Things" (pp. 1–23), explains in detail the relationships among symbols, referents, and interpreters.

4   HNN Staff, "So What Does Jihad Really Mean?" *History News Network*, accessed June 18, 2002, www.historynewsnetwork.org/articles/article.html?id=774.

5   "'Jihad' Dropped from Harvard Student's Speech," CNN.com, accessed June 18, 2002, wysiwyg://153/ http://fyi.cnn.com/2002/f . . . dnews/05/31/harvard .jihad.ap/index.html.

6   Karlyn Kohrs Campbell, *The Rhetorical Act*, 2nd ed. (Belmont, CA: Wadsworth, 1996), 119.

7   National Center for Educational Statistics, *National Assessment of College Student Learning: Identifying College Graduates' Essential Skills in Writing, Speech and Listening, and Critical Thinking*, NCES 95-001 (Washington, DC: GPO, May 1995), 122.

8   Robert Ennis, "A Taxonomy of Critical Thinking Dispositions and Abilities," in *Teaching Thinking Skills: Theory and Practice*, ed. Joan Boykoff Baron and Robert Sternberg (New York: W. H. Freeman, 1987), 10.

9   June Stark, "Critical Thinking: Taking the Road Less Traveled," *Nursing* 95 (November 1995): 55.

10 National Assessment of Educational Progress, *Reading, Writing and Thinking: Results from the 1979–80 National Assessment of Reading and Literature*, Report No. 11-L-01 (Washington, DC: GPO, October 1981), 5.

Chapter 2

1   Elisha Brown, "How a Freelance Journalist Broke the Melania Trump Plagiarism Story in 3 Tweets." Vox. com, accessed January 17, 2017, http://www.vox. com/2016/7/21/12247504/jarrett-hill-melania-trump-plagiarism.

2   Stephanie Busari, "Nigerian President Removes Aid Who Plagiarized Obama Speech." CNN. com, accessed January 11, 2017, http://www.cnn. com/2016/09/28/africa/buhari-obama-plagiarism/.

3   Donald K. Smith, *Man Speaking: A Rhetoric of Public Speech* (New York: Dodd, Mead & Co., 1969), 228.

4   Kenneth Blanchard and Norman Vincent Peale, *The Power of Ethical Management* (New York: Fawcett-Ballantine, 1988), 9.

5   Mary Cunningham, "What Price 'Good Copy'?" *Newsweek* (November 29, 1982): 15.

6   James C. McCroskey, *An Introduction to Rhetorical Communication* (Englewood Cliffs, NJ: Prentice-Hall, 1968), 237.

7   Catilin Casey and Kartik Sheth, "The Ethical Grey Zone." Nature.com, accessed January 11, 2017, http://www.nature.com/naturejobs/ science/articles/10.1038/nj7476-427a.

8   Institute for Civility in Government, "Reclaiming Civility in the Public Square: 10 Rules That Work," September 21, 2008, www.instituteforcivility. org/what-we-do/reclaiming-civility-in-the-public-square-book.aspx.

9   Rod L. Troester and Cathy Sargent Mester, *Civility in Business and Professional Communication* (New York: Peter Lang, 2007), 10.

10 Rona Marech, "Thanks for the Civility: Mannerly Campaign Spread Nationwide," Baltimoresun.com, November 1, 2007, www.choosecivilitymc.org/ published/dat/baltimore_sun.pdf.

11 Institute for Civility in Government.

12 Alexander Lindey, *Plagiarism and Originality* (New York: Harper & Brothers, 1952), 2.

13 John L. Waltman, "Plagiarism: Preventing It in Formal Research Reports," *ABCA Bulletin* (June 1980): 37.

14 Adeeba Folami, "The Meaning of Global Plagiarism." Legal Beagle, accessed January 11, 2017, http://legal-beagle.com/6148594-meaning-global-plagiarism.html.

15 Michael T. O'Neill, "Plagiarism: Writing Responsibly," *ABCA Bulletin* (June, 1980): 34, 36.

16 Erik Vance, "Genetically Modified Conservation," *Conservation Magazine* (July/September 2010). Reprinted as "Genetic Engineering for Good: A Researcher Modifies Crops to Feed the Hungry and Cut Pesticide Use," *Utne Reader* (January/February 2011): 23.

17 *Paraphrase: Write It in Your Own Words*, Purdue OWL (Online Writing Lab), Purdue U Writing Lab, accessed June 16, 2005, http://owl.english.purdue.edu/handouts/print/research/rphr.html.

18 *Copyright and Fair Use in the Classroom, on the Internet, and the World Wide Web*, Information and Library Sciences, University of Maryland University College, accessed June 30, 2011, www.umuc.edu/library/copy.shtml.

19 U.S. Copyright Office, *Limitation on Exclusive Rights: Fair Use*, accessed June 30, 2011, www.copyright.gov/title17/92chap1.html#107.

20 Georgia Harper, "Using the Four Factor Fair Use Test," *Fair Use of Copyrighted Materials*, University of Texas, Austin, last modified August 10, 2001, www.utsystem.edu/ogc/intellectualproperty/copypol2.htm.

21 "Copyright Exceptions," Purdue University Copyright Office, accessed June 29, 2011, www.lib.purdue.edu/uco/CopyrightBasics/fair_use.html.

22 These guidelines have been shaped and reinforced by several excellent sources, including Harper, "Using the Four Factor Fair Use Test"; Georgia Harper, "Copyright Crash Course: Fair Use of Copyrighted Materials," University of Texas Libraries, accessed June 29, 2011, http://copyright.lib.utexas.edu/copypol2.html; "Copyright Exceptions," Purdue University Copyright Office; "Chapter 9, Fair Use," Stanford University Libraries, accessed April 26, 2011, http://fairuse.stanford.edu/Copyright_and_Fair_Use_Overview/chapter9/index.html.

Chapter 3

1 Nancy Daniels, "Public Speaking: The Positive Effect of Nervousness." SelfGrowth.com, accessed January 13, 2017, http://www.selfgrowth.com/articles/public-speaking-the-positive-effects-of-nervousness.

2 Virginia P. Richmond and James C. McCroskey, *Communication: Apprehension, Avoidance, and Effectiveness*, 5th ed. (Boston: Allyn & Bacon, 1998), 41.

3 Chia-Fang Hsu, "Sources of Differences in Communication Apprehension between Taiwanese and Americans," *Communication Quarterly* 52 (2004): 370.

4 Nadene N. Vevea, Judy C. Pearson, Jeffrey T. Child, and Julie L. Semiak, "The Only Thing to Fear Is . . . Public Speaking? Exploring Predictors of Communication in the Public Speaking Classroom," *Journal of the Communication, Speech, & Theatre Association of North Dakota* 22 (2009): 1.

5 Matthew M. Martin and Scott A. Myers, "Students' Communication Traits and Their Out-of-Class Communication with Their Instructors," *Communication Research Reports* 23 (2006): 155.

6 Daniel H. Mansson and Scott A. Myers, "A Reexamination of Swedish and American College Students' Communicative Attributes," *Journal of Intercultural Communication Research* 38 (2009): 9.

7 Karen K. Dwyer and Marlina M. Davidson, "Is Public Speaking Really More Feared Than Death?" *Communication Research Reports* 29 (2012): 107.

8 Richmond and McCroskey, 45.

9 Wendy Wasserstein, "Streeping Beauty: A Rare Interview with Cinema's First Lady", *Interview* (December 1988): 90.

10 James A. Belasco and Ralph C. Stayer, *Flight of the Buffalo* (New York: Warner, 1993), 327–328.

11 Daryl J. Bem, *Belief, Attitudes, and Human Affairs* (Belmont, CA: Brooks/Cole, 1970), 57.

12 Jack Valenti, *Speak Up with Confidence* (New York: William Morrow, 1982), 19.

13 Petri Laukka, Clas Linnman, Fredrik Åhs, Anna Pissiota, Örjan Frans, Vanda Faria, Åsa Michaelgård, Lieuwe Appel, Mats Fredrikson, and Tomas Furmark, "In a Nervous Voice: Acoustic Analysis and Perception of Anxiety in Social Phobics' Speech," *Journal of Nonverbal Behavior* 32 (2008): 195.

14 Joe Ayres and Theodore S. Hopf, "Visualization: A Means of Reducing Speech Anxiety," *Communication Education* 34 (1985): 321.

Chapter 4

1 PBSkidsGO, "Gossip and Rumors: What the Words Mean" (2005), CastleWorks Inc., accessed January 15, 2017, http://pbskids.org/itsmylife/friends/rumors/article2.html.

2 Larry Barker, Renee Edwards, Connie Gaines, Karen Gladney, and Frances Holley, "An Investigation of Proportional Time Spent in Various Communication Activities by College Students," *Journal of Applied Communication Research* 8 (1980): 101–109.

3 Robert L. Montgomery, *Listening Made Easy* (New York: AMACOM, 1981), n.p.

4 Monique Boekaerts, "Being Concerned with Well-being and with Learning," *Educational Psychologist* 28 (1993): 149–167.

5 Lyle V. Mayer, *Fundamentals of Voice and Diction*, 8th ed. (Dubuque, IA: William C. Brown, 1988), 178; Laura Janusik, "Listening Facts," *International Listening Association*, accessed June 27, 2011, http://d1025403.site.myhosting.com/files.listen.org/Facts.htm.

6 "Active Listening Skills," accessed January 16, 2017, http://www.taftcollege.edu/lrc/class/assignments/actlisten.html.

Chapter 5

1 Christopher Beam, "Code Black." State.com, accessed January 18, 2017, http://www.slate.com/articles/news_and_politics/politics/2010/01/code_black.html.

2 Ibid.

3 Ibid.

4 Jeffrey F. Milem, "Why Race Matters," *Academe* (September–October 2000): 28.

5 "The Brief History of the ENIAC Computer," accessed February 9, 2017, http://www.smithsonianmag.com/history/the-brief-history-of-the-eniac-computer-3889120/.

6 Abraham H. Maslow, *Motivation and Personality*, 2nd ed. (New York: Random House, 1970), 35–47.

7 Maslow, 38.

8 Maslow, 41.

9 Ari Posner, "The Culture of Plagiarism," *New Republic* (April 18, 1988): 19.

Chapter 6

1 Leonard J. Rosen and Laurence Behrens, *The Allyn & Bacon Handbook,* 4th ed. (Boston: Allyn & Bacon, 2000), 68.

Chapter 7

1 Patricia Senn Breivik, *Student Learning in the Information Age* (Phoenix, AZ: Oryx Press, 1998), 2.

2 Wayne C. Booth, Gregory G. Colomb, and Joseph M. Williams, *The Craft of Research* (Chicago: University of Chicago Press, 1995), 35.

3 Search Engine Journal. "Latest Search Market Share Numbers: Google Search Up Across All Devices." Accessed May 5, 2017: https://www.searchenginejournal.com/august-2016-search-market-share/172078/

4 Frederick J. Friend, "Google Scholar: Potentially Good for Users of Academic Information," *The Journal of Electronic Publishing*, 9 (2006). doi:10.3998/3336451.0009.105

5 "Google Scholar," Lehigh University, Library & Technology Services, last modified April 14, 2005, www.lehigh.edu/helpdesk/docs/google/

6 Michael K. Bergman, "White Paper: The Deep Web: Surfacing Hidden Value," *The Journal of Electronic Publishing,* 7 (August 2001), accessed August 19, 2011, http://hdl.handle.net/2027/spo.3336451.0007.104

7 Stephen Dingman, email to the authors, September 2, 2005.

8 Bergman, 1.

9 "Wikipedia FAQ/Schools," Wikipedia, last modified June 10, 2011, http://en.wikipedia.org/wiki/Wikipedia:FAQ/Schools.

10 Alison J. Head and Michael Eisenberg, "How Today's College Students Use Wikipedia for Course-Related Research," *First Monday* 15 (March 2010), accessed July 25, 2011, www.uic.edu/htbin/cgiwrap/bin/ojs/index.php/fm/article/view/2830/2476.

11 We adapted this checklist from Serena Fenton and Grace Reposa, "Evaluating the Goods," *Technology & Learning* (September 1998): 28–32; "Module IX: Evaluating Information Sources," McConnell Library, Radford University, accessed September 2, 2002, http://lib.runet.edu/highlanderguide/evaluation/intro.html; Esther Grassian, "Thinking Critically about Web 2.0 and Beyond," UCLA College Library, last modified November 4, 2006, www.sscnet.ucla.edu/library/modules/Judge/CLThinkWeb20.pdf; Keith Stanger, "Criteria for Evaluating Internet Resources," University Library, Eastern Michigan University, accessed August 30, 2002, http://online.emich.edu/~lib_stanger/ineteval.htm.

12 "Preface," *Ulrich's Periodicals Directory 2009*, serials dir. Laurie Kaplan (New Providence, NJ: ProQuest, 2008), vii.

13 Joann Keyton, *Communication Research: Asking Questions, Finding Answers,* 3rd ed. (Boston: McGraw-Hill Higher Education, 2011).

14 Lawrence R. Frey, Carl H. Botan, and Gary L. Kreps, *Investigating Communication: An Introduction to Research Methods,* 2nd ed. (Boston, MA: Allyn & Bacon, 2000), 1–507.

15 Frey, Botan, and Kreps.

Chapter 8

1 Robert Half, "Memomania," *American Way* (November 1, 1987): 21.

2 B. Scott Titsworth, "Students' Notetaking: The Effects of Teacher Immediacy and Clarity," *Communication Education* (October 2004): 317.

3 Glenn Leggett, C. David Mead, Melinda Kramer, and Richard S. Beal, *Prentice Hall Handbook for Writers,* 11th ed. (Englewood Cliffs, NJ: Prentice-Hall, 1991), 417–18. We have drawn on examples these authors use in their excellent section on connecting language.

4 Robert DiYanni and Pat C. Hoy, *The Scribner Handbook for Writers,* 3rd ed. (New York: Longman, 2001), 196.

5 DiYanni and Hoy, 197.

Chapter 9

1 Joseph J. Chesebro and Melissa Bekelja Wanzer, "Instructional Message Variables," in *Handbook of Instructional Communication: Relational and Rhetorical Perspectives 2006,* eds. Timothy P. Mottet, Virginia P. Richmond, and James C. McCroskey (Boston: Pearson, 2006), 89–116.

2 Kyle Zrenchik, "9/11 Rescue Workers: The Forsaken Heroes," *Winning Orations, 2007* (Mankato, MN: Interstate Oratorical Association, 2007), 42. Coached by Ray Quiel.

3 *Encarta World English Dictionary* (New York: St. Martin's, 1999), 1600.

4 Chiwoneso Beverley Tinago, "The Problem with Food Aid," *Winning Orations, 2009* (Mankato, MN: Interstate Oratorical Association, 2009), 38–39. Coached by Jennifer Talbert.

5 Paul Starbuck, "Exercise Anorexia: The Deadly Regimen," *Winning Orations, 2007* (Mankato, MN: Interstate Oratorical Association, 2007), 5. Coached by Ana Petero.

6 Zrenchik, 42.

7 C. Everett Koop, address, National Press Club, Washington, DC, September 8, 1998.

8 Tony Martinet, "Ribbons: Function or Fashion," *Winning Orations, 2004* (Mankato, MN: Interstate Oratorical Association, 2004), 79. Coached by Christina Ellis.

Chapter 10

1 Angela Wnek, Untitled Speech, *Winning Orations, 2012* (Mankato, MN: Interstate Oratorical Association, 2012), 143. Coached by Scott Placke.

2 Hillary Rodham Clinton, "Remarks on the Working Women's Forum," Speech, Working Women's Forum, Chennai, India, July 20, 2011, accessed September 29, 2011, www.state.gov/secretary/rm/2011/07/168835.htm.

3 Ann Bainbridge Frymier and Gary M. Shulman, "What's in It for Me?: Increasing Content Relevance to Enhance Students' Motivation," *Communication Education* 44, no. 1 (1995): 40–50.

4 Jake Gruber, "Heart Disease in Women," *Winning Orations, 2001* (Mankato, MN: Interstate Oratorical Association, 2001), 16. Coached by Judy Santacaterina.

5 Scott A. Myers, "The Relationship between Perceived Instructor Credibility and College Student In-Class and Out-of-Class Communication," *Communication Reports* 17, no. 1 (2004): 129–137.

6 Tess Drager, "Clostridium Difficile: The Killer Bacterium," *Winning Orations, 2013* (Mankato, MN: Interstate Oratorical Association, 2013), 79. Coached by Brian Klosa.

7 Kimberly Paine, "Red Light Running," Winning Orations, 2001 (Mankato, MN: Interstate Oratorical Association, 2001), 42. Coached by Susan Miskelly.

8 Viqar Mohammad, "Ovarian Cancer," *Winning Orations, 2007* (Mankato, MN: Interstate Oratorical Association, 2007), 17. Coached by Judy Santacaterina.

9 Mohammad, 19.

Chapter 11

1 Many people who teach creative writing prefer visual brainstorming, or "branching," to the traditional linear outlines such as the ones we illustrate. For interesting discussions of how outlining by visual brainstorming draws on both sides of the brain, see Henriette Anne Klauser, *Writing on Both Sides of the Brain: Breakthrough Techniques for People Who Write* (San Francisco: HarperSanFrancisco, 1987), 47–55; and Gabriele Lusser Rico, *Writing the Natural Way: Using Right-Brain Techniques to Release Your Expressive Powers* (New York: Tarcher/Putnam, 2000).

2 Austin Willis, "Gum Chewers," Speech Delivered at Penn State Hazleton, Hazleton, Pennsylvania, Fall 2013. Used with permission.

Chapter 12

1 Richard Lederer, *Anguished English: An Anthology of Accidental Assaults upon Our Language* (Charleston, SC: Wyrick, 1987), 8.

2 Gloria Cooper, ed., *Red Tape Holds Up New Bridge, and More Flubs from the Nation's Press* (New York: Perigee, 1987), n.p.

3 This discussion of two ways of responding to language is based on Louise M. Rosenblatt, *The Reader, the Text, the Poem: The Transactional Theory of the Literary Work* (Carbondale: Southern Illinois University Press, 1978), particularly Chapter 3, "Efferent and Aesthetic Reading."

4 Donald J. Trump, "President Donald Trump Rally" (presentation, Melbourne, FL, February 18, 2017), accessed February 21, 2017, https://www.youtube.com/watch?v=TIo3lBkoceU.

5 Joseph L. Chesebro and Melissa B. Wanzer, "Instructional Message Variables," in *Handbook of Instructional Communication: Rhetorical & Relational Perspectives 2006,* eds. Timothy P. Mottet, Virginia P. Richmond, and James C. McCroskey (Boston: Pearson, 2006), 89.

6 Miriam Ringo, *Nobody Said It Better!* (Chicago: Rand, 1980), 201.

7 Gozzi, 438.

8 Elyse Sommer and Dorrie Weiss, eds., *Metaphors Dictionary* (Detroit: Gale, 1995), xi.

9 Phillip J. Wininger, "The Unwanted Neighbor," *Winning Orations, 2001* (Mankato, MN: Interstate Oratorical Association, 2001), 36, 38. Coached by Judy Woodring.

10 Elie Wiesel, "The Shame of Hunger," in *Representative American Speeches: 1990–1991*, ed. Owen Peterson (New York: Wilson, 1991), 70–74.

11 Travis Kirchhefer, "The Deprived," *Winning Orations, 2000* (Mankato, MN: Interstate Oratorical Association, 2000), 151. Coached by Ron Krikac.

12 Sarah Meinen, "The Forgotten Four-Letter Word," *Winning Orations, 1999* (Mankato, MN: Interstate Oratorical Association, 1999), 26–29. Coached by Dan Smith.

13 William Safire, "On Language: Marking Bush's Inaugural," *New York Times Magazine* (February 5, 1989): 12.

14 Our guidelines have been shaped and reinforced by suggestions in these two excellent publications:

Publication Manual of the American Psychological Association, 6th ed. (Washington, DC: American Psychological Association, 2010), 70–77; and Rosalie Maggio, *Talking about People: A Guide to Fair and Accurate Language* (Phoenix, AZ: Oryx, 1997).

15 Rosalie Maggio, *The Bias-Free Word Finder: A Dictionary of Nondiscriminatory Language* (Boston: Beacon, 1991), 7.

16 Maggio, *Talking about People*, 1.

17 Lewis, M. Paul, ed., *Ethnologue: Languages of the World*, 16th ed. (Dallas, TX: SIL International, 2009), online version accessed August 10, 2011, www.ethnologue.com/.

18 Quoted in George Plimpton, ed., *The Writer's Chapbook: A Compendium of Fact, Opinion, Wit, and Advice from the 20th Century's Preeminent Writers* (New York: Viking, 1989), 176.

Chapter 13

1 Karlyn Kohrs Campbell, *The Rhetorical Act*, 2nd ed. (Belmont, CA: Wadsworth, 1996), 119.

2 Achim Nowak, *Power Speaking: The Art of the Exceptional Speaker* (New York: Allworth, 2004), 11.

3 Barack Obama (speech, Tucson, Arizona), accessed March 17, 2017, http://www.telegraph.co.uk/news/worldnews/us-politics/8256760/Barack-Obama-Tucson-Speech-in-full.html

4 Shelby Chaiken, "Communicator Physical Attractiveness and Persuasion," *Journal of Personality and Social Psychology* 37 (1979): 1387.

5 Deborah Blum, "Face It! Facial Expressions Are Crucial to Emotional Health," *Psychology Today* (September 19, 1998): 32. Blum uses Paul Ekman's estimate of 5,000 facial expressions. Ray Birdwhistell posited the number 250,000 in his *Kinesics and Context: Essays on Body Motion Communication* (Philadelphia: University of Pennsylvania Press, 1970), 8.

6 Donna Frick-Horbury and Robert E. Guttentag, "The Effects of Restricting Hand Gesture Production on Lexical Retrieval and Free Recall," *American Journal of Psychology* (Spring 1998): 45–46.

7 "Gestures May Trigger Ability to Recall Words," *Roanoke Times* (June 10, 2005): A12. See also Sharon Begley, "Living Hand to Mouth," *Newsweek* (November 2, 1999): 69.

8 Nick Linardopoulos, "Teaching and Learning Public Speaking Online," *MERLOT Journal of Online Learning and Teaching* (March 2010): 198–209.

9 Ruth Anne Clark and David Jones, "A Comparison of Traditional and Online Formats in a Public Speaking Course," *Communication Education* (April 2001): 109–124.

10 iTalk LLC, "Creating and Delivering Online Presentations," iTalk LLC (December 2000), accessed February 12, 2017, http://www.italk.com/company/Effective_Online_Presentations.pdf

Chapter 14

1 Timothy P. Mottet, Virginia P. Richmond, and James C. McCroskey, *Handbook of Instructional Communication: Rhetorical & Relational Perspectives* (Boston: Pearson, 2006).

2 Paul Schrodt and Paul L. Witt, "Students' Attributions of Instructor Credibility as a Function of Students' Expectations of Instructional Technology Use and Nonverbal Immediacy," *Communication Education* 55, no. 1 (2006); 1.

3 Chris Gurrie and Brandy Fair, "(Re)Discovering PowerPoint: Retooling the PowerPoint Pedagogy for 2009 and Beyond," National Communication Association Convention (Chicago, November 12, 2009), 1.

4 Dave Paradi, "Ten Secrets for Using PowerPoint Effectively," accessed April 27, 2009, www.thinkoutsidetheslide.com/articles.ten_secrets_for_usingpowerpoint.htm.

5 Guy Kawasaki, "How to Change the World: A Practical Blog for Impractical People," December 30, 2005, http://blog.guykawasaki.com/2005/12/the_102030_rule.html\#axzz1F4K0TMii.

6 These guidelines were part of a handout, "When Not to Use PowerPoint," distributed by Prof. Barbara Strain and Prof. Karen Wilking during a workshop at San Antonio College, Spring 2008. Used with permission.

7 Nick Morgan, *Give Your Speech, Change the World* (Boston: Harvard Business School, 2005), 139.

8 Prezi, "Presenting a Better Way to Present," *Prezi*, accessed February 26, 2017, https://prezi.com/.

9 Michael Talman, *Understanding Presentation Graphics* (San Francisco: SYBEX, 1992), 270.

10 Edward R. Tufte, *Visual Explanations: Images and Quantities, Evidence and Narrative* (Cheshire, CT: Graphics Press, 1997), 74.

11 We adapted this list of guidelines from multiple sources, including Ann Luck, *Visual Aid Checklist for Interactive Video Presentation* (1997). Used with permission of the author. Also from Joyce Kupsch and Pat R. Graves, *Create High Impact Business Presentations* (Lincolnwood, IL: NTC Learning Works—NTC/Contemporary, 1998), 89–90, 95–96, 107–09.

12 Edward R. Tufte, *The Visual Display of Quantitative Information* (Cheshire, CT: Graphics Press, 1983), 121. See also Tufte's richly illustrated later works: *Envisioning Information* (Cheshire, CT: Graphics Press, 1990) and *Visual Explanations*.

Chapter 15

1 Apple Inc., "Apple Special Event," September 7, 2016, accessed February 28, 2017, http://www.apple.com/apple-events/september-2016/.

2 Pew Research Center: Internet, Science, & Tech, Pew.com, "Americans' Internet Access: 2000-2015," accessed February 27, 2017, http://www.pewinternet.org/2015/06/26/americans-internet-access-2000-2015/.

3 Internet Live Stats, "Internet Users," InternetLiveStats.com, accessed February 27, 2017, http://www.internetlivestats.com/internet-users/.

4 Melissa Janoske, "Renaissance Fairs: The New Vaudeville," Speech Delivered at Radford University, Radford, VA, Spring 2002. Used with permission.

Chapter 16

1 Zig Ziglar, "The Power of Persuasion," accessed April 14, 2017, http://westsidetoastmasters.com/resources/laws_persuasion/chap1.html.

2 Katherine Hawkins, "Preliminary Development of a Measure of Faculty/Advisor Communication Apprehension," *Communication Research Reports* 8, no. 2 (1991): 127.

3 "The 30-Second President," narr. Bill Moyers, *A Walk through the 20th Century with Bill Moyers*, PBS, 1984.

4 Charles U. Larson, *Persuasion: Reception and Responsibility*, 9th ed. (Belmont, CA: Wadsworth, 2001), 10.

5 Neel Bhatt, Untitled Speech, *Winning Orations, 2004* (Mankato, MN: Interstate Oratorical Association, 2004), 21. Coached by David Moscovitz.

6 *The Rhetoric of Aristotle*, trans. Lane Cooper (New York: Appleton, 1960), 8.

7 Paul Schrodt and Amber N. Finn, "Students' Perceived Understanding: An Alternative Measure and Its Association with Perceived Teacher Confirmation, Verbal Aggressiveness, and Credibility," *Communication Education* 60 (2011): 231.

8 James Benjamin, *Principles, Elements, and Types of Persuasion* (Fort Worth, TX: Harcourt Brace, 1997), 122, 124.

9 James C. McCroskey and Jason J. Teven, "Goodwill: A Reexamination of the Construct and its Measurement." *Communication Monographs* 66 (1999): 66.

10 Paul Schrodt, Paul L. Witt, and Paul D. Turman, "Instructor Credibility as a Mediator of Instructors' Prosocial Communication Behaviors and Students' Learning Outcomes," *Communication Education* 58 (2009): 350.

11 James C. McCroskey, *An Introduction to Rhetorical Communication*, 7th ed. (Boston: Allyn, 1997), 87–88.

12 Jessica J. Jones, "Are You Guilty?" *Winning Orations*, *2004* (Mankato, MN: Interstate Oratorical Association, 2004), 93. Coached by Barbara F. Sims.

13 Raymie E. McKerrow, Bruce E. Gronbeck, Douglas Ehninger, and Alan H. Monroe, *Principles and Types of Speech Communication*, 14th ed. (New York: Addison-Longman, 2000), 153–61. See also: Alan H. Monroe, *Principles and Types of Speech* (Chicago: Scott, Foresman & Company, 1935).

14 Daniel Hinderliter, "Eating Better Through Reducing Food Waste," *Winning Orations, 2013* (Mankato, MN: Interstate Oratorical Association, 2013), 109–11. Coached by Mark Hickman.

Chapter 17

1 Ron Cunzburger, "Presidential Candidates," Politics1.com," accessed April 13, 2017, http://www.politics1.com/p2016.htm.

2 Thomas Gilovich, *How We Know What Isn't So* (New York: Free Press, 1991), 6.

3 Aristotle, *The Rhetoric of Aristotle*, trans. Lane Cooper (New York: Appleton, 1932), 220.

4 For a more elaborate discussion of the structure of an argument, see Stephen Toulmin, *The Uses of Argument* (New York: Cambridge University Press, 1974).

5 Patrick Martin, "The Energy Cure that Kills: Hydraulic Fracturing for Natural Gas," *Winning Orations, 2011* (Mankato, MN: Interstate Oratorical Association, 2011), 147. Coached by Karen Morris.

6 Jon Meinen, Untitled Speech, *Winning Orations, 2006* (Mankato, MN: Interstate Oratorical Association, 2006), 17. Coached by Dan Smith.

7 Nicholas Barton, "The Death of Reading," *Winning Orations, 2004* (Mankato, MN: Interstate Oratorical Association, 2004), 32. Coached by Craig Brown and Robert F. Imbody III.

8 Rachel Resnick, "The Nursing Home Catastrophe," *Winning Orations, 2006* (Mankato, MN: Interstate Oratorical Association, 2006), 1. Coached by Josh Miller.

9 Mario Cuomo, Keynote Address, Democratic National Convention, *Vital Speeches of the Day* (August 15, 1984): 647.

10 John M. Ericson and James J. Murphy with Raymond Bud Zeuschner, *The Debater's Guide*, rev. ed. (Carbondale, IL: Southern Illinois University Press, 1987), 139.

11 W. Ward Fearnside and William B. Holther, *Fallacy—The Counterfeit of Argument* (Englewood Cliffs, NJ: Prentice-Hall, 1959), 92.

Chapter 18

1 Donald Ochs, "Introduction of Samuel L. Becker, Central States Communication Association Convention, April 12, 1991," *The CSCA News* (Spring 1991): 2.

2 http://www.chicagotribune.com/news/nationworld/ct-muhammad-ali-funeral-20160610-story.html.

3 Peggy Noonan, *What I Saw at the Revolution* (New York: Random House, 1990), 253.

4 Southern Illinois University Edwardsville, "Student Commencement Speaker Guidelines," SIUE, accessed March 17, 2017, www.siue.edu/commencement/pdf/student-speaker.pdf.

5 Cowell College, "Commencement Speech Guidelines," *University of California, Santa Cruz*, accessed March 17, 2007, http://cowell.ucsc.edu/activities/commencement/gradinfo/speech-guidelines.html.

Appendix A

1 This definition is adapted from Hendrie Weisinger and Norman M. Lobsenz, *Nobody's Perfect: How to Give Criticism and Get Results* (New York: Warner, 1981), 9–10.

2 This model of criticism is adapted from Beverly Whitaker Long, "Evaluating Performed Literature," *Studies in Interpretation*, vol. 2, eds. Esther M. Doyle and Virginia Hastings Floyd (Amsterdam: Rodopi, 1977), 267–81. See also her earlier article: Beverly Whitaker, "Critical Reasons and Literature in Performance," *The Speech Teacher* 18 (November 1969): 191–93. Long attributes this three-part model of criticism to Arnold Isenberg, "Critical Communication," *The Philosophical Review* (July 1949): 330–44.

Appendix B

1 In constructing our suggestions regarding audience questionnaires, we drew from advice in two excellent texts: Lawrence R. Frey, Carl H. Botan, and Gary L. Kreps, *Investigating Communication: An Introduction to Research Methods*, 2nd ed. (Boston: Allyn & Bacon, 2000) and Joann Keyton, *Communication Research: Asking Questions, Finding Answers*, 4th ed. (New York: McGraw-Hill, 2014).

Appendix C

1 Thomas E. Harris and John C. Sherblom, *Small Group and Team Communication*, 3rd ed. (Boston: Allyn & Bacon, 2005), 156.

2 "Kenneth Blanchard Quotes," *Famous Inspirational Quotes*, May 23, 2009, http://www.inspiration-alquotes4u.com/blanchardquotes/index.html.

Appendix D

1 Alison Gopnik, "The Arts and Science of Asking Questions is the Source of All Knowledge," *BrainyQuote.com*, accessed March 17, 2017, https://www.brainyquote.com/quotes/keywords/asking_questions.html.

Appendix E

1 Jennell Chu, "Flash Mobs," Speech Delivered at San Antonio College, San Antonio, Texas, Spring 2011. Used with permission.

2 Austin Willis, "Gum Chewers," Speech Delivered at Penn State Hazleton, Hazleton, Pennsylvania, Fall 2013. Used with permission.

3 Derrick Peña, "Student Involvement," Speech Delivered at Penn State Hazleton, Hazleton, Pennsylvania, Fall 2016. Used with permission.

4 © 2016 Pearson Education, Inc. All rights reserved.

5 Chiwoneso Beverley Tinago, "The Problem with Food Aid," Winning Orations, 2009 (Mankato, MN: Interstate Oratorical Association, 2009), 38–39. Coached by Jennifer Talbert.

6 © 2016 Pearson Education, Inc. All rights reserved.

Glossary

academic search engines   Search engines that are full-text archives of focused, high-quality sources.

acceptance speech   A speech responding to a speech of presentation by acknowledging an award, a tribute, or recognition.

actual example   An example based on a true instance or illustration.

ad hominem   A fallacy that urges listeners to reject an idea because of the allegedly poor character of the person voicing it; name-calling.

alliteration   The repetition of beginning sounds in words that are adjacent, or near one another.

antithesis   The use of parallel construction to contrast ideas.

appeal to tradition   A fallacy that opposes change by arguing that old ways are always superior to new ways.

appearance   An aspect of physical delivery, in particular our grooming and the way we dress.

argument   The process of reasoning from evidence to prove a claim.

argument by analogy   An argument that links two objects or concepts and states that what is true in one case is or will be true in another.

argument by authority   An argument using testimony from an expert source to prove a speaker's claim.

argument by cause   An argument stating that one action or condition caused or will cause another.

argument by example   An inductive form of argument in which the claim is supported by providing examples.

articulation   The mechanical process of forming the sounds necessary to communicate in a particular language.

attitude   A statement expressing an individual's approval or disapproval, like or dislike.

audience analysis   The process of determining the audience members' demographics, psychographics, and needs, which then shapes the preparation, delivery, and evaluation of a speech.

audience disposition   Listeners' feelings of like, dislike, or neutrality toward a speaker, the speaker's topic, or the occasion for a speech.

audience profile   A sketch of relevant characteristics of listeners that assists the speaker in researching, planning, and delivering speeches.

audience segmentation   The strategy of dividing an audience into various subgroups based on their demographic and psychographic profiles.

audience targeting   The strategy of directing a speech primarily toward one or more portions of the entire audience.

audience-generated topics   Speech topics geared to the interests and needs of a speaker's listeners.

audio aid   An audio file (e.g., mp3 file) used to clarify or prove a point by letting listeners hear an example.

bandwagon   A fallacy that determines truth, goodness, or wisdom by popular opinion.

bar graph   A diagram used to show quantitative comparisons among variables.

behavior   An individual's observable action.

belief   A statement that people accept as true.

brainstorming   Noncritical free association to generate as many ideas as possible.

brief example   A short, general point about a specific person, place, object, experience, or condition discussed in a speech.

caring   The extent to which listeners perceive a speaker as understanding, empathetic, and sensitive.

causal division   Organization of a speech from cause to effect, or from effect to cause.

causal transition   Connects one key idea to another by establishing a cause–effect relationship between two key ideas.

central idea   A one-sentence synopsis that specifies the speaker's key ideas.

channel   The means through which a message is sent.

chart   A graphic used to condense a large amount of information, to list the steps in a process, or to introduce new terms.

chronological division   Organization of a speech according to a time sequence.

chronological transition   Connects one key idea to another by showing how one key idea precedes or follows another in time.

circular conclusion   A closure statement that repeats or refers to material used in the attention-getting step of the introduction.

civility   Communication behaviors that reflect respect for others and foster harmonious and productive relationships.

claim   A declarative statement that the speaker intends to prove and persuade the listeners to accept.

cliché   A once-colorful figure of speech that has lost impact through overuse.

closed questions   Questions with a finite set of responses that are either categorical or in a scale format that asks respondents to place themselves along a continuum.

cognitive restructuring   A strategy for reducing communication anxiety by replacing negative thoughts and statements with positive ones.

commencement speech   A brief, often witty graduation speech intended to emphasize the occasion, education, and skills of the speaker and her or his peers.

communication   The process of sharing meaning by sending and receiving symbolic cues.

communication apprehension The fear or anxiety associated with real or anticipated communication with another person or persons.

comparative advantage pattern An organizational pattern in which the speaker illustrates the advantages of one viewpoint, object, or behavior over another viewpoint, object, or behavior.

comparison The process of associating two items by pointing out their similarities.

competence Listeners' views of a speaker's qualifications to speak on a particular topic.

complementary transition Adds one key idea to another, reinforcing the major point of the speech.

complete sentence outline An outline in which all numbers and letters introduce complete sentences.

concepts Abstract, intangible ideas.

conclusion The deductive argument that what is true of the general class is true of the specific instance.

conditions The state of something or someone, such as the economy, health, or an infrastructure.

connotation The emotional association(s) that a word or phrase may evoke in individual listeners.

contrast The process of distinguishing two items by pointing out their differences.

contrasting transition Connects one key idea to another by showing how the two key ideas differ.

coordinate ideas Ideas that have equal value in a speech.

credibility Listeners' perceptions of a speaker's competence, trustworthiness, and caring.

critical thinking The logical, reflective examination of information and ideas to determine what to believe or do.

criticism Feedback offered for the purpose of improving a speaker's public speaking skills.

cultural relativism With regard to listening, interpreting the speaker's message based on the speaker's lived experiences and cultural norms, enhancing the listeners' ability to understand the speaker's perspective.

database A large collection of information arranged for quick retrieval by computer using key words entered by a researcher.

decoding The process of attaching meaning to symbols received.

deductive argument An argument stating that what is true generally is or will be true in a specific instance.

deep Web Huge databases of Internet information posted by public, government, corporate, and private agencies and available only by specific queries.

definition An explanation of the meaning of a word, phrase, or concept.

definition by etymology Explanation of the origin of the word being defined.

definition by example Providing an instance or illustration of the word being defined.

definition by operation Explanation of how the object or concept being defined works, what it does, or what it was designed to do.

definition by synonym Substitution of a word having similar meaning for the word being defined.

delivery The way a speaker presents a speech, through voice qualities, bodily actions, and language.

demographics The characteristics of the audience, such as age, sex, sexual orientation, race, ethnicity, education, religion, economic status, and group membership.

denotation The dictionary definition of a word or phrase.

derived credibility The image listeners develop of a speaker as he or she speaks.

diagram A graphic, usually designed on a computer or drawn on poster board, showing the parts of an object or organization or the steps in a process.

direct question A question that asks for an overt response from listeners.

encoding The process of selecting symbols to carry a message.

environment The occasion, social context, and physical setting for communication.

ethics Standards used to determine right from wrong, good from bad, in both thought and action.

ethnocentric listeners Listeners who interpret the speaker's message based on their own lived experiences and cultural background rather than the speaker's experiences and cultural background.

ethos Speaker credibility.

eulogy A speech of tribute praising a person who has recently passed away.

evaluate Assessing the merits of the stimuli you received.

evidence Supporting materials a speaker uses to prove a claim.

example A sample or illustration of a category of people, places, objects, actions, experiences, or conditions.

extended example A lengthy and elaborate example that allows for a detailed picture of a person, place, object, experience, or condition discussed in the speech.

eye contact Gaze behavior in which a speaker looks at listeners' eyes.

facial expression The tension and movement of various parts of a speaker's face.

factual distractions Listening disturbances caused by attempts to recall minute details of what is being communicated.

fair use provision Section 107 of U.S. copyright law allowing limited noncommercial use of copyrighted materials for teaching, criticism, scholarship, research, or commentary.

fallacy A flaw in the logic of an argument.

false analogy A fallacy that occurs when an argument by analogy compares entities that have critical differences.

false authority A fallacy that uses testimony from sources who have no expertise on the topic in question.

false dilemma A fallacy that confronts listeners with two choices when, in reality, more options exist. (Sometimes called the either–or fallacy.)

feedback Verbal and nonverbal responses between communicators about the clarity or acceptability of messages.

figurative comparison Associations between two items that do not share actual similarities.

figurative contrast   Distinctions between two items that do not have actual similarities.

film and video   Moving projections used to enhance a speaker's point.

formal outline   A complete sentence outline written in sufficient detail so that a person other than the speaker could understand it.

frequency count   A measure of the number of times that a certain event or response occurs.

general purpose   The broad goal of a speech—to inform, to persuade, or to entertain.

gestures   Movements of a speaker's hands, arms, and head while delivering a speech.

global plagiarism   Plagiarism that occurs when someone presents an entire speech or paper created by someone else as his or her own.

handout   Copies of any presentational aid—pictures, diagrams, graphs, charts, or maps—distributed to the audience members.

hasty generalization   A fallacy that makes claims from insufficient or unrepresentative examples.

hearing   The continuous, natural, and passive process of receiving aural stimuli.

hypothetical example   An example based on an imaginary or fictitious instance or illustration.

impromptu speaking   Speaking with little or no advance preparation.

inclusive language   Language free from certain expressions or words that might be considered to exclude particular groups of people.

incremental plagiarism   Plagiarism that occurs when someone fails to cite his or her sources when presenting information.

inductive argument   Use of collected evidence that supports a general claim.

inflection   Patterns of change in a person's pitch while speaking.

initial credibility   A speaker's image or reputation before speaking to a particular audience.

intentional plagiarism   The deliberate, unattributed use of another's ideas, words, or pattern of organization.

interpret   Decoding, or attaching meanings to the stimuli.

interpreter   Any person using symbols to send or receive messages.

issues   Points of controversy in which people hold opposing or multiple opinions, such as abortion.

jargon   The special language used by people in a particular activity, business, or group.

judgments   A critic's opinions about the relative merits of a speech; the most common and superficial level of speech criticism.

key ideas   The two to five main points you will discuss in your speech.

key word or phrase outline   An outline in which all numbers and letters introduce words or groups of words.

line graph   A diagram used to depict changes among variables over time.

listener   The receiver or decoder of the message.

listening   The intermittent, learned, and active process of giving attention to aural stimuli.

literal comparison   Associations between two items that share actual similarities.

literal contrast   Distinctions between two items that share some actual similarities.

logos   Logical appeal.

major premise   A claim about a general group of people, events, or conditions.

map   A graphic representation of a real or imaginary geographic area.

Maslow's hierarchy   A model of five basic human needs—physiological, safety, belongingness and love, esteem, and self-actualization—in an ordered arrangement.

message   Ideas communicated verbally and nonverbally.

metaphor   An implied comparison of two things without the use of *as* or *like*.

mind mapping   A technique for refining an idea by visually linking more specific ideas that extend from the original idea.

minor premise   A statement placing a person, an event, or a condition into a general class.

Monroe's motivated sequence   A persuasive pattern composed of (1) getting the audience's attention, (2) establishing a need, (3) offering a proposal to satisfy the need, (4) inviting listeners to visualize the results, and (5) requesting action.

movement   A speaker's motion from place to place during speech delivery.

narration   The process of describing an action or series of occurrences using storytelling.

need–plan division   A variation of problem–solution organization that (1) establishes a need or deficiency, (2) offers a proposal to meet the need, (3) shows how the plan satisfies the need, and (4) suggests a plan for implementing the proposal.

noise   Anything that distracts from effective communication.

nonsexist language   Language that treats both sexes fairly and avoids stereotyping either one.

norms   The values a critic believes necessary to make any speech good, effective, or desirable.

object   An actual item or three-dimensional model of an item used during the delivery of a speech.

occasion-generated topics   Speech topics derived from particular circumstances, seasons, holidays, or life events.

open-ended questions   Questions that enable respondents to answer questions about their attitudes, beliefs, values, and behaviors in their own words.

oral footnote   Verbalized credit for ideas and supporting materials in your speech that are not your own.

organizing question   A question that, when answered, indicates the ideas and information necessary to develop your topic.

parallelism   The expression of ideas using similar grammatical structures.

paraphrase   To express the meaning of another person's work (written or spoken) using different words.

paraplage   Plagiarism consisting of half original writing and half quotation from an unattributed source.

patchwork plagiarism   Plagiarism that occurs when someone presents parts of various speeches or papers as his or her own.

pathos   Emotional appeal.

pause   An intentional or unintentional period of silence in a speaker's vocal delivery.

personal narrative   A story told from the viewpoint of a participant in the action and using the pronouns *I* or *we*.

personification   A figure of speech that attributes human qualities to a concept or inanimate object.

persuasion   The process of influencing another person's values, beliefs, attitudes, or behaviors.

physical delivery   Nonauditory delivery; all aspects of delivery excluding the speaker's words and voice.

physical noise   Distractions originating in the physical environment.

physiological noise   Distractions originating in the bodies of communicators.

picture   A photograph, painting, drawing, or print used to make a point more vivid or convincing.

pie, or circle, graph   A circular diagram used to show the relative proportions of a whole.

pitch   The highness or lowness of a speaker's voice.

plagiarism   The unattributed use of another's ideas, words, or pattern of organization.

post hoc ergo propter hoc   A chronological fallacy that says that a prior event caused a subsequent event.

posture   The position or bearing of a speaker's body while delivering a speech.

PowerPoint   Software that enables speakers to supplement their presentations with text, graphics, images, audio, and video.

presentational aids   Visual and/or auditory aids used to enhance the clarity and impact of your message.

preview   A statement that orients the audience by revealing the speaker's key ideas.

Prezi   A one-slide presentation that includes both text and visuals such as graphs, photos, and diagrams.

Primacy theory   The assumption that a speaker should place the strongest argument at the beginning of the body of a speech.

primary research   The process of generating new knowledge and information by collecting, analyzing, and interpreting new data (e.g., conducting a focus group, administering a questionnaire).

problem–cause–solution division   An alternative to the problem–solution division that divides the speech into a discussion of what the problem is, factors contributing to the problem, and how to resolve the problem.

problem–solution division   A rigid organizational pattern that establishes a compelling problem and offers one or more convincing solutions.

process   A series of steps producing an outcome.

projection   A manner of displaying presentational aids by casting their images onto a screen or other background.

pronunciation   How the sounds of a word are to be said and which parts are to be stressed.

proposition   A declarative sentence expressing a judgment or an opinion a speaker wants listeners to accept.

proposition of fact   An assertion about the truth or falsity of a statement.

proposition of policy   A statement requesting support for a course of action.

proposition of value   An assertion about the relative worth of an idea or action.

pro–con assessment   Organization of a speech according to arguments for and against some policy, position, or action followed by a final key idea in which the speaker supports the strongest position.

pro–con division   Organization of a speech according to arguments for and against some policy, position, or action.

psychographics   Characteristics of the audience, such as values, beliefs, and attitudes, which influence behaviors.

psychological noise   Distractions originating in the thoughts of communicators.

public speaking anxiety   A fear of speaking to an audience when delivering a speech.

qualitative research   Research aimed at gathering descriptive, nonnumerical data, in pursuit of new knowledge.

quantitative research   Research aimed at gathering numerical data in pursuit of new knowledge.

questionnaire   A set of written questions designed to elicit information about listeners' knowledge, beliefs, attitudes, or behaviors regarding your specific speech topic.

random word association   Recording of words and ideas that come to mind when thinking about a randomly selected word.

rate   The speed at which a speech is delivered.

reasons   Statements that justify a critic's judgments.

receive   Getting auditory stimuli.

Recency theory   The assumption that a speaker should place the strongest argument at the end of the body of a speech.

red herring   A fallacy that introduces irrelevant issues to deflect attention from the subject under discussion.

referent   The object or idea each interpreter attaches to a symbol.

referent   The object or idea each interpreter attaches to a symbol.

refutation pattern   An organizational pattern in which the speaker attempts to disprove claims and opinions that oppose the speaker's position.

refute   To dispute; to counter one argument with another.

repetition   Restating words, phrases, or sentences for emphasis.

research The process of gathering evidence and arguments to understand, develop, and explain a speech topic.

research-generated topics Speech topics discovered by investigating a variety of sources.

resolve Deciding what to do with the stimuli you received or how to respond.

rhetorical question A question designed to stimulate thought without demanding an overt response.

scope The breadth of an area or subject matter.

search engine A tool for locating information on the Internet by matching items in a search string with pages that the engine indexes.

secondary research The process of gathering, reviewing, and summarizing existing information (e.g., conducting library research, online research).

select Choosing which stimuli to focus on.

self-generated topics Speech topics based on the speaker's interests, experiences, and knowledge.

semantic distractions Listening disturbances caused by confusion over the meanings of words.

sexist language Language that excludes one sex, creates special categories for one sex, or assigns roles based solely on sex.

signpost Numbers (*one, two*, or *three*) or words (*initially, second*, or *finally*) that signal to the listener the speaker's place in the speech.

simile A comparison of two things using the words *as* or *like*.

slippery slope A fallacy of causation stating that one action inevitably sets a chain of events in motion.

spatial division Organization of a speech according to the geography or physical structure of the subject.

speaker The sender, source, or encoder of the message.

speaking extemporaneously Delivering a speech from a combination of your notes and knowledge of the topic

speaking from manuscript Delivering a speech from a text written word for word and practiced in advance.

speaking from memory Delivering a speech that is recalled word for word from a written text.

speaking outline A brief outline for the speaker's use alone, containing source citations and delivery prompts.

specific purpose A statement of the general purpose of the speech, the speaker's intended audience, and the goal or outcome.

speech of introduction A speech introducing a featured speaker to an audience.

speech of presentation A speech conferring an award, a prize, or some other recognition on an individual or group.

speech of tribute A speech honoring a person, group, or event.

speech to actuate A persuasive speech designed to influence listeners' behaviors.

speech to convince A persuasive speech focused on influencing audience attitudes and beliefs, without advocating a specific action.

speech to entertain A speech designed to make a point through the creative, organized use of amusing supporting materials.

speech to inform A speech designed to convey new or useful information in a balanced, objective way.

speech to inspire A persuasive speech designed to influence listeners' feelings.

speech to persuade A speech designed to influence listeners' attitudes, beliefs, values, or behaviors.

statistics Data collected and presented in the form of numbers.

subordinate ideas Ideas that support more general or more important points in a speech.

subpoints Ideas that support the key idea which, in turn, supports the central idea.

syllogism The pattern of a deductive argument, consisting of a major premise, a minor premise, and a conclusion.

symbol Anything to which people attach meaning.

terminal credibility The image listeners develop of a speaker by the end of a speech and for a period of time after it.

testimony Quotations or paraphrases of an authoritative source to clarify or prove a point.

third-person narrative A story told from the viewpoint of a witness and using the pronouns *he, she*, or *they*.

tone The relationship established by language and grammar between speakers and their listeners.

topical division Organization of a speech according to aspects, or subtopics, of the subject.

transition A statement that connects one key idea of the speech with another key idea.

trustworthiness Listeners' views of a speaker's honesty, morality, and objectivity.

understand A sense-making process in which you integrate the stimuli into your frame of reference by considering both the content and context of the stimuli.

unintentional plagiarism The careless or unconscious unattributed use of another's ideas, words, or pattern of organization.

validity The accuracy with which your supporting materials support your claim.

value Judgment of what is right or wrong, desirable or undesirable, usually expressed as words or phrases.

visualization A strategy for reducing communication anxiety by picturing yourself delivering a successful speech.

vocal delivery The way in which speakers orally present the content of their speech; also known as paralanguage.

vocalized pause A sound or word such as *ah, like, okay, um, so*, and *you know* inserted to fill the silence between a speaker's words or thoughts.

volume The relative loudness or softness of a speaker's voice.

working outline An informal, initial outline recording a speaker's process of narrowing, focusing, and balancing a topic.

Text and illustrations Credits

Chapter 1   Page 5: HNN Staff, "So What Does Jihad Really Mean?" History News Network, accessed June 18, 2002, http://www.historynewsnetwork.org/articles/article. html?id=774"; p.8: Karlyn Kohrs Campbell, The Rhetorical Act, 2nd ed. (Belmont, CA: Wadsworth, 1996), 119.; p.11: Robert Ennis, "A Taxonomy of Critical Thinking Dispositions and Abilities," in Teaching Thinking Skills: Theory and Practice, ed. Joan Boykoff Baron and Robert Sternberg (New York: Freeman, 1987), 10.; p.11: National Assessment of Educational Progress, Reading, Writing and Thinking: Results from the 1979–80 National Assessment of Reading and Literature. Report No. 11-L-01 (Washington, DC: GPO, October 1981), 5.; p.11: Adapted from Robert J. Marzano, Ronald S. Brandt, Carolyn Sue Hughes, Beau Fly Jones, Barbara Z. Presseisen, Stuart C. Rankin, and Charles Suhor, Dimensions of Thinking: A Framework for Curriculum and Instruction, Alexandria, VA: Association for Supervision and Curriculum Development (1988), 66, 70–112.

Chapter 2   Page 27: Georgia Harper, "Using the Four Factor Fair Use Test," Fair Use of Copyrighted Materials, University of Texas, Austin, last modified August 10, 2001, http://www .utsystem.edu/ogc/intellectualproperty/copypol2.htm.; p.23: Rona Marech, "Thanks for the Civility: Mannerly Campaign Spread Nationwide," Baltimoresun.com, November 1, 2007, http://www.choosecivilitymc.org/published/dat/baltimore _sun.pdf.; p.23: Institute for Civility in Government.; p.25: Erik Vance, Genetically Modified Conservation, Conservation Magazine, August 27, 2010; p.27: "Copyright Exceptions," Purdue University Copyright Office, accessed June 29, 2011, http://www.lib.purdue.edu/uco/CopyrightBasics/fair_use .html.; p.15: Donald K. Smith, Man Speaking: A Rhetoric of Public Speech (New York: Dodd, 1969), 228.; p.17: Kenneth Blanchard and Norman Vincent Peale, The Power of Ethical Management (New York: Fawcett-Ballantine, 1988), 9; p.19: James C. McCroskey, An Introduction to Rhetorical Communication (Upper Saddle River, NJ: Prentice, 1968), 237.; p.22: Rod L. Troester and Cathy Sargent Mester, Civility in Business and Professional Communication (New York: Peter Lang, 2007), 10.; p.23: Alexander Lindey, Plagiarism and Originality (New York: Harper, 1952), 2.; p.24: John L. Waltman, "Plagiarism: Preventing It in Formal Research Reports," ABCA [American Business Communication Association] Bulletin, June 1980, 37.; p.26: Copyright and Fair Use in the Classroom, on the Internet, and the World Wide Web, Information and Library Sciences, University of Maryland University College, accessed June 30, 2011, http://www.umuc.edu/library/copy .shtml.; p.31: U.S. Copyright Office, Limitation on Exclusive Rights: Fair Use, accessed June 30, 2011, http://www .copyright.gov/title17/92chap1.html#107.; p.18: Mary Cunningham, "What Price 'Good Copy'?" Newsweek (November 29, 1982): 15.; p.25: Michael T. O'Neill, "Plagiarism: Writing Responsibly," ABCA Bulletin (June, 1980): 34, 36.

Chapter 3   Page 30: Nancy Daniels, "Public Speaking: The Positive Effect of Nervousness." SelfGrowth.com. http://www.selfgrowth.com/articles/public-speaking- the-positive-effects-of-nervousness (accessed January 13, 2017).; p.30: Karen K. Dwyer and Marlina M. Davidson, "Is Public Speaking Really More Feared Than Death?" Communication Research Reports 29 (2012): 107.; p.31: Virginia P. Richmond and James C. McCroskey, Communication: Apprehension, Avoidance, and Effectiveness, 5th ed. (Boston: Allyn & Bacon, 1998), 45; p.31: James A. Belasco and Ralph C. Stayer, Flight of the Buffalo (New York: Warner, 1993), 327–28.; p.34: Jack Valenti, Speak Up with Confidence (New York: William Morrow, 1982), 19.; p.36–37: Joe Ayres and Theodore S. Hopf, "Visualization: A Means of Reducing Speech Anxiety," Communication Education 34 (1985): 321.; p.31: Interview Magazine, 1988.

Chapter 4   Page 46: Robert L. Montgomery, Listening Made Easy (New York: AMACOM, 1981), n.p.; p.55: John Marshall, chief justice of the United States from 1801 to 1835; p.45: "The Big Lebowski". Joel and Ethan Coen. Universal Studios, 1998.; p.46: PBSkidsGO (2005). "Gossip and Rumors: What the Words Mean." CastleWorks Inc. http://pbskids.org/itsmylife/friends/rumors/article2 .html (accessed January 15, 2017).

Chapter 5   Page 65: From Motivation and Personality, 1st ed., by Abraham H. Maslow, © 1954. Electronically reproduced by permission of Pearson Education, Inc., Upper Saddle River, New Jersey.; p.58: Christopher Beam, "Code Black." State.com. http://www.slate.com/articles/news_and_politics /politics/2010/01/code_black.html (accessed January 18, 2017).; p.58: Christopher Beam, "Code Black." State.com. http://www.slate.com/articles/news_and_politics/politics /2010/01/code_black.html (accessed January 18, 2017).

Chapter 7   Page 87: Patricia Senn Breivik, Student learning in the information age (1998). (Phoenix, AZ: Oryx Press, 1998), 2.; p.87: Wayne C. Booth, Gregory G. Colomb, and Joseph M. Williams, The Craft of Research (Chicago: University of Chicago Press, 1995), 35.; p.89: Frederick J. Friend, "Google Scholar: Potentially Good for Users of Academic Information," The Journal of Electronic Publishing, 9, no. 1 (2006). do:10.39 98/3336451.0009.105.; p.89: "Google Scholar," Lehigh University, Library & Technology Services, last modified April 14, 2005, http://www.lehigh.edu/helpdesk/docs/google/.; p.89: Michael K. Bergman, "White Paper: The Deep Web: Surfacing Hidden Value," The Journal of Electronic Publishing, 7, no. 1 (August 2001) accessed August 19, 2011, http://hdl .handle.net/2027/spo.3336451.0007.104.; p.90: "Wikipedia FAQ/Schools," Wikipedia, last modified June 10, 2011, http://en.wikipedia.org/wiki/Wikipedia:FAQ/Schools.

Chapter 8   Page 105: James Percelay, " Snaps: The Original Yo' Mama Joke Book" Harper Collins 1994; p.108: B. Scott Titsworth, "Students' Notetaking: The Effects of Teacher Immediacy and Clarity," Communication Education (October 2004): 317.; p.109 110, 113: Austin Willis; p.100: Robert Half, "Memomania," American Way (November 1, 1987): 21.; p.: Pearson Education.

Chapter 9 Page 119: Kyle Zrenchik, "9/11 Rescue Workers: The Forsaken Heroes," Winning Orations, 2007 (Mankato, MN: Interstate Oratorical Association, 2007), 42. Coached by Ray Quiel.; p.120: Index Crime Statistics, Chicago Police Department; p.120: The New York Public Library desk reference, 4th ed New York: Hyperion, 2002. The Stonesong Press; p.120: Encarta World English Dictionary (New York: St. Martin's, 1999), 1600; p.122: Chiwoneso Beverley Tinago, "The Problem with Food Aid," Winning Orations, 2009 (Mankato, MN: Interstate Oratorical Association, 2009), 38–39. Coached by Jennifer Talbert; p.122: Sally Deneen, The Facebook Age: Mark Zuckerberg, Success, March 2011. http://www.success.com/article/the-facebook-age-mark-zuckerberg; p.123: Paul Starbuck, "Exercise Anorexia: The Deadly Regimen," Winning Orations, 2007 (Mankato, MN: Interstate Oratorical Association, 2007), 5. Coached by Ana Petero.; p.124: C. Everett Koop, address, National Press Club, Washington, DC, September 8, 1998; p.123: Kyle Zrenchik, "9/11 Rescue Workers: The Forsaken Heroes," Winning Orations, 2007 (Mankato, MN: Interstate Oratorical Association, 2007), 42. Coached by Ray Quiel.; p.124: Tony Martinet, "Ribbons: Function or Fashion," Winning Orations, 2004 (Mankato, MN: Interstate Oratorical Association, 2004), 79. Coached by Christina Ellis; p.129: Mayo Clinic website, http://www.mayoclinic.org/diseases-conditions/chronic-fatigue-syndrome/basics/definition/con-20022009; accessed March 1, 2017; p.119: Ashkan Naderi; p.124: Ashkan Naderi.

Chapter 10 Page 132: Eudora Welty. Conversations with Eudora Welty By Peggy Whitman Prenshaw, page 309; p.133: Angela Wnek, Untitled Speech, Winning Orations, 2012 (Mankato, MN: Interstate Oratorical Association, 2012), 143. Coached by Scott Placke.; p.136: Hillary Rodham Clinton, "Remarks on the Working Women's Forum," Speech, Working Women's Forum, Chennai, India, July 20, 2011, accessed September 29, 2011, http://www.state.gov/secretary/rm/2011/07/168835.htm.; p.136: SOURCE: Pearson Education, Inc.; p.138: Jake Gruber, "Heart Disease in Women," Winning Orations, 2001 (Mankato, MN: Interstate Oratorical Association, 2001), 16. Coached by Judy Santacaterina.; p.142: Kimberly Paine, "Red Light Running," Winning Orations, 2001 (Mankato, MN: Interstate Oratorical Association, 2001), 42. Coached by Susan Miskelly.; p.144: Pearson Education Inc.; p.133: Angela Wnek, Untitled Speech, Winning Orations, 2012 (Mankato, MN: Interstate Oratorical Association, 2012), 143. Coached by Scott Placke.; p.134: King, Martin L., Jr. "I Have a Dream." Speech. Lincoln Memorial,. Washington, D. C. 28 Aug. 1963. American Rhetoric. Web. 25 Mar. 2013.; p.143: Viqar Mohammad, "Ovarian Cancer," Winning Orations, 2007 (Mankato, MN: Interstate Oratorical Association, 2007), 17. Coached by Judy Santacaterina.

Chapter 11 Page 154: A. P. Allen & A. P. Smith (2011). A Review of the Evidence that Chewing Gum Affects Stress, Alertness and Cognition. Journal of Behavioral and Neuroscience Research 2011, Vol. 9(1), 7–23; p.154: Andrew J. Johnson and Christopher Miles (2008). Chewing gum and context-dependent memory: The independent roles of chewing gum and mint flavour. British Journal of Psychology (2008), 99, 293–306. The British Psychological Society; p.154: Tucha, L., & Koerts, J. (2012). Gum chewing and cognition: An overview. Neuroscience & Medicine, 3, 243–250.

Chapter 12 Page 160: Richard Lederer, Anguished English: An Anthology of Accidental Assaults upon Our Language (Charleston, SC: Wyrick, 1987), 8.; p.160: Gloria Cooper, ed., Red Tape Holds up New Bridge, and More Flubs from the Nation's Press (New York: Perigee, 1987), n.p; p.161: Donald J. Trump, "President Donald Trump Rally" (presentation, Melbourne, FL, February 18, 2017 accessed February 21, 2017 https://www.youtube.com/watch?v=TIo3lBkoceU).; p.164: Miriam Ringo, Nobody Said It Better! (Chicago: Rand, 1980), 201.; "p.166: METAPHORS DICTIONARY by Elyse Sommer, copyright © 2001 Visible Ink Press®, Reprinted by permission of Visible Ink Press.; p.166: Phillip J. Wininger, "The Unwanted Neighbor," Winning Orations, 2001 (Mankato, MN: Interstate Oratorical Association, 2001), 36, 38. Coached by Judy Woodring; p.166: Elie Wiesel, "The Shame of Hunger," in Representative American Speeches: 1990–1991, ed. Owen Peterson (New York: H.W.Wilson, 1991), 70–74.; p.166: Travis Kirchhefer, "The Deprived," Winning Orations, 2000 (Mankato, MN: Interstate Oratorical Association, 2000), 151. Coached by Ron Krikac; p.166: "John F. Kennedy, inauguration speech, January 20, 1961." Public Papers of the Presidents of the United States: John F. Kennedy, 1961. Office of the Federal Register. Washington: Office of the Federal Register, National Archives and Records Service, General Services Administration;" p.166: Abraham Lincoln, Gettysburg Address, November 19, 1863. Abraham Lincoln. "Nicolay Copy" of the Gettysburg Address, 1863. Holograph manuscript. Page 2. Manuscript Division, Library of Congress Digital ID# al0186p1 p.167: Sarah Meinen, "The Forgotten Four-Letter Word," Winning Orations, 1999 (Mankato, MN: Interstate Oratorical Association, 1999), 26–29. Coached by Dan Smith.; p.167: William Safire, "On Language: Marking Bush's Inaugural," New York Times Magazine, February 5, 1989, 12.; p.168: Rosalie Maggio, The Bias-Free Word Finder: A Dictionary of Nondiscriminatory Language (Boston: Beacon, 1991), 7.; p.169: Rosalie Maggio, Talking about People: A Guide to Fair and Accurate Language (Phoenix, AZ: Oryx, 1997); p.170: Quoted in George Plimpton, ed., The Writer's Chapbook: A Compendium of Fact, Opinion, Wit, and Advice from the 20th Century's Pre-eminent Writers (New York: Viking, 1989), 176.

Chapter 13 Page 173: Karlyn Kohrs Campbell et al, The Rhetorical Act: Thinking, Speaking and Writing Critically, 5e, Wadsworth Publishing Company, 2014; p.177: Achim Nowak, Power Speaking: The Art of the Exceptional Public Speaker (New York: Allworth, 2004), 11.; p.177: Barack Obama, "Remarks by the President at a Memorial Service for the Victims of the Shooting in Tucson, Arizona," Speech Delivered in Tuscon, Arizona, January 12, 2011.

Chapter 14 Page 193: Source: Winston Churchill, speech to the House of Commons of the Parliament of the United Kingdom, 13 May 1940.; p.194: Chris Gurrie and Brandy Fair, "(Re)Discovering PowerPoint: Retooling the PowerPoint Pedagogy for 2009 and Beyond," National Communication Association Convention, Chicago, November 12, 2009, 1; p.194–195: Nick Morgan, Give Your Speech, Change the World (Boston: Harvard Business School, 2005), 139.; p.196: Michael Talman, Understanding Presentation Graphics (San Francisco: SYBEX, 1992), 270.

Chapter 15 Page 207: John Train (1988) Even More Remarkable Names, New York: C.N. Potter: Distributed by Crown, 1979.; p.211–212: Melissa Janoske, "Renaissance Fairs: The New Vaudeville," Speech Delivered at Radford University, Radford, Virginia, Spring 2002. Used with permission.

Chapter 16 Page 216: "The 30-Second President," narr. Bill Moyers, A Walk through the 20th Century with Bill Moyers, PBS, September 19, 1984.; p.216: Charles U. Larson, Persuasion: Reception and Responsibility, 9th ed. (Belmont, CA: Wadsworth, 2001), 10.; p.218: Neel Bhatt, Untitled Speech, Winning Orations, 2004 (Mankato, MN: Interstate Oratorical Association, 2004), 21. Coached by David Moscovitz.; p.222: Jessica J. Jones, "Are You Guilty?" Winning Orations, 2004 (Mankato, MN: Interstate Oratorical Association, 2004), 93. Coached by Barbara F. Sims.; p.229–230: Daniel Hinderliter, "Eating Better Through Reducing Food Waste," Winning Orations, 2013 (Mankato, MN: Inter-state Oratorical Association, 2013), 109–11. Coached by Mark Hickman.

Chapter 17 Page 234: Thomas Gilovich, How We Know What Isn't So (New York: Free, 1991) 6.; p.234: Aristotle, The Rhetoric of Aristotle: An Expanded Translation with Supplementary Examples for Students of Composition and Public Speaking, trans. Lane Cooper (New York: Appleton, 1932), 220.; p.237: Patrick Martin, "The Energy Cure that Kills: Hydraulic Fracturing for Natural Gas," Winning Orations, 2011 (Mankato, MN: Interstate Oratorical Association, 2011), 147. Coached by Karen Morris.; p.238: Jon Meinen, Untitled Speech, Winning Orations, 2006 (Mankato, MN: Interstate Oratorical Association, 2006), 17. Coached by Dan Smith.; p.239: Nicholas Barton, "The Death of Reading," Winning Orations, 2004 (Mankato, MN: Interstate Oratorical Association, 2004), 32. Coached by Craig Brown and Robert F. Imbody, III.; p.239: Rachel Resnick, "The Nursing Home Catastrophe," Winning Orations, 2006 (Mankato, MN: Interstate Oratorical Association, 2006), 1. Coached by Josh Miller.; p.242: Mario Cuomo, Keynote Address, Democratic National Convention, Vital Speeches of the Day (August 15, 1984): 647.; p.243: John M. Ericson and James J. Murphy with Raymond Bud Zeuschner, The Debater's Guide, rev. ed. (Carbondale, IL: Southern Illinois University Press, 1987), 139.; p.246: W. Ward Fearnside and William B. Holther, Fallacy—The Counterfeit of Argument (Upper Saddle River, NJ: Prentice, 1959), 92.

Chapter 18 Page 253–254: Source: Don Ochs, "Introduction of Samuel L. Becker, Central States Communication Association Convention, April 12, 1991," The CSCA News, Spring 1991, 2.; p.258: Billy Crystal's Eulogy. June 10, 2016 in Louisville, KY. (https://www.nytimes.com/2016/06/11/sports/lonnie-billy-crystal-bill-clinton-eulogies-for-muhammad-ali.html?_r=0); p.258: Peggy Noonan, What I Saw at the Revolution (New York: Random House, 1990), 253.; p.258: Cowell College, "Commencement Speech Guidelines," University of California, Santa Cruz, accessed March 17, 2007, http://cowell.ucsc.edu/activities/commencement/gradinfo/speech-guidelines.html.

Appendix A: Page 265: Bambi (1942) Walt Disney Productions. Based on the book Bambi, A Life in the Woods (1928) by Austrian author Felix Salten. Translation by Whittaker Chambers was published in North America by Simon & Schuster.

Appendix C: Page 274: Thomas E. Harris and John C. Sherblom, Small Group and Team Communication, 3rd ed. (Boston: Allyn, 2005) 156.; p.274: Kenneth Blanchard (1998). The Heart of a Leader: Insights on the art of influence. Colorado: David C. Cook.

Appendix D: Page 277: Alison Gopnik, The Philosophical Baby: What Children's Minds Tell Us About Truth, Love, and the Meaning of Life. (2009). New York: Farrar, Straus and Giroux.

Appendix E: Page 288–289: Nick Guardi, Special Occasion: Eulogy. [2015] © Pearson Education, Inc. All rights reserved.; p.286–288: Chiwoneso Beverley Tinago, "The Problem with Food Aid," Winning Orations, 2009 (Mankato, MN: Interstate Oratorical Association, 2009), 38–39. Coached by Jennifer Talbert.; p.284–286: Ashley Burdick, Mental Illness. [2015] © Pearson Education, Inc. All rights reserved.; p.282–284: Derrick Peña, "Student Involvement," Speech Delivered at Penn State Hazleton, Hazleton, Pennsylvania, Fall 2016. Used with permission; p.280–282: Austin Willis, "Gum Chewers," Speech Delivered at Penn State Hazleton, Hazleton, Pennsylvania, Fall 2013. Used with permission.; p.279–280: Jennell Chu, "Flash Mobs," Speech Delivered at San Antonio College, San Antonio, Texas, Spring 2011. Used with permission.

Photo Credits

Name Index

Subject Index